W9-ABC-141

Longman A-Level Course in

PHYSICS
Volume 1

Longman

Loo Kwok Wai
Ong Bee Hoo

Pearson Education South Asia Pte Ltd
23/25, First Lok Yang Road, Singapore 629733

Associated companies, branches and
representatives throughout the world

First published 2003
Second reprint 2004

ISBN 981-4105-09-0

Set in Palatino 10/13 pt
Produced by Pearson Education South Asia Pte Ltd
Printed in Singapore

Acknowledgements

The examination questions have been reproduced by
permission of the University of Cambridge Local
Examinations Syndicate & SNP Pan Pacific Publishing Pte Ltd.

The University of Cambridge Local Examinations Syndicate
bears no responsibility for the example answers to questions
taken from its past question papers which are
contained in this publication.

Preface

Longman A Level Course Physics (Volume 1) is written for students taking the new Cambridge 9248 A-level syllabus. It covers in detail, the four core sections: (I) General Physics, (II) Newtonian Mechanics, (III) Matter, (IV) Oscillation and Waves. These are normally taught in the first year of a Junior College Physics course. Topics on Electricity and Magnetism, Modern Physics and the four option topics are discussed in Longman A Level Course Physics (Volume 2). The latter is normally taught in the second year of the Junior College Physics course.

The aim of this text is to help students attain a deeper understanding of key Physics concepts and its applications. The following are some features found in this book:

- The text is written in concise point form.
- The topics are arranged in order of the new Cambridge 9248 syllabus.
- Worked Examples from past year A-level examination questions and illustrations are provided to help students in understanding.
- An exercise is provided at the end of each chapter. Each exercise consists of Multiple-Choice Questions and Structured Questions used in the A-level examinations.
- A concept map is provided at the end of each chapter.
- A glossary of key Physics terms and definitions and a summary of important Physics formulae learnt during the course are included.
- Appendices

Contents

Physical Quantities and Units

PHYSICAL QUANTITIES

SI UNITS

THE AVOGADRO CONSTANT

SCALARS AND VECTORS

Syllabus Objectives

In this chapter you should be able to:

- show an understanding that all physical quantities consist of a numerical magnitude and a unit.
- recall the following base quantities and their units: mass (kg), length (m), time (s), current (A), temperature (K), amount of substance (mol).
- express derived units as products or quotients of the base units and use the named units listed.
- use base units to check the homogeneity of physical equations.
- show an understanding of and use the conventions for labelling graph axes and table columns as set out in the ASE publication *SI Units, Signs, Symbols and Abbreviations*, except where these have been superseded by *Signs, Symbols and Systematics (The ASE Companion to 5–16 Science, 1995)*.
- use the following prefixes and their symbols to indicate decimal sub-multiples or multiples of both base and derived units: pico (p), nano (n), micro (μ), milli (m), centi (c), deci (d), kilo (k), mega (M), giga (G), tera (T).
- make reasonable estimates of physical quantities included within the syllabus.
- show an understanding of the significance of the Avogadro constant as the number of atoms in 0.012 kg of carbon-12.
- use molar quantities where one mole of any substance is the amount containing a number of particles equal to the Avogadro constant.
- distinguish scalar and vector quantities and give examples of each.
- add and subtract coplanar vectors.
- represent a vector as two perpendicular components.

1

PHYSICAL QUANTITIES

- In Physics, quantities that can be measured are known as physical quantities. Two examples are shown in Fig 1.1.
- All physical quantities consist of a precise numerical value and a standard or a unit.

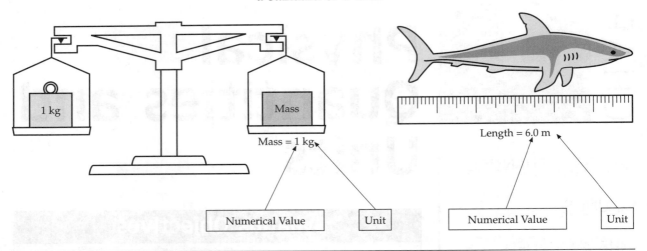

Fig 1.1 Two examples of Physical Quantities

SI UNITS

- In 1960, scientist at the General Conference of Weights and Measures adopted the international usage of a metric system of measurement called International System of Units (abbreviated S. I. in all languages).

- The S. I. system of units distinguishes seven physical quantities as base or fundamental quantities (Table 1.1). These base quantities were chosen arbitrarily and form the building blocks of all derived physical quantities. Their corresponding units are called Base Units.

Base quantities	Base units	
	Name	Symbol
Mass	kilogram	kg
Length	metre	m
Time	second	s
Electric current	ampere	A
Temperature	kelvin	K
Amount of substance	mole	mol
Luminous intensity	candela	cd

Table 1.1 Base quantities and base units

- The definitions of six commonly used base units are as follows:
(a) The kilogram (kg) is the unit of mass and is equal to the mass of a platinum-iridium cylinder kept near Paris, France.

(b) The metre (m) is the unit of length and is equal to the path travelled by light in a vacuum during a time interval of 1/299 792 458 of a second.

(c) The second (s) is the unit of time and is equal to the duration of 9 192 631 770 periods of the radiation corresponding to the transition between the two hyperfine levels of the ground state of the Caesium 133 atom.

(d) The ampere (A) is the unit of the electric current. It is the constant current that exerts a force of 2×10^{-7} N per metre length on two straight, parallel and infinitely long wire of negligible cross-sectional area when that current flows through it.

(e) The kelvin (K) is the unit of temperature. It is the fraction of 1/273.16 of the thermodynamic temperature of the triple point of water.

(f) The mole (mol) is the amount of substance that contains 6.02×10^{23} particles.

- Another feature of the S. I. units makes use of prefixes to indicate decimal multiples or submultiples of all units. The standard prefixes are shown in Table 1.2.

Prefix	Symbol	Sub-multiple	Prefix	Symbol	Multiple
atto	a	10^{-18}	deca	da	10^1
femto	f	10^{-15}	hecto	h	10^2
pico	p	10^{-12}	kilo	k	10^3
nano	n	10^{-9}	mega	M	10^6
micro	μ	10^{-6}	giga	G	10^9
milli	m	10^{-3}	tera	T	10^{12}
centi	c	10^{-2}	peta	P	10^{15}
deci	d	10^{-1}	exa	E	10^{18}

Table 1.2 Standard prefixes

Derived Quantities and Derived Units

- A derived quantity is related to the base quantities through a defining equation. Likewise, derived units can be traced to the base units. It is the product or quotient or a combination of products and quotients of the base units.

  For example:

  (a) Volume = length (m) $\times$ breadth (m) $\times$ height (m)

  The derived unit for volume is m^3.

  (b) Density $= \dfrac{\text{mass (kg)}}{\text{volume (m}^3)}$

  The derived unit for density is kg m^{-3}.

  (c) Velocity $= \dfrac{\text{displacement (m)}}{\text{time (s)}}$

  The derived unit for velocity is m s^{-1}.

(d) Acceleration = $\dfrac{\text{change in velocity (m s}^{-1})}{\text{time (s)}}$

The derived unit for acceleration is m s^{-2}.

(e) Force = mass (kg) $\times$ acceleration (m s^{-2})

The derived unit for force is kg m s^{-2} or newton (N).

- Further examples of derived quantities and its units are shown in Table 1.3.

Derived quantities	Derived units	Alternative units
Area	m^2	—
Momentum	kg m s^{-1}	—
Pressure	kg m^{-1} s^{-2}	pascal
Work Done	kg m^2 s^{-2}	joule
Power	kg m^2 s^{-3}	watt
Electric Charge	A s	coulomb
Potential Difference	kg m^2 A^{-1} s^{-3}	volt
Resistance	kg m^2 A^{-2} s^{-3}	ohm
Frequency	s^{-1}	hertz

Table 1.3   Derived quantities and its units

- It should be noted that certain derived units can be replaced by simpler names. For example kg m s^{-2} is normally replaced with newton (N).

- There are some physical quantities that have no units. Some examples of these are relative density, refractive index and strain. In addition, all real numbers and some mathematical constants like π have no units. They are sometimes called dimensionless constants.

Uses of Base Units

- Base units are used to find units of unknown quantities in an equation. The units of an unknown derived quantity in a physical equation can be found by substituting known units into the defining equation.

The energy of a photon of light of frequency f is given by hf, where h is the Planck constant. What are the base units of h?

Cambridge

The defining equation is $E = hf$

$$h = \frac{E}{f}$$

Units of $h = \dfrac{\text{kg m}^2 \text{ s}^{-2}}{\text{s}^{-1}} = \text{kg m}^2 \text{ s}^{-1}$

4

Q The drag coefficient C_D of a car moving with speed v through air of density ρ is given by $C_D = \dfrac{F}{1/2\rho v^2 A}$ where F is the drag force exerted on the car and A is the maximum cross-sectional area of the car perpendicular to the direction of travel. Show that C_D is dimensionless.

Cambridge

A

$$C_D = \frac{F}{1/2\rho v^2 A}$$

$$\text{Units of } C_D = \frac{(\text{kg m s}^{-2})}{(\text{kg m}^{-3})(\text{m s}^{-1})^2(\text{m}^2)}$$

$$= \frac{\text{kg m s}^{-2}}{\text{kg m s}^{-2}}$$

$$= 1$$

C_D is dimensionless.

- Base units can be used to check the homogeneity of a physical equation. This involves checking units on the left-hand and right-hand side of the equation. If they are the same, the equation is said to be homogeneous or dimensionally consistent. This, however, does not guarantee that the equation is physically correct. There could be an incorrect coefficient, a missing or extra term, or simply a wrong positive or negative sign. Examples of equations that are homogeneous but physically incorrect are shown in Fig 1.2.

Incorrect coefficient: $v = u + 4at$

Extra term $\quad : v = u + at + \sqrt{as}$

Incorrect sign $\quad : T = -2\pi\sqrt{\frac{l}{g}}$

Fig 1.2 Examples of homogeneous physically incorrect equations

5

Q Which expression could be correct for the velocity v of ocean waves in terms of ρ the density of seawater, g the acceleration of free fall, h the depth of the ocean and λ the wavelength?

$$v = \sqrt{g\lambda} \; ; \; v = \sqrt{\frac{g}{h}} \; ; \; v = \sqrt{\rho g h} \; ; \; v = \sqrt{\frac{g}{\rho}}$$

Cambridge

A

Units of $v = \text{m s}^{-1}$

Units of $\sqrt{g\lambda} = (\text{m s}^{-2} \, \text{m})^{1/2}$
$$= \text{m s}^{-1}$$

Units of $\sqrt{\dfrac{g}{h}} = \left(\dfrac{\text{m s}^{-2}}{\text{m}}\right)^{1/2}$
$$= \text{s}^{-1}$$

Units of $\sqrt{\rho g h} = \left[\left(\dfrac{\text{kg}}{\text{m}^3}\right)(\text{m s}^{-2})(\text{m})\right]^{1/2}$
$$= [\text{kg m}^{-1} \text{s}^{-2}]^{1/2}$$

Units of $\sqrt{\dfrac{g}{\rho}} = \left[\dfrac{\text{m s}^{-2}}{\text{kg m}^{-3}}\right]^{1/2}$
$$= [\text{kg}^{-1} \text{m}^4 \text{s}^{-2}]^{1/2}$$

The equation $v = \sqrt{g\lambda}$ could be correct as it is homogeneous.

Q The experimental measurement of the heat capacity C of a solid as a function of temperature T is to be fitted to the expression

$$C = \alpha T + \beta T^3$$

What are possible units of α and β?

Cambridge

A

The defining equation for heat capacity is $C = \dfrac{Q}{\Delta\theta}$

Units of $C = \text{J K}^{-1}$

As the equation is dimensionally consistent,

(Units of α) K = Units of C

Units of $\alpha = \dfrac{\text{J K}^{-1}}{\text{K}}$
$$= \text{J K}^{-2}$$

Similarly

(Units of β) K^3 = Units of C

Units of $\beta = \dfrac{\text{J K}^{-1}}{\text{K}^3}$
$$= \text{J K}^{-4}$$

6

(a) (i) How do you check a formula for homogeneity? Why does this method of checking not give definite confirmation that an equation is correct?

(ii) Express the unit of force and of charge in terms of the SI base units kilogram, metre, second and ampere. Hence, by reference to Coulomb's law $F = \dfrac{1}{4\pi\varepsilon_0}\dfrac{Q_1 Q_3}{r^2}$, express the units of ε_0, the permittivity of a vacuum, in terms of these base units.

(b) A unit for μ_0, the permeability of a vacuum, is kg m s^{-2} A^{-2}. Use the unit, and your unit for ε_0, to decide which one of the following relations between ε_0, μ_0 and c, the speed of light in a vacuum, is homogeneous.

$\varepsilon_0\mu_0 = c^2$; $\varepsilon_0\mu_0 = c$; $\varepsilon_0\mu_0 = c^{-1}$; $\varepsilon_0\mu_0 = c^{-2}$

Cambridge

(a) (i) If the formula is homogeneous, the units on the left side of the formula must be identical with the units on the right side. An equation that is dimensionally consistent may be physically incorrect.

(ii) $F = ma$

Units of force = kg m s^{-2}

$Q = It$

Units of charge = A s

$$F = \frac{1}{4\pi\varepsilon_0}\frac{Q_1 Q_2}{r^2}$$

$$\varepsilon_0 = \frac{1}{4\pi F}\frac{Q_1 Q_2}{r^2}$$

Units of $\varepsilon_0 = \dfrac{\text{(A s)(A s)}}{\text{(kg m s}^{-2})(\text{m}^2)}$

$= $ A^2 s^4 kg^{-1} m^{-3}

(b) $\varepsilon_0\mu_0 = c^2$ ———————— (1)

Units of $\varepsilon_0\mu_0 = $ (A^2 s^4 kg^{-1} m^{-3})(kg m s^{-2} A^{-2})

$= $ m^{-2} s^2

Units of c^2 are m^2 s^{-2}.

Equation (1) is **not homogeneous**.

$\varepsilon_0\mu_0 = c$ ———————— (2)

Units of c are m s^{-1}.

Equation (2) is **not homogeneous**.

$\varepsilon_0\mu_0 = c^{-1}$ ———————— (3)

Units of c^{-1} are m^{-1} s.

Equation (3) is **not homogeneous**.

$\varepsilon_0\mu_0 = c^{-2}$ ———————— (4)

Units of c^{-2} are m^{-2} s^2.

Equation (4) is **homogeneous**.

7

(a) The kilogram, the metre and the second are base units. Name two other base units.
(b) Explain why the unit of energy is said to be a derived unit.
(c) The density π and the pressure p of a gas are related by the expression

$$c = \sqrt{\frac{\gamma p}{\rho}}$$

where c and γ are constants.
(i) 1. Determine the base units of density ρ.
    2. Show that the base units of pressure p are kg m^{-1} s^{-2}.
(ii) Given that the constant γ has no unit, determine the unit of c.
(iii) Using your answer to (ii), suggest what quantity may be represented by the symbol c.

Cambridge

(a) ampere and kelvin
(b) The unit of energy is a derived unit because it can be expressed as the product and/or quotient of base units.
Units of energy = kg m^2 s^{-2}

(c) (i) 1. density $(\rho) = \dfrac{\text{mass } (m)}{\text{volume } (v)}$

    Base units of density $= \dfrac{\text{kg}}{\text{m}^3}$

    $= $ kg m^{-3}

    2. pressure $(p) = \dfrac{\text{force } (F)}{\text{area } (A)}$

    Base units of pressure $= \dfrac{\text{kg m s}^{-2}}{\text{m}^2}$

    $= $ kg m^{-1} s^{-2}

(ii) $c = \sqrt{\dfrac{\gamma p}{\rho}}$

    Unit of $c = \sqrt{\dfrac{\text{kg m}^{-1}\text{ s}^{-2}}{\text{kg m}^{-3}}}$

    $= $ m s^{-1}

(iii) The quantity c is either speed or velocity.

Conventions for Labelling Axes on Graphs and Table Columns

- A physical quantity consists of a numerical value and a unit. For example, time $= 10.0$ s

$$\therefore \frac{\text{time}}{\text{s}} = 10.0$$

Similarly, velocity $= 5$ m s^{-1}

$$\therefore \frac{\text{velocity}}{\text{m/s}} = 5$$

(a) (i) How do you check a formula for homogeneity? Why does this method of checking not give definite confirmation that an equation is correct?

(ii) Express the unit of force and of charge in terms of the SI base units kilogram, metre, second and ampere. Hence, by reference to Coulomb's law $F = \dfrac{1}{4\pi\varepsilon_0}\dfrac{Q_1 Q_3}{r^2}$, express the units of ε_0, the permittivity of a vacuum, in terms of these base units.

(b) A unit for μ_0, the permeability of a vacuum, is kg m s^{-2} A^{-2}. Use the unit, and your unit for ε_0, to decide which one of the following relations between ε_0, μ_0 and c, the speed of light in a vacuum, is homogeneous.

$\varepsilon_0\mu_0 = c^2$; $\varepsilon_0\mu_0 = c$; $\varepsilon_0\mu_0 = c^{-1}$; $\varepsilon_0\mu_0 = c^{-2}$

Cambridge

(a) (i) If the formula is homogeneous, the units on the left side of the formula must be identical with the units on the right side. An equation that is dimensionally consistent may be physically incorrect.

(ii) $F = ma$

Units of force = kg m s^{-2}

$Q = It$

Units of charge = A s

$$F = \frac{1}{4\pi\varepsilon_0}\frac{Q_1 Q_2}{r^2}$$

$$\varepsilon_0 = \frac{1}{4\pi F}\frac{Q_1 Q_2}{r^2}$$

Units of $\varepsilon_0 = \dfrac{(\text{A s})(\text{A s})}{(\text{kg m s}^{-2})(\text{m}^2)}$

$= \text{A}^2 \text{ s}^4 \text{ kg}^{-1} \text{ m}^{-3}$

(b) $\varepsilon_0\mu_0 = c^2$ ——————— (1)

Units of $\varepsilon_0\mu_0 = (\text{A}^2 \text{ s}^4 \text{ kg}^{-1} \text{ m}^{-3})(\text{kg m s}^{-2} \text{ A}^{-2})$

$= \text{m}^{-2} \text{ s}^2$

Units of c^2 are m^2 s^{-2}.

Equation (1) is **not homogeneous**.

$\varepsilon_0\mu_0 = c$ ——————— (2)

Units of c are m s^{-1}.

Equation (2) is **not homogeneous**.

$\varepsilon_0\mu_0 = c^{-1}$ ——————— (3)

Units of c^{-1} are m^{-1} s.

Equation (3) is **not homogeneous**.

$\varepsilon_0\mu_0 = c^{-2}$ ——————— (4)

Units of c^{-2} are m^{-2} s^2.

Equation (4) is **homogeneous**.

7

(a) The kilogram, the metre and the second are base units. Name two other base units.
(b) Explain why the unit of energy is said to be a derived unit.
(c) The density π and the pressure p of a gas are related by the expression

$$c = \sqrt{\frac{\gamma p}{\rho}}$$

where c and γ are constants.
(i) 1. Determine the base units of density ρ.
  2. Show that the base units of pressure p are $kg\ m^{-1}\ s^{-2}$.
(ii) Given that the constant γ has no unit, determine the unit of c.
(iii) Using your answer to (ii), suggest what quantity may be represented by the symbol c.

Cambridge

(a) ampere and kelvin
(b) The unit of energy is a derived unit because it can be expressed as the product and/or quotient of base units.
Units of energy $= kg\ m^2\ s^{-2}$

(c) (i) 1. density $(\rho) = \dfrac{\text{mass }(m)}{\text{volume }(v)}$

Base units of density $= \dfrac{kg}{m^3}$

$= kg\ m^{-3}$

2. pressure $(p) = \dfrac{\text{force }(F)}{\text{area }(A)}$

Base units of pressure $= \dfrac{kg\ m\ s^{-2}}{m^2}$

$= kg\ m^{-1}\ s^{-2}$

(ii) $c = \sqrt{\dfrac{\gamma p}{\rho}}$

Unit of $c = \sqrt{\dfrac{kg\ m^{-1}\ s^{-2}}{kg\ m^{-3}}}$

$= m\ s^{-1}$

(iii) The quantity c is either speed or velocity.

Conventions for Labelling Axes on Graphs and Table Columns

- A physical quantity consists of a numerical value and a unit.
  For example, time $= 10.0$ s

$$\therefore\ \frac{\text{time}}{\text{s}} = 10.0$$

Similarly, velocity $= 5\ m\ s^{-1}$

$$\therefore\ \frac{\text{velocity}}{\text{m/s}} = 5$$

8

- A table of velocity and time should be headed as shown in Table 1.4. Since units are included in the heading, there is no necessity to write units within the columns.

- A graph is a representation of how two physical quantities are related. Axes on a graph should be labelled with the physical quantity and its associated units. Numbers written on the axes should be entirely numerical. This is illustrated in Fig 1.3.

velocity	time
m/s	s
0	0.0
5	10.0
10	20.0
15	30.0
20	40.0
25	50.0

Table 1.4   Table column

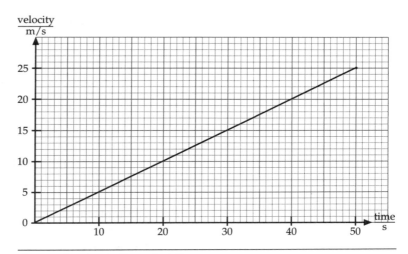

Fig 1.3   Graph velocity against time

THE AVOGADRO CONSTANT

- The Avogadro constant N_A is equal to the number of atoms in exactly 0.012 kg of carbon-12.

- This number was found experimentally to be $6.02 \times 10^{23} \ \text{mol}^{-1}$. N_A has the unit of mol^{-1} or per mol (abbreviation of mole).

- One mole of any substance is the amount containing a number of particles equal to the Avogadro constant. It could be atoms, molecules, protons, neutrons or even grains of sand.

- The mass of one mole of a substance is known as the molar mass and is measured in kg mol^{-1}.

- The volume of one mole of a substance is known as the molar volume.

- Mass of one atom or molecule,

$$m = \frac{\text{Molar mass } (M)}{\text{Avogadro constant } (N_A)}$$

Hence $M = N_A \, m$

9

- The number of moles of a substance can be found by using the following formulas.
  Number of moles of a substance,

  $$n = \frac{\text{mass of the substance } (m')}{\text{Molar mass } (M)}$$

  $m' = n\,M$

  Number of moles of a substance,

  $$n = \frac{\text{number of atoms or molecules } (N)}{\text{Avogadro constant } (N_A)}$$

  $N = n\,N_A$

- The molar mass for elements is known as the relative atomic mass or RAM. It is the atomic mass expressed in grams.

- The relative atomic mass of an element, A_r is given by

  $$A_r = 12 \times \frac{\text{average mass of one atom of the element}}{\text{mass of one atom of } {}^{12}C}$$

  For example, the RAM for hydrogen and carbon-12 atoms are 1.008 g and 12 g respectively.

- The molar mass for molecules is known as Relative Molecular Mass or RMM. It is the molecular mass expressed in grams. The relative molecular mass of an element, M_r, is given by

  $$M_r = 12 \times \frac{\text{average mass of one molecule of the substance}}{\text{mass of one atom of } {}^{12}C}$$

- The relative molecular mass is the sum of the relative atomic masses of all the atoms in the molecule.

(a) The value of the Avogadro constant is 6.02×0^{23} per mole.
 (i) Define the mole.
 (ii) Calculate the mass of an atom of ^{12}C, using the above value of the Avogadro constant.
(b) A solid iron cube of side 20 mm has a mass of 6.3×10^{-2} kg. One mole of iron atoms has a mass of 5.6×10^{-2} kg.
 (i) How many iron atoms are there in the cube?
 (ii) Hence find the maximum volume that an iron atom could occupy in the solid state.
 (iii) Use your answer to (b) (ii) above to estimate the diameter of an iron atom.

Cambridge

10

A

(a) (i) The mole is the amount that contains 6.02×10^{23} particles.

(ii) $N_A\, m = M$ where m is the mass of an atom of ^{12}C,
N_A is the Avogadro constant,
M is the molar mass of ^{12}C.

$$m = \frac{M}{N_A}$$

$$= \frac{0.012}{6.02 \times 10^{23}}$$

$$= 1.99 \times 10^{-26} \text{ kg}$$

$$= 2.0 \times 10^{-26} \text{ kg}$$

(b) (i) Number of moles of iron atom $= \dfrac{\text{mass of solid iron cube}}{\text{molar mass}}$

$$= \frac{6.3 \times 10^{-2} \text{ kg}}{5.6 \times 10^{-2} \text{ kg}}$$

$$= 1.125 \text{ moles}$$

Number of iron atoms in the cube $= (\text{Number of moles})\, N_A$
$$= (1.125)(6.02 \times 10^{23})$$
$$= 6.77 \times 10^{23}$$
$$= 6.8 \times 10^{23}$$

(ii) Maximum volume of one atom of iron $= \dfrac{\text{volume of cube}}{\text{number of iron atoms}}$

$$= \frac{(0.020)^3}{6.77 \times 10^{23}}$$

$$= 1.18 \times 10^{-29} \text{ m}^3$$

$$= 1.2 \times 10^{-29} \text{ m}^3$$

(iii) An iron atom of diameter d can be placed in a cube of length d. Make the assumption that the volume of the cube of length d is equal to the maximum volume of an iron atom i.e.

$$d^3 = 1.18 \times 10^{-29}$$
$$\therefore d = 2.3 \times 10^{-10} \text{ m}$$

SCALARS AND VECTORS

Scalar Quantities

- Scalar quantities are physical quantities that can be represented by a magnitude only. It does not have a direction. Examples are the temperature of a liquid and the mass of an object. Both of these quantities cannot be represented with a direction.

- The addition and subtraction of scalar quantities are governed by the rules of ordinary algebra. For example, the total mass of two objects is the sum of their individual masses.

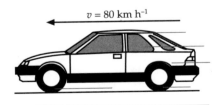

Fig 1.3a Car moving due west

11

Vector Quantities

- A physical quantity that can be represented by a magnitude and a direction in space is known as a vector. For example, the velocity of a car can be described with a magnitude, $v = 80$ km/h and a direction such as due west (Fig 1.3a). If the direction of travel of this car is not specified, the magnitude is simply called speed (a scalar).

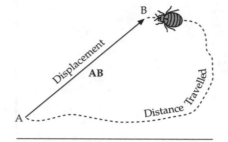

Fig 1.3b   Displacement and distance

- In Fig 1.3b an ant crawls from the initial position A along a curve to a final position B. A vector can be used to indicate the change in position of the ant. An arrow is drawn directly from A to B. This vector is known as displacement. In this case, the displacement is very different from the actual distance travelled by the ant.

- A vector in general can be represented by an arrow whose length is proportional to its magnitude and its direction by the orientation of the arrow.

- To distinguish vectors from scalars, vectors are written with special symbols. The following are some common examples of symbols used to represent vectors: $\mathbf{AB}$, $\overrightarrow{AB}$, $\underline{s}$.

- If only the magnitude is required, it is written as $|\mathbf{AB}|$, $|\overrightarrow{AB}|$ and $|\underline{s}|$ or simply s.

- Table 1.5 shows a list of scalar and vector quantities.

Scalar quantity	Vector quantity
distance	displacement
speed	velocity
temperature	acceleration
energy	force
power	momentum
mass	weight
density	moment
pressure	torque
volume	electric field
time	magnetic flux density

Table 1.5   Examples of scalars and vectors

- In Fig 1.4, only vectors $\mathbf{A}$ and $\mathbf{B}$ are equal. This means that
magnitude of $\mathbf{A}$ = magnitude of $\mathbf{B}$ and
direction of $\mathbf{A}$ = direction of $\mathbf{B}$.

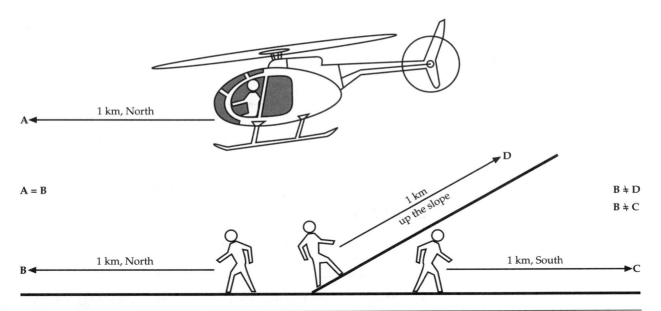

A — 1 km, North

A = B

B — 1 km, North →

B ← 1 km, North

1 km up the slope → D

1 km, South → C

B ≠ D
B ≠ C

Fig 1.4   Illustration of displacement

- A vector **P** can be multiplied by any ordinary number to increase or decrease its length or to reverse its direction. This is illustrated in Fig 1.5.

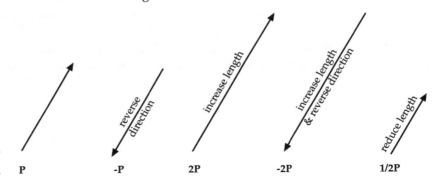

Fig 1.5   Multiply vectors with a scalar

P   -P   2P   -2P   1/2P

reverse direction · increase length · increase length & reverse direction · reduce length

Addition and Subtraction of Vectors

- Vectors can be added or subtracted. Vector addition or subtraction involves finding the resultant or the vector sum of two or more vectors. This resultant has effects that are entirely the same as the combined action of its separate vectors.

Addition of Vectors in the Same Direction

- When vectors are in the same direction, the resultant is obtained by adding the magnitudes of the separate vectors. The direction of the resultant remains the same as the

13

individual vectors. In Fig 1.6, the resultant of vectors $\mathbf{A}$ and $\mathbf{B}$ is $\mathbf{R}$ and acting to the right i.e. $\mathbf{A} + \mathbf{B} = \mathbf{R}$.

Fig 1.6   Vector addition

Addition of Vectors in Opposite Directions

• This can be considered as the addition of a negative vector or a vector subtraction.
  Hence in Fig 1.7, $\mathbf{P} + (-\mathbf{Q}) = \mathbf{P} - \mathbf{Q} = \mathbf{S}$.

• The direction of vector $\mathbf{S}$ is in the direction of the bigger vector.

Fig 1.7   Vector subtraction

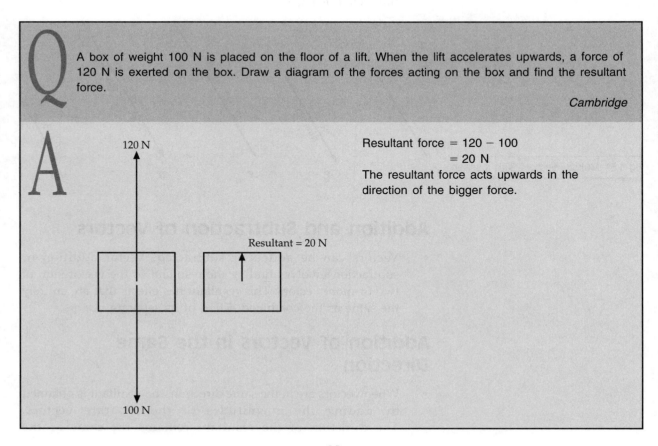

Q A box of weight 100 N is placed on the floor of a lift. When the lift accelerates upwards, a force of 120 N is exerted on the box. Draw a diagram of the forces acting on the box and find the resultant force.

Cambridge

A

Resultant force = 120 − 100
= 20 N
The resultant force acts upwards in the direction of the bigger force.

14

Addition of Vectors in Different Directions

- Two or more coplanar vectors can be added by using the parallelogram method or the head to tail method.

- The procedures of the parallelogram method are outlined below.
  (a) Draw two vectors **A** and **B** acting at O and inclined at an angle of θ to each other.
  (b) Construct a parallelogram as shown in Fig 1.8.
  (c) Draw the diagonal from O to the opposite corner of the parallelogram.
  (d) This is the resultant of **A** and **B** and is denoted by a double-headed arrow.

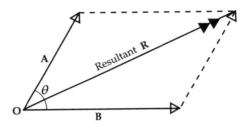

Fig 1.8 Parallelogram method

- The procedures for the head to tail method are outlined below.
  (a) Vector **A** in Fig 1.8 is drawn such that the head of vector **B** touches the tail of vector **A**.
  (b) The resultant **R** can be obtained by drawing an arrow from the tail of **B** to the head of **A** (Fig 1.9).
  (c) Conversely, the same **R** can also be obtained by moving **B** to join **A** as shown in Fig 1.10. It does not matter which order the vectors are added. In both diagrams, a closed triangle is formed by **R**.

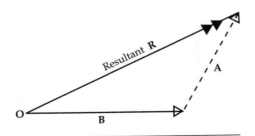

Fig 1.9 Head to tail method

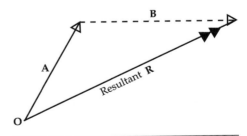

Fig 1.10 Head to tail method

15

(d) The same method can also be applied to three or more vectors. The resultant of vectors **A**, **B** and **C** in Fig 1.11 is illustrated in Fig 1.12.

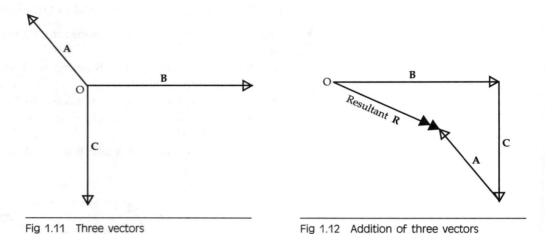

Fig 1.11   Three vectors

Fig 1.12   Addition of three vectors

Components of Vectors

- An alternative method to describe vectors requires the use of the Cartesian coordinate system (Fig 1.13). The vector is represented by an arrow from the origin $(0, 0)$ to the point (x, y).

Fig 1.13   Position vector

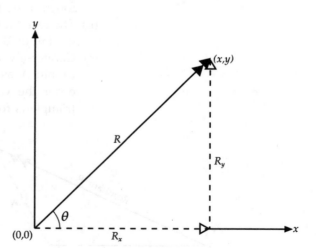

- This vector is known as the position vector. It can be considered as the resultant of two perpendicular vectors R_x and R_y along the x and y-axis respectively. R_x is known as the x-component of R and R_y is known as the y-component of R.

16

- To represent a vector completely, this book uses the magnitude-angle notation (R and θ) where R is the magnitude of $\mathbf{R}$ and θ is angle made by x-axis to the vector $\mathbf{R}$ in the anticlockwise direction.

- From the Fig. 1.13, $\sin \theta = \dfrac{R_y}{R}$, where θ is the angle measured anticlockwise from the x-axis.

  Therefore $R_y = R \sin \theta$.

  $\cos \theta = \dfrac{R_x}{R}$

  $\therefore R_x = R \cos \theta$

  The magnitude of R is given by:

  $R = \sqrt{R_x^2 + R_y^2}$

  The direction of R is given by:

  $\tan \theta = \dfrac{R_y}{R_x}$

Q A beetle crawls on a wall. Its location is determined by the coordinates $x = 60$ mm and $y = 80$ mm with respect to the origin. Determine the magnitude and direction of the position vector $\mathbf{r}$.

A The magnitude of the position vector $\mathbf{r}$ is given by the length from (0, 0) to (60, 80).

From Pythagoras' theorem,

$|\mathbf{r}| = \sqrt{80^2 + 60^2}$

$= \sqrt{6400 + 3600}$

$= 100$ mm

The direction of the vector is given by θ.

$\tan \theta = \dfrac{80}{60}$

Hence $\theta = \tan^{-1} \dfrac{80}{60} = 53.1°$

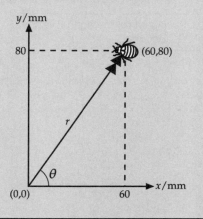

17

Analytical Method of Vector Addition

- In the analytical method of vector addition, the x-components of all individual vectors are added together to give the x-component of the resultant vector (R_x). Similarly, the y-components of all vectors can be added together to give the y-component of the resultant (R_y). This is illustrated diagrammatically for two vectors in Fig 1.14. The final resultant is the sum of R_x and R_y.

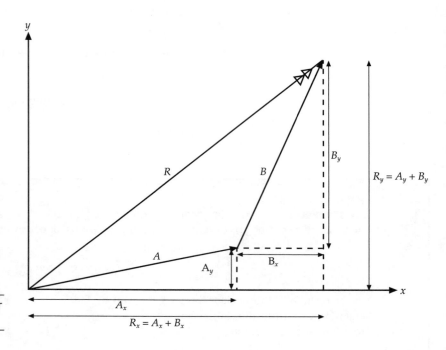

Fig 1.14   Analytical method of vector addition

- The addition of vectors by the analytical method is illustrated schematically in the following equations.

$$\begin{array}{ccccc} \mathbf{A} & = & \mathbf{A}_x & + & \mathbf{A}_y \\ + & & + & & + \\ \mathbf{B} & = & \mathbf{B}_x & + & \mathbf{B}_y \\ \\ \mathbf{R} & = & \mathbf{R}_x & + & \mathbf{R}_y \end{array}$$

Three men, Smith, Brown and Jones are attempting to push a large object in the direction Ox. Smith exerts a force of 200 N at a direction $30°$ to Ox and Brown exerts a force of 400 N at $60°$ to Ox as shown in the diagram.

What is the magnitude and direction of the smallest force Jones should exert such that the resultant of all three forces acts along Ox?

Cambridge

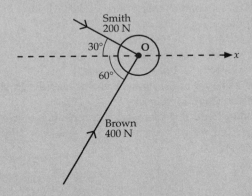

Scale 1 cm : 100 N

The smallest force exerted by Jones would be a force that is perpendicular to Ox. The resultant of the three forces will act along Ox.

Magnitude of Jones' force
$= 2.4 \times 100$
$= 240$ N

Direction of Jones' force
$=$ Downwards at $90°$ to Ox.

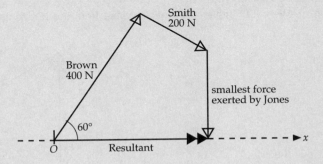

19

Q An aircraft is climbing with a steady speed of 100 m s^{-1} at an angle of 30° to the horizontal.

(a) Using a scale of 1 cm to represent a speed of 20 m s^{-1}, draw a line, starting from P on the diagram, to represent the velocity of the aircraft at that instant.

(b) On the same diagram in (a), construct lines to represent the vertical and the horizontal components of the velocity of the aircraft. Hence, determine
  (i) the vertical component of the velocity;
  (ii) the horizontal component of the velocity.

(c) A short time later its velocity is 100 m s^{-1} vertically.
  (i) Using the same scale as in (a), draw a vector diagram to show the initial and final velocities and the change in velocity.
  (ii) Determine the magnitude and direction of the change in velocity.

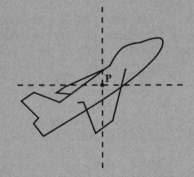

A (a) and (b)

Scale of 1 cm : 20 m s^{-1}
From the scale diagram,
  (i) vertical component = 2.5 × 20 = 50 m s^{-1}
  (ii) horizontal component = 4.2 × 20 = 84 m s^{-1}

(c) Change in velocity = final velocity − initial velocity
$\Delta \mathbf{V} = \mathbf{V}_2 - \mathbf{V}_1$ where $\mathbf{V}_2$, the final velocity, is 100 m s^{-1} vertically and $\mathbf{V}_1$, the initial velocity, is 100 m s^{-1} at an angle of 30° to the horizontal.
$\therefore \mathbf{V}_2 = \mathbf{V}_1 + \Delta \mathbf{V}$

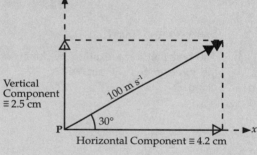

(i) The vector diagram for the initial, final velocities and the change in velocity is illustrated in the diagram.
(ii) Magnitude of $\Delta \mathbf{V}$ = 100 m s^{-1}
Direction of $\Delta \mathbf{V}$ = 150° measured anticlockwise from the horizontal.

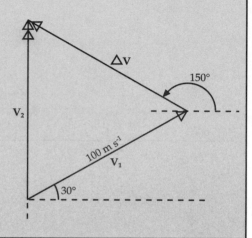

 Two forces, F_1 and F_2 of magnitude 15.0 N and 10.0 N respectively are applied at point O. Both forces are inclined at an angle of 50° to the x-axis.

Calculate

(a) the x and y components of each of the forces;

(b) the vector sum of the x-components of these forces;

(c) the vector sum of the y-components of these forces;

(d) the resultant of these forces.

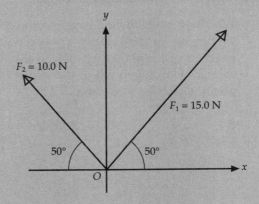

(a) $F_{1x} = 15.0 \cos 50°$
$= 9.64$ N
$F_{1y} = 15.0 \sin 50°$
$= 11.5$ N
$F_{2x} = -10.0 \cos 50°$
$= -6.43$ N
$F_{2y} = 10.0 \sin 50°$
$= 7.66$ N

(b) Vector sum of the x-components $F_x = F_{1x} + F_{2x}$
$= 9.64 - 6.43$
$= 3.21$ N

(c) Vector sum of y-components $F_y = F_{1y} + F_{2y}$
$= 11.5 + 7.66$
$= 19.2$ N

(d) Resultant $F = \sqrt{F_x{}^2 + F_y{}^2} = \sqrt{3.21^2 + 19.2^2}$
$= 19.47$
$= 19.5$ N

$$\tan \theta = \frac{F_y}{F_x}$$

$$= \frac{19.2}{3.21}$$

$$\theta = 80.5°$$

Exercise 1

Multiple Choice Questions

1   Which of the following could be the correct expression for the velocity v of ocean waves in terms of ρ the density of seawater, g the acceleration of free fall, h the depth of the ocean and λ the wavelength?

   A $\sqrt{g\lambda}$ **B** $\sqrt{\dfrac{g}{h}}$

   C $\sqrt{\rho g h}$ **D** $\sqrt{\dfrac{g}{\rho}}$

2   In terms of the kilogram (kg), metre (m), second (s) and kelvin (K), what are the base units of specific heat capacity?
   A $m\,s^{-2}K^{-1}$ **B** $m\,s^{-1}K^{-1}$
   C $m^2\,s^{-2}K^{-1}$ **D** $m^2\,s^{-1}K^{-1}$

3   Which list of S I units contains only base units?
   A kelvin, metre, mole, ampere, kilogram
   B kilogram, metre, second, ohm, mole
   C kilogram, newton, metre, ampere, ohm
   D newton, kelvin, second, volt, mole

4   If p is the momentum of an object of mass m, the expression $\dfrac{p^2}{m}$ has base units identical to
   A energy.   **B** force.
   C power.   **D** velocity.

5   The mass of one carbon-12 atom is

   A $\dfrac{12}{6.0 \times 10^{23}}$ kg.

   B $\dfrac{0.012}{6.0 \times 10^{23}}$ kg.

   C $\dfrac{6.0 \times 10^{23}}{0.012}$ kg.

   D $\dfrac{1}{12 \times 6.0 \times 10^{23}}$ kg.

6   A sample of carbon-12 has a mass of 3.0 g. Which expression gives the number of atoms in the sample? (N_A is the symbol for the Avogadro constant.)
   A $0.0030\ N_A$ **B** $0.25\ N_A$
   C $3.0\ N_A$ **D** $4.0\ N_A$

7   Which line in the table correctly identifies force, kinetic energy and momentum as scalar or vector quantities?

	force	kinetic energy	momentun
A	scalar	scalar	vector
B	scalar	vector	vector
C	vector	scalar	scalar
D	vector	scalar	vector

8   Which pair includes a vector quantity and a scalar quantity?
   A displacement; acceleration
   B power; speed
   C work; potential energy
   D force; kinetic energy

9   Forces of 4 N and 6 N act at a point. Which one of the following could not be the magnitude of their resultant?
   A 1 N   **B** 4 N
   C 8 N   **D** 10 N

10   Two forces act on a circular disc as shown in Fig. 1.15.

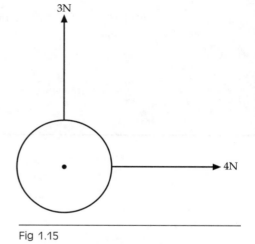

Fig 1.15

22

Which arrow best shows the line of action of the resultant force?

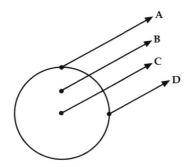

11 A particle has an initial velocity of 15 m s^{-1} in the Ox direction as shown in Fig. 1.16. At a later time its velocity is 15 m s^{-1} at an angle of 60° to Ox. (Directions are indicated by measuring angles anticlockwise from the direction Ox.)

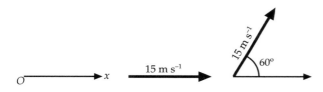

Fig 1.16

The change in velocity that has taken place in this interval is

A zero.
B 26 m s^{-1} at an angle of 30° to Ox.
C 15 m s^{-1} at an angle of 120° to Ox.
D 26 m s^{-1} at an angle of 210° to Ox.

Structured Questions

1 The unit J s^{-1} can be used as the unit of power instead of the watt. Give a unit for each of the following quantities using appropriate combinations of metre (m), second (s), ampere (A), joule (J) and volt (V) only.

Quantity
energy
pressure
electrical charge
electrical resistance

2 The theory of gas flow through small diameter tubes at low pressures is an important consideration of high vacuum technique. One equation which occurs in the theory is

$$Q = \frac{kr^3(p_1 - p_2)}{l}\sqrt{\frac{M}{RT}}$$

where k is a number without units, r is the radius of the tube, p_1 and p_2 are the pressures at each end of the tube of length l, M is the molar mass of the gas (unit: kg mol^{-1}), R is the molar gas constant (unit: J K^{-1} mol^{-1}) and T is the temperature. Use the equation to find the base unit of Q.

3 Bernoulli's equation, which applies to fluid flow, states that $p = h\rho g + \frac{1}{2}\rho v^2 = k$ where p is a pressure, h a height, ρ a density, g an acceleration, v a velocity and k a constant. Show that the equation is dimensionally consistent and state an SI unit for k.

Cambridge

4 (a) Some physical quantities are often paired together, one of the pair being a vector and the other a scalar. Identify the vector quantity in each of the following pairs.
    (i) velocity and speed
    (ii) weight and mass
    (iii) energy and momentum
    (iv) gravitational field strength and gravitational potential

   (b) Two vectors **A** and **B** are at right angles to each other. Draw a vector diagram to show how the sum of the vectors could be found.

   (c) A car changes its velocity from 30 m s^{-1} due east to 25 m s^{-1} due south.
    (i) Draw a vector diagram to show the initial and final velocities and change in velocity.
    (ii) Calculate the change in speed.
    (iii) Calculate the change in velocity.

Cambridge

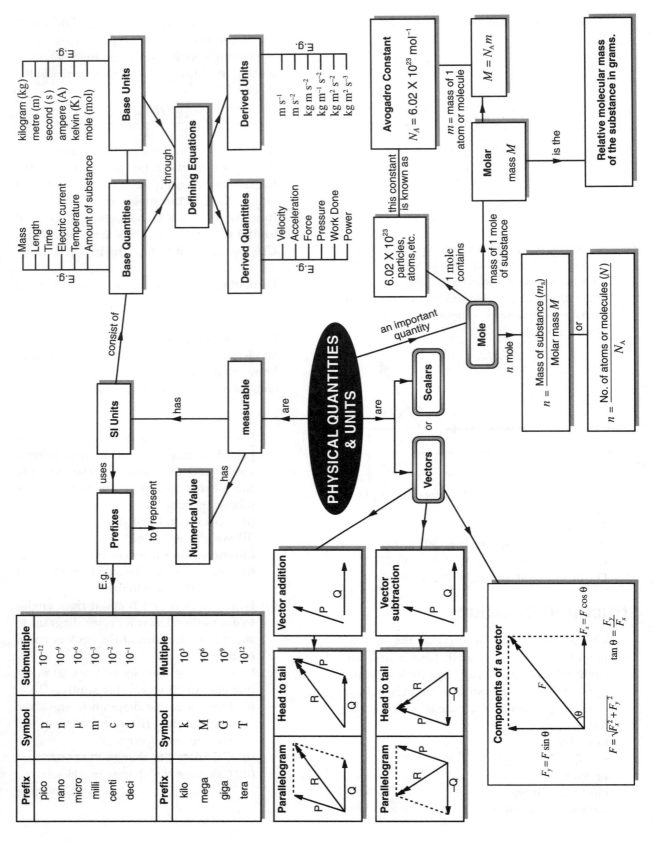

PHYSICAL QUANTITIES & UNITS

measurable — are — PHYSICAL QUANTITIES & UNITS

measurable → has → **SI Units**

measurable → has → **Numerical Value**

SI Units → uses → **Prefixes** → to represent → Numerical Value

Base Quantities consist of SI Units

Base Quantities (E.g.):
- Mass
- Length
- Time
- Electric current
- Temperature
- Amount of substance

Base Units (E.g.):
- kilogram (kg)
- metre (m)
- second (s)
- ampere (A)
- kelvin (K)
- mole (mol)

Base Quantities → through → **Defining Equations** → **Base Units**

Derived Quantities → through **Defining Equations** → **Derived Units**

Derived Quantities (E.g.):
- Velocity
- Acceleration
- Force
- Pressure
- Work Done
- Power

Derived Units (E.g.):
- m s⁻¹ → $m\ s^{-1}$
- $m\ s^{-2}$
- $kg\ m\ s^{-2}$
- $kg\ m^{-1}\ s^{-2}$
- $kg\ m^2\ s^{-2}$
- $kg\ m^2\ s^{-3}$

Prefixes

Prefix	Symbol	Submultiple
pico	p	10^{-12}
nano	n	10^{-9}
micro	μ	10^{-6}
milli	m	10^{-3}
centi	c	10^{-2}
deci	d	10^{-1}

Prefix	Symbol	Multiple
kilo	k	10^{3}
mega	M	10^{6}
giga	G	10^{9}
tera	T	10^{12}

Scalars or Vectors

PHYSICAL QUANTITIES & UNITS → are → **Scalars** or **Vectors**

Vectors

Vector addition — Head to tail, Parallelogram

Vector subtraction — Head to tail, Parallelogram

Components of a vector

$$F_y = F \sin \theta$$
$$F_x = F \cos \theta$$
$$F = \sqrt{F_x^2 + F_y^2}$$
$$\tan \theta = \frac{F_y}{F_x}$$

Mole

PHYSICAL QUANTITIES & UNITS → an important quantity → **Mole**

1 mole contains **6.02 X 10²³ particles, atoms, etc.**

this constant is known as **Avogadro Constant** $N_A = 6.02 \times 10^{23}\ mol^{-1}$

n mole — mass of 1 mole of substance → **Molar mass M**

m = mass of 1 atom or molecule

$$M = N_A m$$

Molar mass M → is the → **Relative molecular mass of the substance in grams.**

$$n = \frac{\text{Mass of substance } (m_s)}{\text{Molar mass } M}$$

or

$$n = \frac{\text{No. of atoms or molecules } (N)}{N_A}$$

24

2 Measurement Techniques

MEASUREMENTS

ERRORS AND UNCERTAINTIES

Syllabus Objectives

In this chapter you should be able to:

- use techniques for the measurement of length, volume, angle, mass, time, temperature and electrical quantities appropriate to the ranges of magnitude implied by the relevant parts of the syllabus.
  In particular, candidates should be able to:
  - measure temperature, using a thermometer as a sensor;
  - use ammeters and voltmeters with appropriate scales;
  - use a galvanometer in null methods;
  - use a cathode-ray oscilloscope;
  - use a calibrated Hall probe.
- use both analogue scales and digital displays.
- use calibration curves.
- show an understanding of the distinction between systematic errors (including zero errors) and random errors.
- show an understanding of the distinction between precision and accuracy.
- assess the uncertainty in a derived quantity by simple addition of actual, fractional or percentage uncertainties (a rigorous statistical treatment is not required).

MEASUREMENTS I

- Measurement is the basis of experimental science. It involves the observation of physical variables in a controlled environment in order to gain an understanding of the natural world. Through measurements theories are verified, adapted or discarded. A variety of measurement techniques is explored in the following pages.

Measurement of Length

(a) **Metre-rule**

(i) A metre-rule is used to measure length. In order to use it accurately, care must be taken to avoid parallax error. This arises when the eye is not positioned vertically above the mark to be measured (Fig 2.1). At the incorrect position I, the mark seems to correspond to the 5.1 cm line on the scale. When viewed vertically at C it is 5.0 cm.

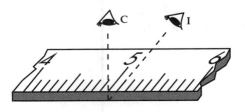

Fig 2.1   Parallax error

(ii) When measuring the length of an object, avoid creating a gap between the ruler and the object to be measured.

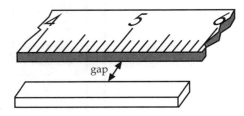

Fig 2.2   Errors could arise from poor alignment

(iii) Check the ruler for end errors before making a measurement. This could arise when the end of the ruler is worn or the zero mark is not at the edge of the object.

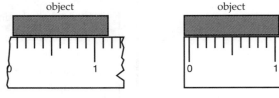

Fig 2.3   End errors that could arise in a measurement

26

Fig 2.4a   Measurement with calliper

(b) **Calliper**

Figs 2.4a and 2.4b show two different kinds of callipers that can be used to measure the diameter of a sphere and the internal diameter of a tube. In both instruments, the open jaws are placed on a metre-rule and the required lengths are read off.

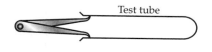

Fig 2.4b   Measurement with calliper

(c) **Vernier calliper**

(i) A vernier calliper consists of a small scale (vernier scale) which can slide along a main scale to give a more accurate reading (Fig 2.5). The procedures for using the vernier calliper to measure the diameter of a sphere is given below:

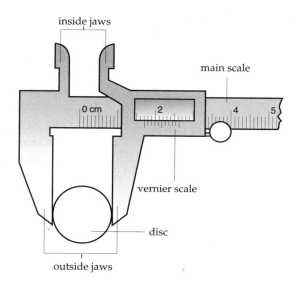

Fig 2.5   Measurement with vernier callipers

– Check for zero error
– Grip sphere firmly
– Read the value
– Take several readings at different points
– Find the average

Diameter of the sphere = 1.71 cm

(ii) The vernier scale has a length of 0.9 cm subdivided into ten divisions. Each division has a length of 0.09 cm.

(iii) In Fig 2.6a, M_0 on the main scale corresponds to V_0 on the vernier scale. There is no zero error. The distances between the M_1 and V_1 mark, M_2 and V_2 mark and so on becomes progressively larger. Fig 2.6b shows a vernier calliper with

27

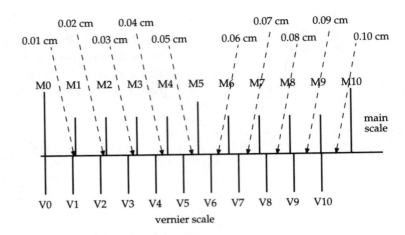

Fig 2.6a   The main scale and the vernier scale of vernier callipers

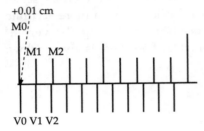

Fig 2.6b   Positive zero error

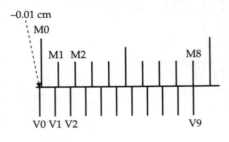

Fig 2.6c   Negative zero error

positive zero error. In this case, M_1 coincides with V_1. The V_0 mark on the vernier scale would have moved a distance of 0.01 cm to the right. Its zero error is +0.01 cm. Fig 2.6c shows an example of negative zero error. The M_8 mark in this case coincides with the V_9 mark, hence V_0 would have moved a distance of 0.01 cm to the left. The zero error is taken as –0.01 cm to distinguish it from the zero error in Fig 2.6b.

(iv) This positive or negative zero error must be subtracted from the reading of the diameter of the sphere to obtain the corrected reading.

From Fig 2.6b, zero error = +0.01 cm
Diameter of sphere = 1.71 cm (Fig 2.5)
Corrected reading of sphere = 1.71 − (+0.01)
$\qquad\qquad\qquad\qquad\qquad$ = 1.70 cm

From Fig 2.6c, zero error = −0.01 cm
Diameter of sphere = 1.71 cm (Fig 2.5)
Corrected reading of sphere = 1.71 − (−0.01)
$\qquad\qquad\qquad\qquad\qquad$ = 1.72 cm

(v) Fig 2.7 shows another type of vernier calliper that can read to an accuracy of 0.02 mm. The vernier scale has a length of 4.9 cm subdivided into 50 divisons.

Fig 2.7   The main scale and the vernier scale of a vernier calliper

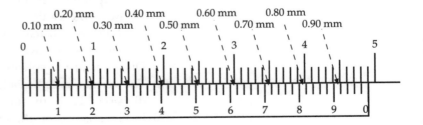

(d) Micrometer screw gauge

(i) A micrometer screw gauge can be used to measure small lengths accurately. The instrument has two scales: one on the sleeve and another on the thimble. One complete revolution or the movement of 50 divisions of the thimble causes the spindle to move 0.5 mm. Movement of one division on the thimble causes the spindle to move 0.01 mm horizontally. Fig 2.8 shows how the micrometer is used to measure the diameter of a sphere.

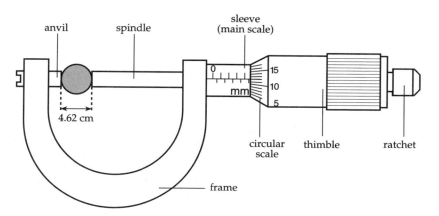

Fig 2.8   Micrometer screw gauge

Procedures for using the micrometer
- Check for zero error
- Place object between the anvil and the spindle
- Turn ratchet a few times
- Tighten lock
- Read sleeve and thimble
- Take several readings at different points
- Find the average
  Sleeve reading = 4.5 mm
  Thimble reading = 0.12 mm
  Diameter of sphere = 4.62 mm

(ii) When there is zero error the final reading must be adjusted. This is illustrated in Fig 2.9.

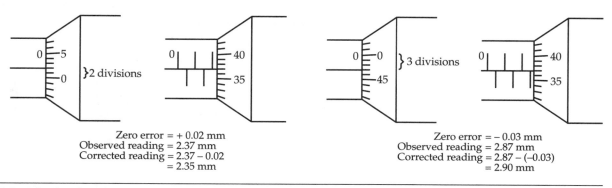

Zero error = + 0.02 mm
Observed reading = 2.37 mm
Corrected reading = 2.37 − 0.02
= 2.35 mm

Zero error = − 0.03 mm
Observed reading = 2.87 mm
Corrected reading = 2.87 − (−0.03)
= 2.90 mm

Fig 2.9   Adjusting for zero errors

Measurement of Volume

- The S. I. unit for the measurement of volume is m^3. As volume measured in the laboratory are small, alternative units such as dm^3, cm^3 and mm^3 are used. It should also be noted that $1\ dm^3$ is equal to 1 litre (l) and $1\ cm^3$ is equal to 1 ml. Although the litre is not an S. I. unit, it is an accepted unit used together with other S. I. units. Fig 2.10 shows how these quantities are related.

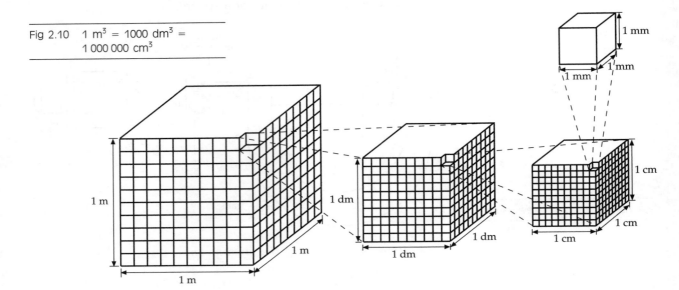

Fig 2.10 $1\ m^3 = 1000\ dm^3 = 1\ 000\ 000\ cm^3$

- To measure the volume of a liquid a measuring cylinder can be used. The smallest cylinder gives the most accurate reading. For example, in a 500-cm^3 cylinder, every 5 cm^3 is marked compared with 1 cm^3 for a 100-cm^3 cylinder. For more accurate readings a burette should be used. Alternatively a graduated flask or a pipette may be used if fixed volumes of liquids are required.

- To avoid parallax error, readings should be taken from the lowest point of a concave meniscus (Fig 2.11). In the case of mercury which has a convex meniscus, readings should be taken from the highest point.

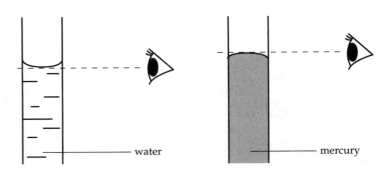

Fig 2.11   Correct way to measure volume in a measuring cylinder

water   mercury

Measurement of Angles

- The most common instrument used to measure angle is the protractor. Readings will be inaccurate if there is parallax error or poor alignment of the protractor. Fig 2.12 illustrates the incorrect and correct method of alignment when measuring the angle θ of the slope.

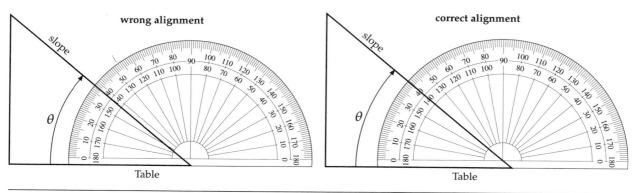

Fig 2.12   Correct alignment for measuring angles

Fig 2.13a   Spring balance

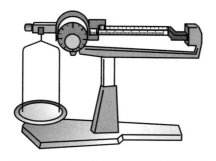

Fig 2.13b   Beam balance

Measurement of Mass and Weight

- Mass is measured by one of the following measuring instruments.

  (a) **Spring balance**
    (i) A spring balance (Fig 2.13a) makes use of the force of gravity acting on an object to extend or compress a spring.
    (ii) It measures weight but since weight is proportional to mass, the balance is often calibrated in grams or kilograms.
    (iii) As gravitational force varies over the surface of the earth, readings taken by the spring balance will vary too.

  (b) **Triple beam balance or lever balance**
    (i) This instrument measures the mass of an object. It is done by balancing the unknown mass with a set of known accurate masses (Fig 2.13b).
    (ii) The readings are independent of gravitational force and are the same throughout the world.

  (c) **Electronic balance or top pan balance**
    (i) The mass to be measured is placed on a top pan (Fig 2.13c). The force of gravity deforms a substance within the balance. This alters the resistance and the current flowing through. The variation of the current with mass are then calibrated in grams.

31

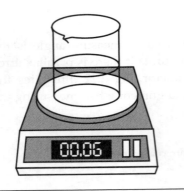

Fig 2.13c Electronic balance

(ii) One of the advantages of using this instrument is its reliability, accuracy and the small movement of the scale pan.

(iii) To make the task of weighing as simple as possible, most of the electronic balances have built-in features such as zeroing, calibration, dual range and a clear digital display.

- Weight
  (a) As the weight of any object is proportional to its mass, the weight is given by $W = mg$ where m is the mass of the object and g is the gravitational acceleration.
  (b) The unit used to measure weight is the newton. Most balances do not give readings in newton. The exception are some spring balances and a small number of electronic balances.

Measurement of Time

- Simple pendulum
  (a) One period of a simple pendulum is the time taken for one complete swing (centre – right – centre – left – centre)
  (b) The Period (T) of a simple pendulum is dependent only on the length of the pendulum and gravitational acceleration.

- Stopwatch
  (a) Analog stopwatches shown in Fig 2.14b can be read to 0.1 s.
  (b) Digital stopwatches shown in Fig 2.14c can be read to 0.01s. The limit of accuracy is the smallest decimal place on the digital display.

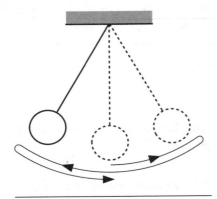

Fig 2.14a Simple pendulum

Fig 2.14b Analog stopwatch

Fig 2.14c Digital stopwatch

32

- Ticker tape timer
  - (a) It consists of a vibrator that operates at a frequency of 50 Hz. When a strip of paper is pulled through the vibrator, a series of dots is produced.
  - (b) The time interval between dots is 0.02 s.

- Scaler
  - (a) It measures time to 0.001 s.
  - (b) It can also be used as an electronic counter.

- Stroboscope
  - (a) It is capable of measuring the time of rotation of an object.
  - (b) It produces flashes at regular intervals. If the rotational speed of an object coincides with the flash rate, the rotating object will appear stationary. The time of rotation is measured from the time between the flashes.

Measurement of Temperature

- Mercury in glass thermometer
  - (a) The most common laboratory instrument that measures temperature conveniently is the mercury-in-glass thermometer. It has a range of $-10°C$ to $110°C$.
  - (b) When taking a reading, it is essential that the eye be at the same level as the mercury meniscus. This is to prevent parallax error.
  - (c) Temperatures should be measured to tenths of a degree. This should be possible if a hand lens is used and temperatures are steady. In Fig 2.15, the value of R_2 read from the thermometer is $31.0°C$.

- Digital thermometer
  - (a) The digital thermometer shown in Fig 2.16 makes use of a thermocouple as its temperature sensor.
  - (b) The thermocouple is embedded in a probe and one end of it is connected to the thermometer display console.
  - (c) Temperatures within the range of $-50°C$ to $1300°C$ can be read on the digital liquid crystal display. An accuracy of $0.1°C$ can be obtained from this instrument.

Measurement of Electric Current (Ammeter)

- An ammeter is used to measure electric current. Care must be taken to connect the ammeter in series with other components in the circuit.

- The positive terminal of the ammeter should be connected to the positive terminal of the battery (Fig 2.17). Similarly, the negative terminal of the ammeter leads to the negative terminal of the battery. If this is not done, the needle will get stuck as it moves below the zero mark in an anti-clockwise direction. This

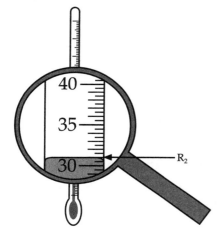

Fig 2.15   Mercury in glass thermometer

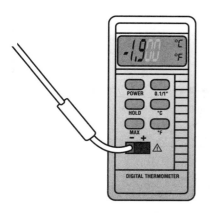

Fig 2.16   Digital thermometer

33

can be easily rectified by interchanging the wires connected to the ammeter.

- Errors in reading the scale of the ammeter are common. For example, in using an ammeter with a range of 0 to 1 A, it is easy to ignore the decimal place and read a current of 0.5 A as 5.0 A. Some ammeters are equipped with a mirror mounted under the needle. This is used to guide the eye to a position directly above the needle. In this position, the image of the needle is covered up and parallax error is eliminated.

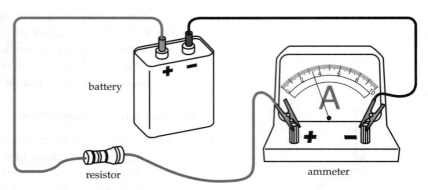

Fig 2.17   Measurement with an ammeter

Measurement of Potential Difference (Voltmeter)

- The voltmeter must be connected in parallel to the resistor whose potential difference is required (Fig 2.18).

- The positive terminal of the voltmeter must again be connected to the positive terminal of the battery. Similarly, the negative terminal of the voltmeter leads to the negative terminal of the battery.

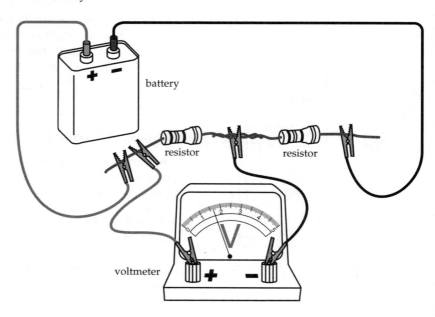

Fig 2.18   Measurement with a voltmeter

Galvanometer

- A galvanometer is an electrical meter that measures small currents in either direction. The zero mark is at the center of the scale. This instrument is commonly used in the potentiometer or wheatstone bridge circuit. In Fig 2.19, the bridge is balanced when the potential at A equals the potential at B. This is achieved by adjusting the variable resistor R_v until the galvanometer needle points to the zero mark at the center of the scale. The use of the galvanometer in this way is known as the null method of balancing. When the circuit is balanced, the unknown resistance (R_x) is related to the known resistances R_v, R_1 and R_2 by

$$R_x = R_v \left(\frac{R_1}{R_2} \right)$$

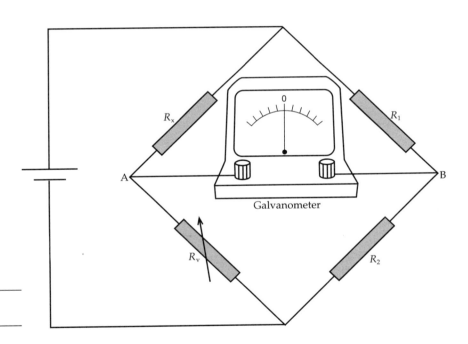

Fig 2.19   Measurement with a galvanometer

- Digital multimeter
  (a) A digital multimeter (Fig 2.20) is a versatile electronic instrument that can be used as an ammeter, a voltmeter or an ohmmeter.
  (b) By incorporating shunts, multipliers, variable resistors and an in-build battery, it is capable of measuring both a. c. and d. c. current and voltages as well as resistances in an electric circuit.

35

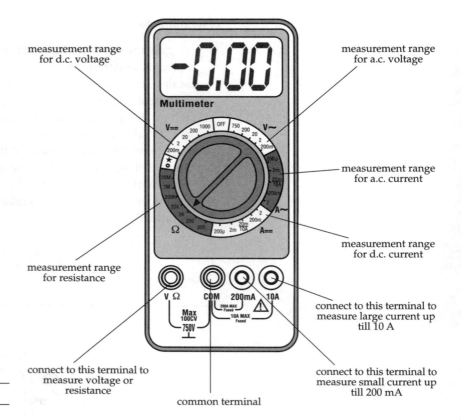

measurement range for d.c. voltage

measurement range for a.c. voltage

Multimeter

measurement range for a.c. current

measurement range for resistance

measurement range for d.c. current

V Ω   COM   200mA   10A

Max 100CV 750V

connect to this terminal to measure large current up till 10 A

connect to this terminal to measure voltage or resistance

common terminal

connect to this terminal to measure small current up till 200 mA

Fig 2.20   Digital multimeter

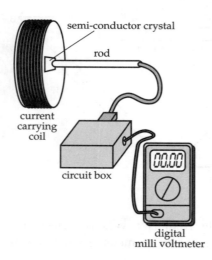

semi-conductor crystal

rod

current carrying coil

circuit box

digital milli voltmeter

Fig 2.21   Calibrated Hall probe measures magnetic flux density

- Calibrated Hall Probes
  (a) Hall probes are electronic devices that can measure magnetic flux density. It consists of a small semiconductor crystal fixed to one end of a rod and connected via a circuit box to a digital milli-voltmeter (see Fig 2.21).
  (b) Before making a measurement, the probe must be calibrated with a magnetic field of known strength. This can be done by placing the probe perpendicular to the magnetic field. When the circuit box is switch on a current will flow through the semiconductor crystal. A potential difference known as the Hall voltage will appear across the crystal. This voltage will be directly proportional to the magnetic flux density. The sensitivity of the probe in millivolts per tesla can be found. Subsequently, when the probe is placed in a unknown magnetic field, its flux density can be determined.

- Cathode Ray Oscilloscope
  Cathode ray oscilloscopes are sophisticated electronic instruments (Fig 2.22a) that can measure a. c. or d. c. voltages and display electronic signals on a phosphor- coated screen. Fig 2.22b shows the internal structure of a cathode ray oscilloscope.

36

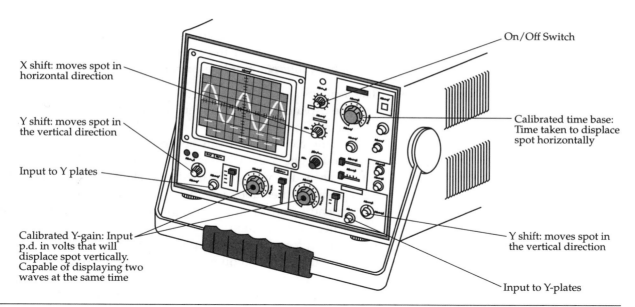

Fig 2.22a Dual Beam Cathode Ray Oscilloscope

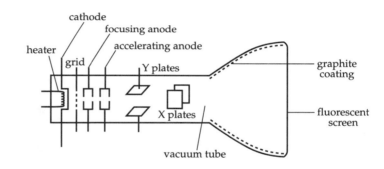

Fig 2.22b CRO

- Cathode – An indirectly heated metal piece emits electrons by thermionic emission. The on/off switch (Fig 2.22b) operates the cathode.

- Grid – The negatively charged metal mesh placed in front of the cathode limits the amount of electrons moving through. This in turn affects the brightness on the screen. The on/off switch incorporates a brightness control which operates the grid.

- Anode – Consists of an accelerating and foscussing anode. Both are connected to a high positive potential relative to the cathode. This causes electrons to accelerate to high speeds. The focus control adjust the sharpness on the screen by changing the potential on the focussing anode.

- Vacuum Tube – It is highly evacuated so that electrons will meet with minimum obstruction as it travels to the screen.

- The Display Screen – The screen is coated with either a blue phosphor or a green phosphor. Light energy are emitted when energetic electrons collide with the screen. It is important to

37

earth the screen so that in-coming electrons from the cathode will not accumulate on the screen but will leak to the earth through an internal graphite coating.

- The Y-plates
  (a) The Y-plates control the vertical deflection of the electron beam.
  (b) D.c. or a.c. voltages can be applied to this set of plates through the Y-INPUT (Fig 2.22a & b).
  (c) When a d.c. voltage is used, the stationary spot of light appears either above or below the centre of the screen, depending on whether the applied voltage is in the positive or negative direction.
  (d) With an a.c. voltage, the spot of light moves up and down with the same frequency as the input voltage. As the frequency increases the movement becomes so rapid that the eye will perceive the rapid vertical motion of the spot of light as a straight line (Fig 2.23).

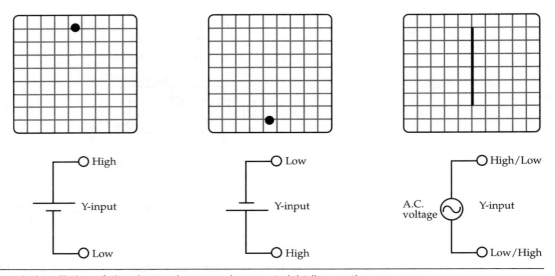

Fig 2.23   Rapid vertical oscillation of the electron beam produces a straight line on the c.r.o screen

(e) The Y-shift is able to move the spot of light or line vertically upwards or downwards. This can be used to centre the spot on the screen.
(f) The calibrated Y-gain or voltage sensitivity controls an in-built amplifier that is connected to the Y-plates. Input voltages are amplified sufficiently to make a visible deflection of the electron spot on the screen. The different settings on the Y-gain indicates how much the input voltage is needed to displace the spot of light by 1 division. It is calibrated in volts/division or mV/division. When the Y-gain is selected, d.c. or a.c. voltages can be found as follows.

38

D.C. voltage, $V = d$ (division) $\times$ Y-gain (V/division)

where d is the displacement of the spot from the centre of the screen.

Peak to peak voltage, $V_{pp} = L$ (division) $\times$ Y-gain (V/division)

where L is the entire length of the vertical trace on the screen.

Peak voltage, $V_p = \dfrac{1}{2} V_{pp}$

- X-Plates
  (a) The X-plates control the horizontal deflection of the electron beam.
  (b) A common use of the Oscilloscope is to connect an inbuilt time-base generator to the x-plates. This produces a varying saw-tooth voltage illustrated in Fig 2.24.

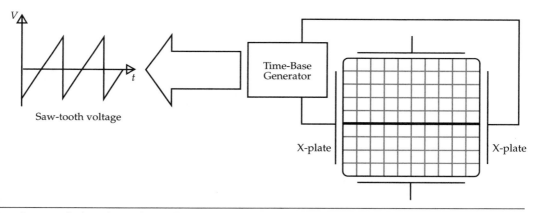

Saw-tooth voltage

Fig 2.24   Saw-tooth voltage applied to the x-plates of the c.r.o.

- As the voltage on the x-plates increases, the beam of electrons will move across the screen with constant speed. A moving spot of light can be seen.
- At the end of the sweep, it flies back to the origin due to a reversal of the voltage across the x-plates.
- If the frequency is high, the moving dot appears as a horizontal straight line across the screen.
- The X-gain or time-based controls the time it takes the spot of light on the screen to travel one division horizontally. It is calibrated in millisecond/division or μs/division. For example, a setting of 5 ms/division causes the spot of light to move 1 division in 5 ms.

Time taken to cross a screen 10 divisions wide

$= 10$ divisions $\times \dfrac{50 \text{ ms}}{\text{division}}$

$= 0.5$ s

39

(c) A less common use is to connect an external voltage source to the X-plates through the X-input terminal. One lead goes into the X-input while the other goes into the ground terminal.

- Uses of the Cathode-Ray Oscilloscope
The cathode ray oscilloscope is a very versatile instrument. Its uses are illustrated in Table 2.1

Table 2.1   Uses of the CRO

Uses	Gain	Screen
1) Measure d. c. voltages – Switch off time-base. 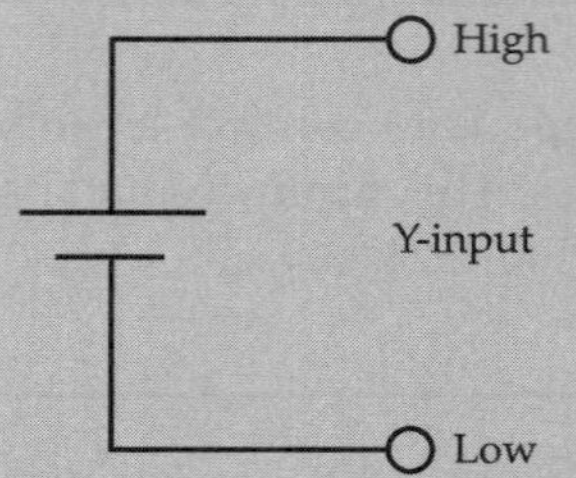 High — Y-input — Low	Volts/Div 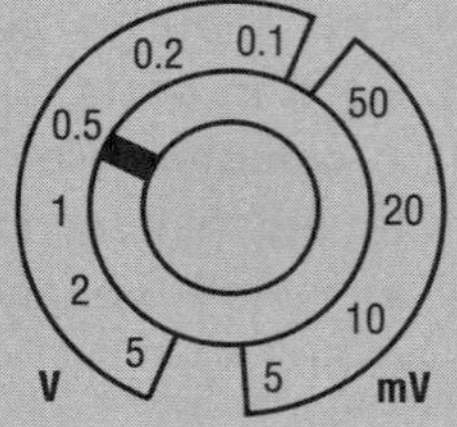 0.5 V/div	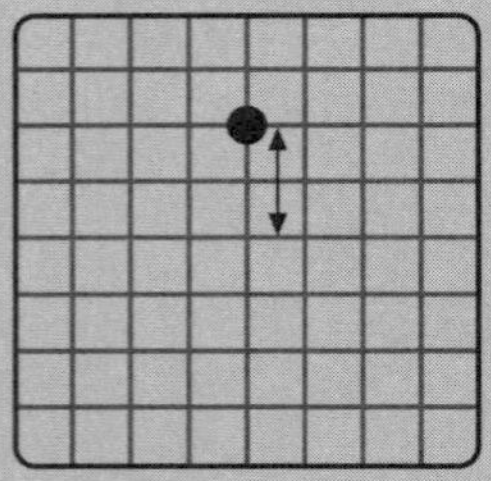 $V = 2$ div $\times$ 0.5 V/div $= 1.0$ V
2) Measure a. c. voltages – switch off time-base. 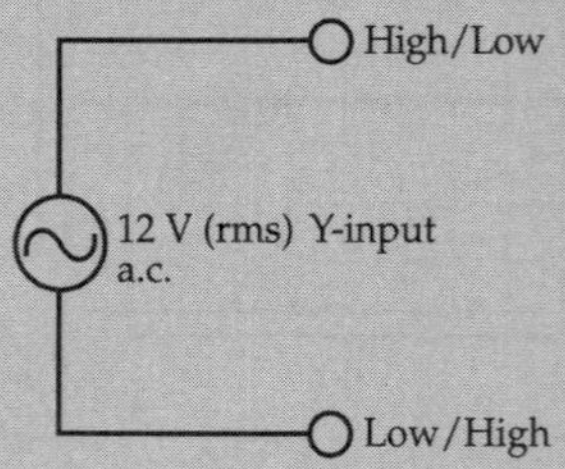 High/Low — 12 V (rms) Y-input a.c. — Low/High	Volts/Div 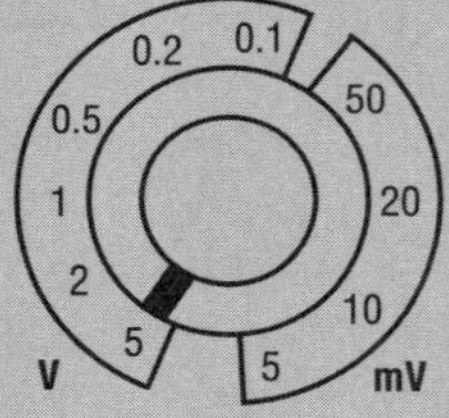 5 V/div	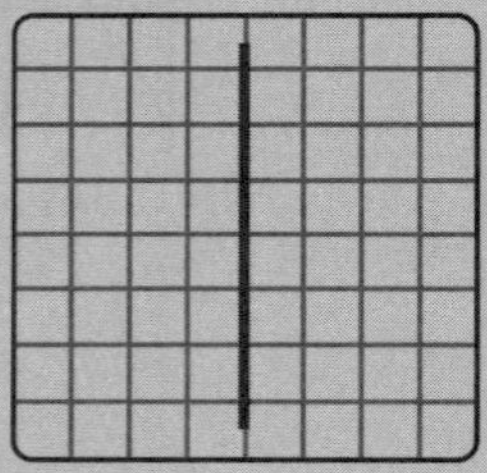 $V_{PP} = 6.8$ div $\times$ 5.0 V/div $= 34.0$ V $V_P = \dfrac{34.0}{2} = 17$ V
3) Measuring time and frequency – Obtain steady trace. – Measure number of divisions occupied by 1 cycle. – Multiply by time/div.	Time/Div 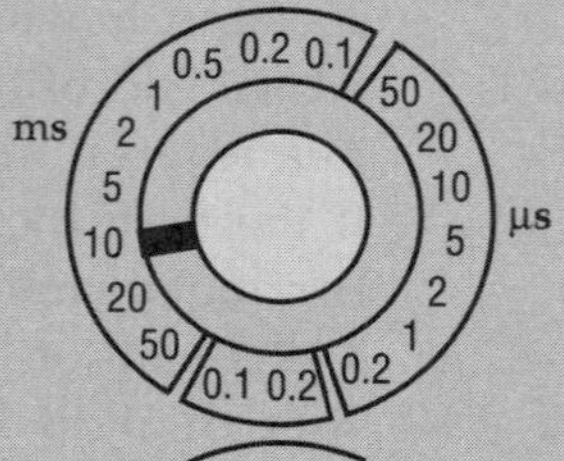 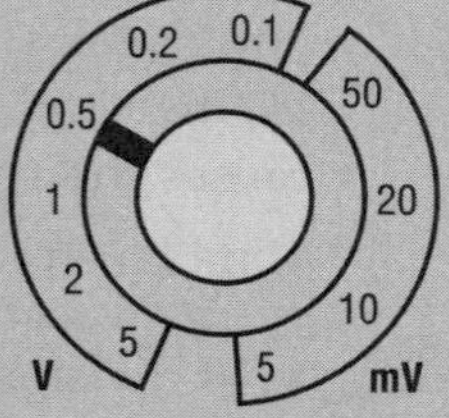 Volts/Div	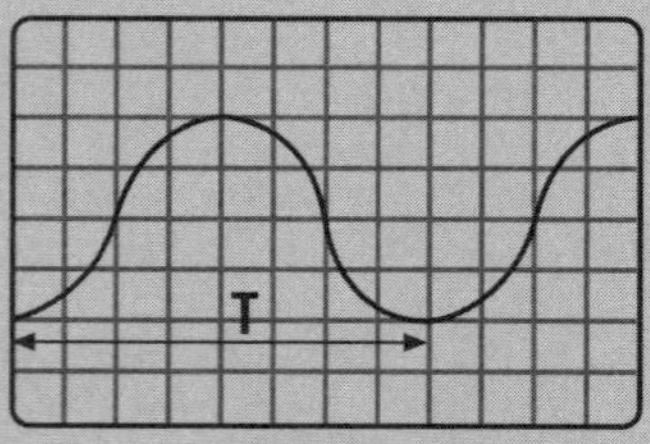 Period (T) $= 8$ div $\times$ 10 ms/div $= 80$ ms Frequency $= \dfrac{1}{80 \times 10^{-3}}$ $= 12.5$ Hz

40

ERRORS AND UNCERTAINTIES

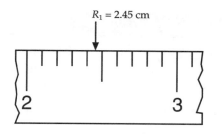

$R_1 = 2.45$ cm

Fig 2.25 A reading obtained from a metre-rule

Uncertainty in a Reading

- A reading is the single determination of a value at one point on a measuring scale.

- Generally, a reading can be estimated to $\frac{1}{2}$ of the smallest division on a measuring scale. In the case of a ruler, it would be 0.5 mm or 0.05 cm. Hence the value of R_1 read from a metre-rule in Fig 2.25 is 24.5 mm or 2.45 cm.

- All experimental data has associated with it an element of uncertainty. The maximum range within which the reading is likely to lie is known as its maximum uncertainty. In the above case, it is between 24.0 mm to 25.0 mm or 2.40 cm to 2.50 cm.

Uncertainty in a measurement

- A measurement is the process by which a physical quantity is compared with a standard unit. Very often this involves the determination of two readings. For example the length of a pencil is obtained by taking the difference between two readings from a metre-rule (Fig. 2.26). The uncertainty associated with this length is obtained as follows:

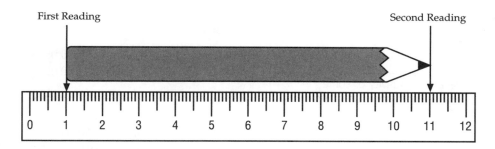

Fig 2.26 A measurement obtained from a metre-rule

Smallest division on the metre-rule = 1 mm or 0.1 cm
The uncertainty for 1 reading = ± 0.5 mm or ± 0.05 cm
Since two readings are involved, uncertainty in the measurement, also known as absolute error
$= \pm(0.5 + 0.5)$ mm
$= \pm 1$ mm or ± 0.1 cm
The measured length = (100 ± 1) mm or (10.0 ± 0.1) cm
The measured value has the same number of decimal places as the maximum uncertainty while the latter is generally expressed to one significant figure only.

- The measured value of any quantity can be characterised by two important terms. They are:
(a) the maximum uncertainty and
(b) the number of significant figures.

41

- The maximum uncertainty is an indication of the scale sensitivity or the accuracy of the measuring instrument used. Table 2.2 shows the sensitivity of some commonly used measuring instruments.

Instrument	Sensitivity	Example
Metre-rule	0.001 m 0.1 cm 1 mm	0.543 m 54.3 cm 543 mm
Vernier calliper	0.01 cm (0.1 mm)	2.53 cm
Vernier calliper (more accurate version)	0.002 cm (0.02 mm)	1.276 cm
Vernier microscope	0.01 cm	6.48 cm
Micrometer screw gauge	0.01 mm	1.57 mm
Digital stopwatch	0.01 s	9.85 s**
Thermometer	0.2°C 0.5°C	27.8°C 67.5°C
Electronic balance	0.01 g 0.001 g	4.03 g 1.789 g
Protractor	1°	39°
Ammeter	0.05 A 0.02 A	2.55 A 0.48 A
Voltmeter	0.05 V	1.25 V

Table 2.2   Sensitivity of some commonly used apparatus

** Since the average human reaction time is about 0.2 s, it is reasonable to round off the time obtained from a digital stopwatch to 1 decimal place (i.e. 9.9 s in the above example).

- The maximum uncertainty determines the number of significant figures a measurement should have. In the example illustrated in Fig 2.26, the maximum uncertainty of ± 0.1 cm restricts the length of the pencil to 1 decimal place in cm. The measured length is therefore written as 10.0 cm. To write it as 10.00 cm is unwarranted as it is beyond the accuracy that a metre-rule can provide. The number of significant figures in a measurement is the number of meaningful digits whose values are known with certainty.

Experimental Errors

- All experiments are affected by errors. Experimental errors can be classified as random errors or systematic errors.

Random Errors

- Random errors produces unpredictable deviations from the actual value such that each reading has equal chance to fall above or below the actual value.

- Random errors cannot be eliminated but can be reduced by finding the average of all the readings obtained. The average temperature of the four random readings in example 1 in Table 2.3 is 30.1°C. This is in good agreement to the actual temperature of 30.2°C. We can say that the value is accurate. By taking the average, the most probable result is obtained.

- When a set of readings has small random errors, it is precise. They are scattered close to the average value. If they are scattered further apart like in example 2, they are not precise.

Systematic Errors

- Systematic error causes a random set of readings to be distributed consistently around an average value that is significantly different from the actual value. The error is predictable.

- In examples 3 and 4 of Table 2.3 the four readings are scattered around the average value of 24.8°C which is significantly different from the actual value of 30.2°C. In this case, the cause could probably be due to wrong calibration or a biased observer. In other apparatus, it could be due to faulty equipment, zero error or an unsuitable laboratory condition. Determining the average value does not reduce the systematic error. The cause of the error must be identified and eliminated.

- When a set of readings has small systematic error, it is accurate. If it has large systematic error, it is inaccurate.

Treatment of Errors

- If a measurement has a value of x and its maximum uncertainty is Δx, it is written as $(x \pm \Delta x)$. Care should be taken to ensure that the measurement have the same number of decimal places as the quoted maximum uncertainty. Hence a length is written as (10.0 ± 0.1) cm and not (10 ± 0.1) cm.

- Although the maximum uncertainty is useful it is also important to know how this quantity compares with the quantity measured. For example an uncertainty of ± 1 mm in a

Example	Random Error	Systematic Error	Diagram	Remarks
1	Small	Small	Actual Temperature = 30.2°C 29.7°C 30.0°C 30.3°C 30.4°C Average Temperature = 30.1°C	Precise and Accurate
2	Large	Small	Actual Temperature = 30.2°C 28.2°C 29.8°C 30.5°C 31.9°C Average Temperature = 30.1°C	Not Precise but Accurate
3	Small	Large	Actual Temperature = 30.2°C 24.5°C 24.7°C 24.9°C 25.1°C Average Temperature = 24.8°C	Precise but Inaccurate
4	Large	Large	Actual Temperature = 30.2°C 23.2°C 24.6°C 25.1°C 26.3°C Average Temperature = 24.8°C	Not Precise and Inaccurate

Table 2.3 Examples of random and systematic error

length of 100 cm is negligible but an error of ± 1 mm in 1 cm is significant. To make this comparison, we use the ratio $\dfrac{\Delta x}{x}$ which is also called the maximum fractional uncertainty. The percentage uncertainty is given by $\left(\dfrac{\Delta x}{x}\right)100\%$.

Addition and Subtraction of Uncertainties

- If we add or subtract two physical quantities, its maximum uncertainties must be added together. Proof of this is shown in Appendix A.

  If $S = A + B$ and ΔA, ΔB and ΔS are the maximum uncertainties of A, B and S respectively.
  $$\Delta S = \Delta A + \Delta B$$
  If $D = A - B$ and ΔA, ΔB and ΔD are the maximum uncertainties of A, B and D respectively.
  $$\Delta D = \Delta A + \Delta B$$
  It should be noted that uncertainties are not eliminated when physical quantities are subtracted. In fact, if A and B are nearly equal quantities, the percentage error is very high.

Q The lengths A and B are (4.2 ± 0.1) cm and (5.5 ± 0.1) cm. Find the percentage uncertainty of S and D where
(a) $S = A + B$
(b) $D = 3A - 2B$

A
(a) $S = 4.2 + 5.5$
$\quad\;\; = 9.7$ cm
$\;\Delta S = 0.1 + 0.1$
$\quad\;\; = 0.2$ cm

Percentage uncertainty of $S = \left(\dfrac{\Delta S}{S}\right)100\%$

$\qquad\qquad\qquad = \left(\dfrac{0.2}{9.7}\right)100\%$

$\qquad\qquad\qquad = 2.1\ \%$

(b) $D = 3\,(4.2) - 2\,(5.5)$
$\quad\;\; = 1.6$ cm
$\;\Delta D = 3\,(0.1) + 2\,(0.1)$
$\quad\;\; = 0.5$ cm

Percentage uncertainty of $D = \left(\dfrac{\Delta D}{D}\right)100\%$

$\qquad\qquad\qquad = \left(\dfrac{0.5}{1.6}\right)100\%$

$\qquad\qquad\qquad = 31\ \%$

Q A student attempts to measure the diameter of a steel ball by using a metre rule to measure four similar balls in a row. The positions of the scale are estimated to be $X = (1.0 \pm 0.2)$ cm and $Y = (5.0 \pm 0.2)$ cm. What is the diameter of a steel ball together with its associated uncertainty?

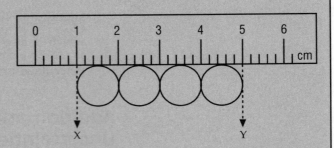

Cambridge

A Length $XY = (5.0 - 1.0) \pm (0.2 + 0.2)$
$= (4.0 \pm 0.4)$ cm

Diameter of steel ball $= \dfrac{1}{4}(4.0 \pm 0.4)$
$= (1.0 \pm 0.1)$ cm

Multiplication and Division

- If two quantities A and B are multiplied together, the maximum fractional uncertainty of the product is the sum of the two fractional uncertainties in A and B. Proof of this is shown in Appendix A.

$$M = A \times B$$

The maximum fractional uncertainty in M is $\dfrac{\Delta M}{M} = \dfrac{\Delta A}{A} + \dfrac{\Delta B}{B}$.

- If two quantities A and B are divided together, the maximum fractional uncertainty of the division is the sum of the two fractional uncertainties in A and B. Proof of this is shown in Appendix A.

$$D = \frac{A}{B}$$

The maximum fractional uncertainty in D is $\dfrac{\Delta D}{D} = \dfrac{\Delta A}{A} + \dfrac{\Delta B}{B}$

- When both multiplication and division are involved, the method for determining the fractional uncertainty still remains the same. For example $Z = \dfrac{AB}{CD}$.

The maximum fractional uncertainty in Z is

$$\frac{\Delta Z}{Z} = \frac{\Delta A}{A} + \frac{\Delta B}{B} + \frac{\Delta C}{C} + \frac{\Delta D}{D}$$

Powers

- If $Z = k A^n$ where k and n are constants, the maximum fractional uncertainty in Z is n times the fractional uncertainty in A. The constant k is assumed to be error free and do not appear in the evaluation of fractional uncertainty. Hence, $\dfrac{\Delta Z}{Z} = n \dfrac{\Delta A}{A}$.

- If $W = k A^{1/n}$, where k and n are constants, the maximum fractional uncertainty in W is $\dfrac{1}{n}$ times the fractional uncertainty of A. Hence, $\dfrac{\Delta W}{W} = \dfrac{1}{n} \dfrac{\Delta A}{A}$.

The length of a piece of paper is measured as (297 ± 1) mm. Its width is measured as (209 ± 1) mm.
(a) What is the fractional uncertainty in its length?
(b) What is the percentage uncertainty in its length?
(c) What is the area of one side of the piece of paper? State your answer with its uncertainty.

Cambridge

(a) Fractional uncertainty in

the length of the paper $= \dfrac{\Delta x}{x}$

$= \dfrac{1}{297}$

$= 0.00337$

(b) Percentage uncertainty

in the length $= \left(\dfrac{\Delta x}{x}\right) 100$

$= (0.00337)(100)$

$= 0.337\%$

(c) Area A = length $(l) \times$ width (w)
$= 297 \times 209$
$= 62\ 073$ mm^2
Fractional uncertainty in area is given by

$\dfrac{\Delta A}{A} = \dfrac{\Delta l}{l} + \dfrac{\Delta w}{w}$

$\Delta A = \left(\dfrac{1}{297} + \dfrac{1}{209}\right)(62\ 073)$

$= 506$ mm^2

Area should be expressed as $(62\ 100 \pm 500)$ mm^2 or $(6.21 \pm 0.05) \times 10^4$ mm^2.

The density of the material of a rectangular block was determined by measuring the mass and linear dimensions of the block. The results obtained, together with their uncertainties are shown below.
mass $= (25.0 \pm 0.1)$ g
length $= (5.00 \pm 0.01)$ cm
breadth $= (2.00 \pm 0.01)$ cm
height $= (1.00 \pm 0.01)$ cm
The density was calculated to be 2.50 g cm^{-3}.
What was the uncertainty in this result?

Cambridge

47

A

$$\text{density} = \frac{\text{mass}}{\text{volume}}$$

$$d = \frac{m}{v}$$

$$d = \frac{m}{lbh}$$

$$\frac{\Delta d}{d} = \frac{\Delta m}{m} + \frac{\Delta l}{l} + \frac{\Delta b}{b} + \frac{\Delta h}{h}$$

$$\frac{\Delta d}{2.50} = \frac{0.1}{25.0} + \frac{0.01}{5.00} + \frac{0.01}{2.00} + \frac{0.01}{1.00}$$

$$\Delta d = 0.0525$$
$$\quad\ = 0.05 \text{ g cm}^{-3}$$

Hence the uncertainty is ± 0.05 g cm^{-3}.

Q

The equation governing the volume rate of flow, $\frac{V}{t}$ of a fluid under streamline conditions through a horizontal pipe of length l and radius r is $\frac{V}{t} = \frac{(\pi p r^4)}{(8l\eta)}$ where p is the pressure difference across the pipe and η is the viscosity of the fluid.

In an experiment to find η for water, a student quoted his result as 1.137×10^{-3} kg m^{-1} s^{-1} and estimated the percentage uncertainties in his measurement of $\frac{V}{t}$, p, l and r as $\pm 3\%$, $\pm 2\%$, $\pm 0.5\%$ and $\pm 5\%$ respectively. How should he have written the value?

Cambridge

A

$$\eta = \frac{\pi p r^4}{8l\left(\frac{v}{t}\right)}$$

The percentage uncertainty in η is given by:

$$\left(\frac{\Delta\eta}{\eta}\right)100\% = \left(\frac{\Delta p}{p}\right)100\% + 4\left(\frac{\Delta r}{r}\right)100\% + \left(\frac{\Delta l}{l}\right)100\% + \frac{\Delta\left(\frac{v}{t}\right)}{\frac{v}{t}}100\%$$

$$= 2\% + 4(5)\% + 0.5\% + 3\%$$
$$= 25.5\%$$

i.e. $\left(\dfrac{\Delta\eta}{1.137 \times 10^{-3}}\right)100\% = 25.5\%$

$$\therefore \Delta\eta = \left(\frac{25.5}{100}\right)(1.137 \times 10^{-3})$$
$$= 2.90 \times 10^{-4} \text{ kg m}^{-1} \text{ s}^{-1}$$
$$= 0.3 \times 10^{-3} \text{ kg m}^{-1} \text{ s}^{-1}$$

η should be written as $(1.1 \pm 0.3) \times 10^{-3}$ kg m^{-1} s^{-1}.

Exercise 2

Multiple Choice Questions

1 The diagrams show the scale reading of a travelling microscope focused in turns on each of the end of a short metal rod.

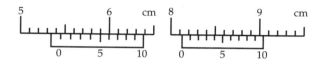

On reading the vernier, an error of one division either way may be made.
What is the length of the rod and the associated error in the measurement?
A 2.66 ± 0.01 cm   B 2.68 ± 0.01 cm
C 2.68 ± 0.02 cm   D 2.70 ± 0.01 cm

2 The diameter of a steel ball is measured using a micrometer screw gauge. A student takes an initial zero reading and then a reading of the diameter.
The diagrams show the enlargements of the screw gauge readings.

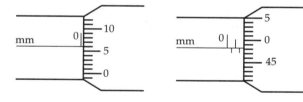

What is the diameter of the ball?
A 1.92 mm   B 1.98 mm
C 2.04 mm   D 3.48 mm

3 A student uses vernier callipers to measure the sides of rectangular wafer of silicon to the nearest tenth of a millimetre. The lengths are 10.4 mm, 6.3 mm and 2.3 mm. Which of the following best expresses the volume of the wafer?
A 1.50696 × 10^2 mm^3 B 1.5 × 10^2 mm^3
C 1.507 × 10^2 mm^3 D 1.51 × 10^2 mm^3

4 A body, dropped from a tower, is timed to take (2.0 ± 0.1) s to fall to the ground. If the acceleration of free fall is taken as 10 m s^{-2}, the calculated height of the tower should be quoted as
A (20 ± 0.2) m   B (20 ± 0.5) m
C (20 ± 1) m   D (20 ± 2) m

5 A petrol gauge in a car indicates the volume V of fuel in the tank. V is given by the angular deflection θ of the pointer on a dial.

Below are the calibration curves for four different gauges.

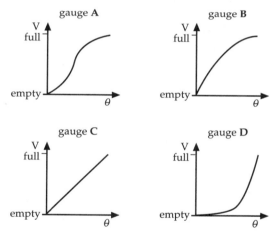

For **low** fuel levels in the tank, which gauge would be most sensitive?

6 Which of the following experimental techniques reduces the systematic error of the quantity being investigated?
A timing a large number of oscillations to find a period
B measuring several internodal distances on a standing wave to find the mean internodal distance
C measuring the diameter of a wire repeatedly and calculating the average
D adjusting an ammeter to remove its zero error before measuring a current

7   When comparing systematic and random errors, the following pairs of properties of errors in an experimental measurement may be contrasted:

P_1 : error can possibly be eliminated
P_2 : error cannot possibly be eliminated
Q_1 : error is of constant sign and magnitude
Q_2 : error is of varying sign and magnitude
R_1 : error will be reduced by averaging repeated measurements
R_2 : error will not be reduced by averaging repeated measurements

Which properties apply to random errors?

A P_1, Q_1, R_2 **B** P_1, Q_2, R_2
C P_2, Q_2, R_1 **D** P_2, Q_1, R_1

8   In a simple electrical circuit, the current in a resistor is measured as (2.50 ± 0.05) mA. The resistor is marked as having a value of 4.7 $\Omega \pm 2\%$. If these values were used to calculate the power dissipated in the resistor, what would be the percentage uncertainty in the value obtained?

A 2 %   **B** 4 %
C 6 %   **D** 8 %

9

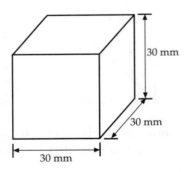

The dimensions of a cube are measured with vernier callipers.
The measured length of each side is 30 mm. If the vernier callipers can be read with an uncertainty of ±0.1 mm, what is the approximate uncertainty in the value of its volume?

A $\dfrac{1}{27}\%$ **B** $\dfrac{3}{10}\%$

C $\dfrac{1}{3}\%$ **D** 1 %

10 Four students each made a series of measurements of the acceleration of free fall g. The table shows the results obtained. Which student obtained a set of results that could be describe as precise but not accurate?

Student	Results, g/m s^{-2}			
A	9.81	9.79	9.84	9.83
B	9.81	10.12	9.89	8.94
C	9.45	9.21	8.99	8.76
D	8.45	8.46	8.50	8.41

11 A micrometer, reading to ±0.01 mm, gives the following results when used to measure the diameter d of a uniform wire: 1.02 mm, 1.02 mm, 1.01 mm, 1.02 mm, 1.02 mm.
When the wire is removed and the jaws are closed, a reading of −0.02 mm is obtained. Which of the following gives the value of d with a precision appropriate to the micrometer?

A 1.0 mm   **B** 1.00 mm
C 1.038 mm   **D** 1.04 mm

12 In an experiment to determine the acceleration of free fall g, the period of oscillation T and length l of a simple pendulum were measured. The uncertainty in the measurement of l was estimated to be 4%, and that of T, 1%.
The value of g was determined using the formula $g = \dfrac{4\pi^2 l}{T^2}$.
What is the uncertainty in the calculated value for g?

A 2%   **B** 3%
C 5%   **D** 6%

Long Questions

1   Distinguish between a *random error* and *a systematic error* in the measurement of a physical quantity.

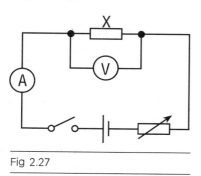

Fig 2.27

The resistance X of an unknown resistor is measured by finding the potential difference across it and the current through it, using the circuit shown in Fig 2.27.

(a) When the switch is closed and the variable resistor is at a certain setting, the readings of the meters are as shown in Figs 2.28 and 2.29 below.

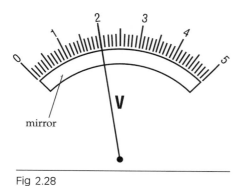

Fig 2.28

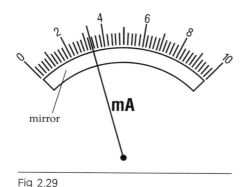

Fig 2.29

Write down the readings of the voltmeter and of the milliammeter.

(b) Give an example of a systematic error that could occur in this experiment.

(c) Some meters have a strip of mirror mounted under the needle and near the scale, as shown in Figs 2.28 and 2.29. Suggest how this may help to eliminate a possible source of error in the experiment.

(d) The variable resistor is adjusted to give a new set of readings which, when repeated, give average values of voltage V and current I of 3.00 ± 0.03 V and 4.9 ± 0.1 mA respectively.

   (i) Estimate the percentage uncertainty in the value of the unknown resistance X as a result of the uncertainties in the average values of V and I.

   (ii) Find the unknown resistance X and express it with its associated uncertainty to the appropriate number of significant figures.

(e) When an experiment like this is performed, rather than taking an average, it is common practice to adjust the variable resistor so as to provide several pairs of values of potential difference and current. These values are then plotted on a graph, from which the value of X may be deduced. Discuss the advantages of this procedure compared with the determination of X from a single pair of readings, as in (a) above.

"The act of measuring any physical quantity disturbs the situation being observed." This statement was made in connection with the measurement of position and momentum on an atomic scale. Discuss briefly whether the measurement of current and voltage in this experiment could be said to disturb the situation being observed.

Cambridge

2   (a) Distinguish between a *random error* and a *systematic error* in the measurement of a physical quantity.

(b) The spring constant k of a spring may be determined by finding the extension of the spring and the load applied, using the apparatus shown in Fig 2.30.

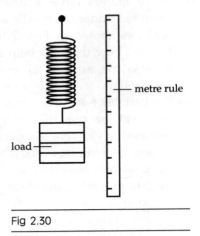

metre rule

load

Fig 2.30

(i) Give one example of a systematic error and one example of a random error which could occur in this experiment.

(ii) Readings of the position of the lower end of the spring are made using the metre rule. Suggest a method by which the error in these readings may be kept to a minimum.

(c) A student obtained the following readings using the apparatus in Fig 2.30

reading on the rule for the lower end of the unextended spring
$$= 13.60 \pm 0.05 \text{ cm,}$$
reading on the rule for the lower end of the extended spring $= 17.95 \pm 0.05$ cm,
$$\text{load} = 4.00 \pm 0.02 \text{ N}$$

It may be assumed that the spring obeys Hooke's law.

(i) Estimate the percentage uncertainty in the determination of k.

(ii) Calculate k and give it with its actual uncertainty to the appropriate number of significant figures.

(d) What is the percentage uncertainty in the determination of the *extension* of the spring if the measurements made in (c) are obtained with a load of 2.00 N?

(e) When performing the experiment, it is common practice to vary the load so that several pairs of values of load and position of the lower end of the spring are obtained, both on increasing and on decreasing the load. The values are then plotted on a graph from which k is determined. Discuss the advantages of this procedure compared with the determination of k as in (c).

Cambridge

52

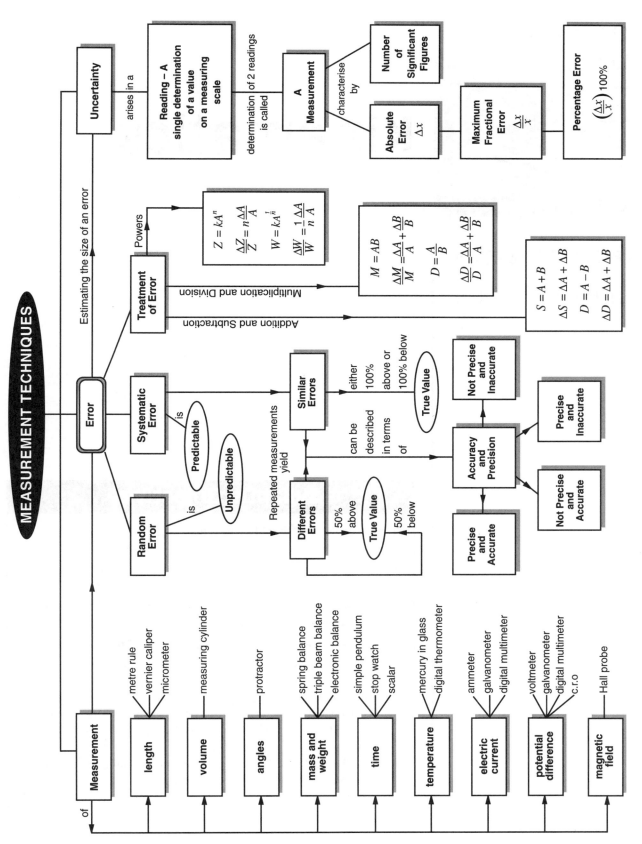

MEASUREMENT TECHNIQUES

Uncertainty — arises in a — **Reading – A single determination of a value on a measuring scale** — determination of 2 readings is called — **A Measurement** — characterise by

- **Number of Significant Figures**
- **Absolute Error** Δx — **Maximum Fractional Error** $\frac{\Delta x}{x}$ — **Percentage Error** $\left(\frac{\Delta x}{x}\right) 100\%$

Estimating the size of an error

Error

Treatment of Error

Powers:
$$Z = kA^n$$
$$\frac{\Delta Z}{Z} = n \frac{\Delta A}{A}$$
$$W = kA^{\frac{1}{n}}$$
$$\frac{\Delta W}{W} = \frac{1}{n} \frac{\Delta A}{A}$$

Multiplication and Division:
$$M = AB$$
$$\frac{\Delta M}{M} = \frac{\Delta A}{A} + \frac{\Delta B}{B}$$
$$D = \frac{A}{B}$$
$$\frac{\Delta D}{D} = \frac{\Delta A}{A} + \frac{\Delta B}{B}$$

Addition and Subtraction:
$$S = A + B$$
$$\Delta S = \Delta A + \Delta B$$
$$D = A - B$$
$$\Delta D = \Delta A + \Delta B$$

Systematic Error — is — **Predictable**

Random Error — is — **Unpredictable**

Repeated measurements yield:
- **Similar Errors** — either 100% above or 100% below — **True Value**
- **Different Errors** — 50% above / 50% below — **True Value**

can be described in terms of — **Accuracy and Precision**
- **Not Precise and Inaccurate**
- **Precise and Inaccurate**
- **Precise and Accurate**
- **Not Precise and Accurate**

Measurement — of:
- **length** — metre rule, vernier caliper, micrometer
- **volume** — measuring cylinder
- **angles** — protractor
- **mass and weight** — spring balance, triple beam balance, electronic balance
- **time** — simple pendulum, stop watch, scalar
- **temperature** — mercury in glass, digital thermometer
- **electric current** — ammeter, galvanometer, digital multimeter
- **potential difference** — voltmeter, galvanometer, digital multimeter, c.r.o
- **magnetic field** — Hall probe

53

Kinematics

RECTILINEAR MOTION

NON-LINEAR MOTION

Syllabus Objectives

In this chapter you should be able to:

- define displacement, speed, velocity and acceleration.
- use graphical methods to represent displacement, speed, velocity and acceleration.
- find displacement from the area under a velocity-time graph.
- use the slope of a displacement-time graph to find the velocity.
- use the slope of a velocity-time graph to find the acceleration.
- derive, from the definitions of velocity and acceleration, equations which represent uniformly accelerated motion in a straight line.
- solve problems using equations which represent uniformly accelerated motion in a straight line, including the motion of bodies falling in a uniform gravitational field without air resistance.
- describe qualitatively the motion of bodies falling in a uniform gravitational field with air resistance.
- describe and explain motion due to a uniform velocity in one direction and a uniform acceleration in a perpendicular direction.

RECTILINEAR MOTION

Motion in a Straight Line

- Kinematics is the description of motion of a particle without referring to the forces and energies that causes motion.

- Motion is the change in position of a particle with respect to time.

(a) Linear Representation

- A particle is a mathematical point that has no size and internal structure. As such it cannot rotate and has only translational motion. It is used to idealise physical objects so that the mathematical treatment of its motion can be simplified.

(b) Planar Representation

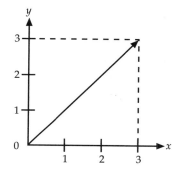

Fig 3.1 Position of a particle

- The position of a particle is determined with reference to the origin of a number line. Fig 3.1 shows the linear and planar representation of the position of a particle.

Displacement and Distance

- The length travelled by a particle without taking into account the direction of its motion is the distance moved by that particle.

- The distance travelled by the particle in a specific direction is the displacement of the particle.
  (a) Hence, displacement $\Delta x = x_f - x_i$ where x_f is the final position and x_i is the initial position (Δ is a Greek symbol used to represent a small change or an increment).
  (b) The direction of displacement is from the initial position to the final position.
  (c) The S. I. unit for displacement is metre (m).

- A comparison between the displacement and the distance travelled by four particles is illustrated in Fig 3.2. As all of them are moving linearly, a number line is used to determine the respective final and initial positions of the particles.

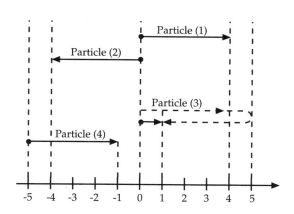

Fig 3.2 Comparison between displacement and distance

55

Particle (1): Displacement $\quad x = 4 - 0 = +4$ cm
Distance travelled $\quad s = 4$ cm

Particle (2): Displacement $\quad x = -4 - 0 = -4$ cm
Distance travelled $\quad s = 4$ cm

Particle (3): Displacement $\quad x = 1 - 0 = +1$ cm
Distance travelled $\quad s = 5 + 4 = 9$ cm

Particle (4): Displacement $\quad x = -1 - (-5) = +4$ cm
Distance travelled $\quad s = 4$ cm

Negative or positive sign for displacement indicates direction. The magnitude of the displacement and the distance travelled are the same only when an object moves in one direction in a straight line.

Average Speed and Constant Speed

- When the speed of a particle changes over a period of time, we could always identify the smallest and the largest speed attained during the period of motion. The average speed lies in between these two extremes. It is defined as the total distance travelled by the particle divided by the total time taken. Mathematically, it is written as:

$$\text{Average speed} = \frac{\text{total distance travelled}}{\text{total time taken}}$$

$$v = \frac{s}{t}$$

- If the average speed is the same for all parts of the motion, then the speed is constant. A particle moving with constant speed travels equal distances in equal periods of time no matter how small the time interval may be.

- The S. I. units for average speed and constant speed are m s^{-1}.

A racing car accelerates uniformly through three gear changes with the following average speeds:
20 m s^{-1} for 2.0 s
40 m s^{-1} for 2.0 s
60 m s^{-1} for 6.0 s
What is the average speed of the car?

Cambridge

Overall average speed $= \dfrac{(20)(2.0) + (40)(2.0) + (60)(6.0)}{2.0 + 2.0 + 6.0}$

$= 48$ m s^{-1}

56

Average Velocity and Instantaneous Velocity

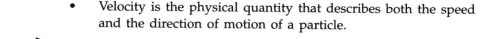

Fig 3.3 One-dimensional motion of a particle

- Velocity is the physical quantity that describes both the speed and the direction of motion of a particle.

- Consider the motion of a particle along a line or in one dimension. It is located at position x_1 at time t_1 and at another position x_2 at a later time t_2 (Fig 3.3).

  The average velocity $<v>$ of a particle is the displacement of the particle divided by the time interval. It is written as:

$$<v> = \frac{\text{final position} - \text{initial position}}{\text{final time} - \text{initial time}}$$

$$= \frac{x_2 - x_1}{t_2 - t_1}$$

$$\text{or} \quad <v> = \frac{\Delta x}{\Delta t}$$

The symbol $<v>$ represents the average velocity.

- The instantaneous velocity v of a particle is the velocity measured at a particular moment. This velocity is obtained by shrinking the time interval in the average velocity towards zero. As Δt decreases, the average velocity approaches a limiting value called the instantaneous velocity.

$$\text{Hence instantaneous velocity } v = \lim_{\Delta t \to 0} \frac{\Delta x}{\Delta t}$$

$$= \frac{dx}{dt}$$

It should be noted that the magnitude of the instantaneous velocity is also called instantaneous speed. The value on the speedometer of a car indicates the instantaneous speed.

- The S. I. units for average velocity and instantaneous velocity are m s^{-1}.

Acceleration

- The average acceleration $<a>$ is defined as the change in velocity divided by the change in time.

  Hence average acceleration is written as:

$$<a> = \frac{v - u}{t_2 - t_1}$$

$$= \frac{\Delta v}{\Delta t}$$

where v is final velocity, u is initial velocity,
       t_2 is final time and t_1 is initial time.

57

Q The motion of a particle travelling along the x-axis is described by the equation $x(t) = 10t + 5t^2$.
(a) Find the displacement of the particle in the time interval between $t_1 = 1$ s and $t_2 = 5$ s.
(b) Find the average velocity in this time interval.
(c) Find the instantaneous velocity at time $t = 3$ s.

A
(a) Δx = final position − initial position
$= x(t_2) - x(t_1)$
$= (10t_2 + 5\,t_2^2) - (10t_1 + 5t_1^2)$
$= 5(t_2^2 - t_1^2) + 10(t_2 - t_1)$
$= 5(5^2 - 1^2) + 10(5 - 1)$
$= 160$ m

(b) Average velocity $<v> = \dfrac{\Delta x}{\Delta t}$

$= \dfrac{160}{4}$

$= 40$ m s^{-1} in the positive direction of the x-axis.

(c) Instantaneous velocity $v = \dfrac{dx}{dt}$

$= \dfrac{d(10t + 5t^2)}{dt}$

$= 10 + 10t$

The instantaneous velocity at $t = 3$ s is $v = 10 + 10(3)$
$= 40$ m s^{-1}

- Instantaneous acceleration a is the limiting value of $\dfrac{\Delta v}{\Delta t}$ as Δt approaches zero or become very small.

Hence $a = \lim\limits_{\Delta t \to 0} \dfrac{\Delta v}{\Delta t}$

$= \dfrac{dv}{dt}$

- The S. I. units for acceleration are m s^{-2}.

- The acceleration of a particle can either be positive or negative. It depends on which direction is chosen as positive. In the following examples, positive direction is towards the right and negative direction is towards the left.

An object falls freely from rest with a constant acceleration of 9.8 m s^{-2} for 3.0 seconds. What is the speed of the object at the end of 3.0 seconds?

 Constant acceleration can be found from the change in velocity divided by the time elapsed during the change.

$$a = \frac{\Delta v}{\Delta t}$$

$$= \frac{v - u}{\Delta t}$$

$$9.8 = \frac{v - 0}{3.0}$$

$$v = 29.4 \text{ m s}^{-1}$$

$$= 29 \text{ m s}^{-1}$$

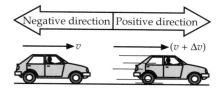

Fig 3.4a   Speed increases in the positive direction

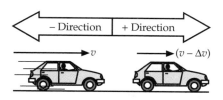

Fig 3.4b   Speed decreases in the positive direction

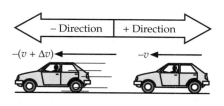

Fig 3.4c   Speed increases in the negative direction

- Consider the motion of a car along a straight road (Fig 3.4). We denote the change in velocity of the car as Δv.

  (a) Motion in the positive direction

  (i) Car is moving to the right and speeding up from v to $(v + \Delta v)$ in Fig 3.4a. The acceleration of the car is:

  $$a = \frac{(v + \Delta v) - v}{\Delta t}$$

  $$= +\frac{\Delta v}{\Delta t}$$

  Acceleration is positive when the car speeds up in the positive direction.

  (ii) Car is moving to the right and slowing down from v to $(v - \Delta v)$ in Fig 3.4b. The acceleration of the car is:

  $$a = \frac{(v - \Delta v) - v}{\Delta t}$$

  $$= -\frac{\Delta v}{\Delta t}$$

  Acceleration is negative when the car slows down in the positive direction. This is called deceleration.

  (b) Motion in the negative direction

  (i) Car is moving to the left and speeding up from $-v$ to $-(v + \Delta v)$ in Fig 3.4c. The acceleration of the car is:

  $$a = \frac{-(v + \Delta v) - (-v)}{\Delta t}$$

  $$= -\frac{\Delta v}{\Delta t}$$

  Acceleration is negative when the car speeds up in the negative direction.

59

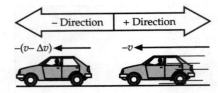

Fig 3.4d Speed decreases in the negative direction

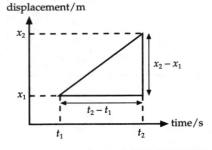

Fig 3.5 Displacement-time graph

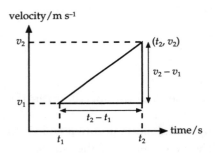

Fig 3.6 Velocity-time graph

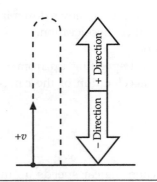

Fig 3.7 Up and down motion of a projected object

(ii) Car is moving to the left and slowing down from $-v$ to $-(v - \Delta v)$ in Fig 3.4d. The acceleration of the car is:

$$a = \frac{-(v - \Delta v) - (-v)}{\Delta t}$$

$$= +\frac{\Delta v}{\Delta t}$$

Acceleration is positive when the car slows down in the negative direction. This is also called deceleration.

- **Displacement-time graph**
  The gradient of the displacement-time graph of an object gives the velocity of that object. The displacement of the object in Fig 3.5 increases from x_1 at time t_1 to x_2 at time t_2 at a constant rate.

  $$\text{Gradient of the } (x - t) \text{ graph} = \frac{x_2 - x_1}{t_2 - t_1}$$

  $$= \frac{\Delta x}{\Delta t}$$

  $$= \text{velocity}$$

- **Velocity-time graph**
  The gradient of the velocity-time graph of an object gives the acceleration of that object. The velocity of the object in Fig 3.6 increases from v_1 at time t_1 to v_2 at time t_2 at a constant rate.

  $$\text{Gradient of the } (v\text{-}t) \text{ graph} = \frac{v_2 - v_1}{t_2 - t_1}$$

  $$= \frac{\Delta v}{\Delta t}$$

  $$= \text{acceleration}$$

Determination of Velocity and Acceleration Graphically

- Velocity and acceleration can be obtained from the slope of the displacement-time graph and the velocity-time graph respectively. Consider the motion of an object tossed vertically upwards from the ground (Fig 3.7). We assume that the object falls freely in a uniform gravitational field with negligible air resistance. Table 3.1 shows the displacement of the object at an interval of 1 second.

- A displacement-time graph can be plotted from the results found in Table 3.1. This graph, in Fig 3.8a shows the displacement of the object as it increases from zero to a maximum at $t = 4.00$ s and decreases to zero again at $t = 8.00$ s.

- The velocity-time graph can be obtained from the displacement-time graph. This is done by drawing tangents to the curve in

$\dfrac{x}{m}$	$\dfrac{t}{s}$
0.0	0.00
35.0	1.00
60.1	2.00
75.0	3.00
80.0	4.00
74.9	5.00
60.0	6.00
35.2	7.00
0.0	8.00

Table 3.1   Displacement of an object
at intervals of
1 second

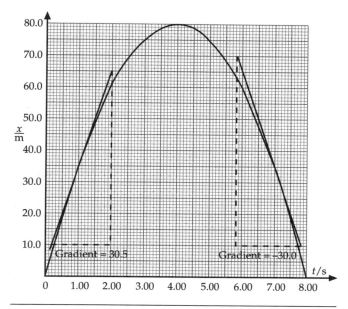

Fig 3.8a   Displacement-time graph

Fig 3.8a at regular intervals. The gradient of each tangent gives the instantaneous velocity of the object. This has a maximum value at the start of the motion and zero when the object is at the maximum displacement. As the object falls back to the ground, the velocity increases in the negative direction. This is depicted as negative velocity and is represented by a straight line below the time axis in the velocity-time graph (Fig 3.8b). The speed of the object just before it strikes the ground is the same as the speed of projection.

$\dfrac{v}{m/s}$	$\dfrac{t}{s}$
39.2	0.00
30.5	1.00
19.3	2.00
9.0	3.00
0.0	4.00
−10.5	5.00
−20.2	6.00
−30.0	7.00
−39.2	8.00

Table 3.2   Velocity of an object at
intervals of 1 second

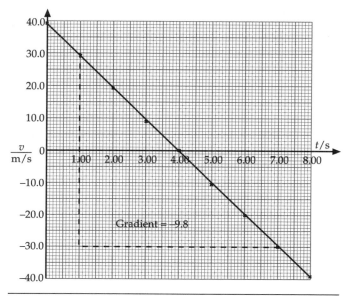

Fig 3.8b   Velocity-time graph

61

- The acceleration-time graph can be obtained by calculating the gradient of the straight line in the velocity-time graph. The gradient obtained, or the acceleration of the object, has a constant value of -9.81 m s^{-2}. This means that when the acceleration is plotted against time (Fig 3.8c), the graph is a straight line below the time axis. The constant, -9.81 m s^{-2} is also known as free-fall acceleration or gravitational acceleration g. It is a vector quantity that affects the motion along the y-axis. Since the upward direction is taken as positive, the acceleration is negative and points downwards irrespective of whether the object moves up or down. This is similar to the illustration in Fig 3.4b and c.

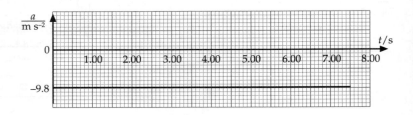

Fig 3.8c   Acceleration-time graph

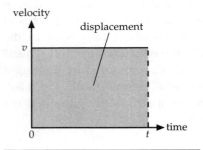

Fig 3.9   Shows the velocity-time graph of a particle moving with constant velocity

- **Area under the velocity-time graph**

  The area under the velocity-time graph of a particle gives the distance travelled or displacement of that particle. The proof of this for a particle moving with constant velocity is shown below.

$$\text{velocity} = \frac{\text{displacement}}{\text{time}}$$

$$v = \frac{s}{t}$$

$$s = vt$$

$$= \text{shaded area under the } (v\text{–}t) \text{ graph}$$

  In general

  Displacement = Area under the $(v\text{–}t)$ graph

- **Further examples of displacement-time graph**

  Analysis of the displacement-time graph can yield information on displacement, velocity and acceleration. Table 3.1 illustrates this.

Graph	Object	Displacement	Velocity	Acceleration (a)	Remarks
Object 1 (Gradient = 0) +5, Object 2 (Gradient = 0) 0, Object 3 (Gradient = 0) -5; displacement vs time	1	$\Delta s = 0$ s is positive	0	0	stationary
	2	$\Delta s = 0$ $s = 0$	0	0	stationary at the origin
	3	$\Delta s = 0$ s is negative	0	0	stationary
Object 4 (constant positive gradient), Object 6 (constant positive gradient), Object 5 (constant negative gradient); displacement vs time	4	s increases at constant rate. Δs is positive.	constant (positive)	0	moves away from origin in the positive direction
	5	s increases in the negative direction at constant rate. Δs is negative.	constant (negative)	0	moves away from the origin in the negative direction
	6	s increases at constant rate. Δs is positive.	constant (positive)	0	moves pass origin towards the positive direction
Object 7 (decreasing positive gradient), Object 8 (increasing positive gradient), Object 9 (decreasing negative gradient); displacement vs time	7	s increases at decreasing rate. Δs is positive.	Decreases in the positive direction	decelerate	slows down as it moves away from the origin in the positive direction
	8	s increases at increasing rate. Δs is positive.	Increases in the positive direction	accelerate	starts from rest and accelerates away from the origin
	9	s is increasing in the negative direction at a decreasing rate. Δs is negative.	Decrease in the negative direction	decelerate	slows down as it moves away from the origin in the negative direction

Graph	Object	Displacement	Velocity	Acceleration	Remarks
	10	s decreases at increasing rate. Δs is negative.	increases (negative)	accelerate	moves back towards the origin
	11	s decreases at constant rate. Δs is negative.	constant (negative)	0	moves pass origin towards the negative direction
	12	s changes at a decreasing rate. Δs is positive.	decrease (positive)	decelerate	moves back towards origin

Table 3.1

- **Further examples of velocity-time graph**

   Analysis of the velocity-time graph can yield information on displacement, velocity and acceleration. Table 3.2 illustrates this.

Graph	Object	Displacement	Velocity (v)	Acceleration (a)	Remarks
	1	Positive	constant (positive)	0	moves in the positive direction
	2	0	0	0	stationary
	3	Negative	constant (negative)	0	moves in the negative direction
	4	Positive	increases in the positive direction at a constant rate	constant (positive)	starts from rest at $t = 0$ s uniform acceleration
	5	Negative	increases in the negative direction at a constant rate	constant (negative)	starts from rest at $t = 0$ s uniform acceleration in the opposite direction
	6	Positive	increases in the positive direction at a constant rate	constant (positive)	has velocity u at $t = 0$ s

	7	Positive	increases in the positive direction	decreases to zero (positive)	moves in the positive direction and attain constant speed after some time
	8	Positive	increases in the positive direction	increases (positive)	starts from rest and move in the positive direction
	9	Negative	increases in the negative direction	increases (negative)	moves in the negative direction
	10	Negative	increases in the negative direction	decreases (negative)	moves in the negative direction
	11	Positive	decreases in the positive direction	increases (negative)	moving in the positive direction and slowing down
	12	Positive	decreases to 0 m s^{-1}	constant (negative)	moving in the positive direction and slowing down
	13	Negative	decreases in the negative direction	constant (positive)	moving in the negative direction and slowing down

Table 3.2

- Methods of solving kinematics problems
  (a) Draw diagrams to gain a better understanding of the problem
  (b) List
    (i) the known quantities that are given,
    (ii) the unknown quantities required.
  (c) Define the positive direction and use the correct sign convention for all the known and unknown quantities. For example a ball is projected upwards from point A in Fig 3.10. The positive direction is defined as the ball's initial direction of travel.

(i) The sign of the displacements for 5 points during the flight is shown in Fig 3.10.

(ii) The sign of the velocities for 5 points during the flight is shown in Fig 3.11.

(c) A summary of the signs for displacement, velocity and acceleration is shown in Table 3.3.

(d) Select the most appropriate equations of motion.

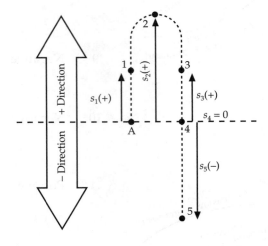

Fig 3.10   Displacements of projected ball

Point	x	v	a
1	+	+	−
2	+	0	−
3	+	−	−
4	0	−	−
5	−	−	−

Table 3.3   Sign convention

Fig 3.11   Velocities of projected ball

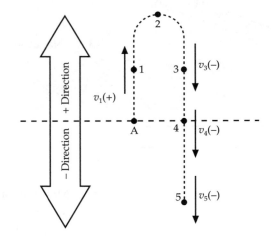

66

Q The graph, Fig 3.12, shows the speed of two cars A and B which are travelling in the same direction over a period of time of 40 s. Car A, travelling at a constant speed of 40 m s^{-1}, overtakes car B at time $t = 0$. In order to catch up with car A, car B immediately accelerates uniformly for 20 s to reach a constant speed of 50 m s^{-1}.

(a) How far does car A travel during the first 20 s?

(b) Calculate the acceleration of car B in the first 20 s.

(c) How far does car B travel in this time?

(d) What additional time will it take for car B to catch up with car A?

(e) How far will each car have then travelled since $t = 0$?

(f) What is the maximum distance between the cars before car B catches up with car A?

Cambridge

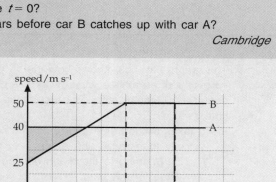

Fig 3.12

A

(a) Distance travelled by car A during the first 20 s is
$$s_A = 20 \times 40$$
$$= 800 \text{ m}$$

(b) Acceleration of car B in the first 20 s is
$$a = \frac{50 - 25}{20}$$
$$= 1.25 \text{ m s}^{-2}$$

(c) Distance travelled by car B during the first 20 s is
$$s_B = \frac{1}{2}(25 + 50)(20)$$
$$= 750 \text{ m}$$

(d) Let t_1 be the additional time taken for car B to catch up with car A.
Distance travelled by car A in time $(20 + t_1)$ is s.
s = Distance travelled by car B in the same time as car A.
$$800 + 40 \, t_1 = 750 + 50 \, t_1$$
$$10 \, t_1 = 50$$
$$t_1 = 5 \text{ s}$$

(e) Hence, the total distance travelled since $t = 0$ is given by:
$$s = 800 + 40 \,(5)$$
$$= 1000 \text{ m}$$

67

(f) When car A overtakes car B, the distance between the
two cars increases continuously until the velocities of the
two cars are equal. This occurs at time t_2.
By similar triangles,

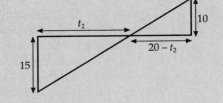

$$\frac{t_2}{20 - t_2} = \frac{15}{10}$$

$$t_2 = 12 \text{ s}$$

The maximum distance between the cars at this moment
is given by:

$$s = 40\ (12) - \frac{1}{2}(25 + 40)\ (12)$$

$$= 90 \text{ m}$$

The graph, Fig 3.13, shows how the
velocity v of an athlete varies with time t
during a 100-metre race. The race starts at
time $t = 0$.

(a) It takes a short time for the athlete's
velocity to increase above zero.
  (i) By referring to the graph deduce a
  value for this time.
  (ii) Give a reason for this delay.

(b) Use the graph to deduce
  (i) the maximum velocity of the athlete,
  (ii) the athlete's maximum acceleration,
  (iii) the distance the athlete travels
  between the times $t = 4.0$ s and
  $t = 8.0$ s.

(c) Assuming that 10 people with
stopwatches are available, outline what
they would need to do in order to
obtain such a graph experimentally.

(d) Sketch the shape of the acceleration-
time graph for this 100-metre race.

(e) Suggest why the men's Olympic record
for 200-metre is less than twice the
time for 100-metre.

Cambridge

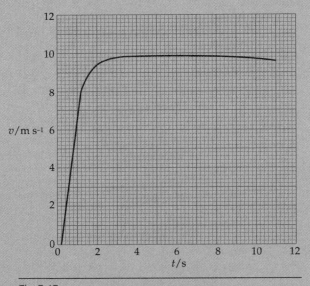

Fig 3.13

68

(a) (i) Time for athlete's velocity to increase above zero = 0.2 s

(ii) The delay is due to the athlete's reaction time.

(b) (i) The maximum velocity of the athlete is 9.82 m s^{-1}.

(ii) The maximum acceleration of the athlete = Gradient of the velocity-time graph at t equals to 0.2 s

$$= \frac{10.0}{1.0}$$

$$= 10 \text{ m s}^{-2}$$

(iii) The distance travelled by the athlete between $t = 4.0$ s and $t = 8.0$ s is $(9.82 \times 4.0) = 39.3$ m

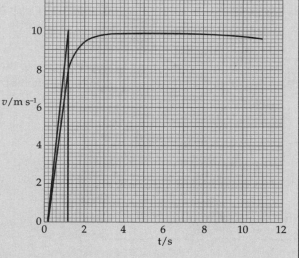

(c) Place ten timers at different measured distances along the track. When the race starts, all ten timers must start their stopwatches at the same time. They are to stop their stopwatches as the athletes pass their positions. The displacement from the starting line and the corresponding time taken by the 10 timers should be tabulated and a displacement-time graph drawn. The instantaneous velocities of the athletes can be found by finding the gradients at 10 different positions on the displacement-time graph. Values of velocities and time are tabulated and a (v-t) graph can be drawn.

Displacement-time graph

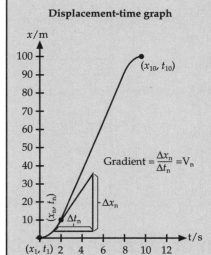

Velocity-time graph

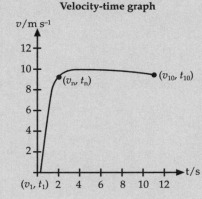

Acceleration-time graph

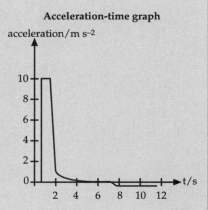

(d) The shape of the acceleration-time graph is as shown.

(e) As the athlete accelerates only once at the start of a 200-metre race, the average speed will be larger than the average speed of a 100-metre race that is counted twice. This means that the Olympic record for a 200-metre race will be smaller than twice the time for a 100-metre race.

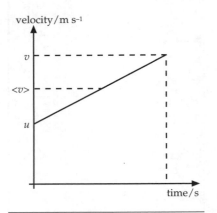

Fig 3.14   Average velocity from a (v–t) graph

Equations of Motion

- Consider the motion of a particle that accelerates from an initial velocity u to a final velocity v with constant acceleration a. Fig 3.14 shows the velocity-time graph of this motion.

- Since the acceleration is constant, the velocity increases at a constant rate. Hence the average velocity is midway between u and v.

$$<v> = \frac{1}{2}(u + v)$$

But $<v> = \dfrac{s}{t}$

$$s = <v>t$$

$$= \frac{1}{2}(u + v)t$$

$$s = \frac{1}{2}(u + v)t \quad\text{———————— (1)}$$

Also $a = \dfrac{v - u}{t}$

$$v = u + at \quad\text{———————— (2)}$$

Substituting $v = u + at$ into equation (1)

$$s = \frac{1}{2}(u + u + at)t$$

$$s = ut + \frac{1}{2}at^2 \quad\text{———————— (3)}$$

Rewriting equation (2) for t and substituting into equation (1)

$$t = \frac{v - u}{a}$$

we have $s = \dfrac{1}{2}(u + v)\left(\dfrac{v - u}{a}\right)$

$$v^2 = u^2 + 2as \quad\text{———————— (4)}$$

Free Fall in a Uniform Gravitational Field without Air Resistance

- All objects falling in the same gravitational field without air resistance have the same acceleration. This is clearly illustrated on the surface of the moon which does not have an atmosphere. If a stone and a feather are tossed upwards on the surface of the moon with the same initial speed, they will rise to the same maximum height in the same time (Fig 3.20). Conversely they

70

will fall together and attain the same speed when they reach the ground if they are dropped from the same height. This is because there is no air resistance on the moon to hinder their motion. The gravitational acceleration remains constant.

Fig 3.15 Absence of air resistance means all objects will fall with the same acceleration

Free Fall in a Uniform Gravitational Field with Air Resistance

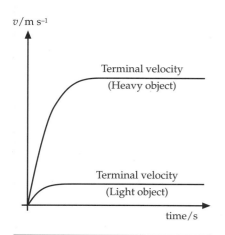

Fig 3.16 The velocity-time graph of free fall motion on the surface of the Earth. The downward direction is taken as positive.

- As the velocity of the object increases during a free fall, the air resistance acting on the object also increases. This opposes the downward motion and causes the acceleration to decrease to zero. At this point, the weight is offset by the air resistance and the object moves with a constant terminal velocity.

- The free fall of an object in a uniform gravitational field with air resistance is illustrated in Fig 3.16. The gradient at each point on the curve represents the object's acceleration. The greatest acceleration occurs when the object is just released. A heavier object with a small surface area takes a longer time to reach terminal velocity. The initial portion of the curve approximates a straight line with gradient (i.e. acceleration) equals to g. This means that the object have constant acceleration at the initial stage of its free-fall motion. The equations of motion can be applied to this object.

71

Q A car is travelling with uniform acceleration along a straight road. The road has marker posts every 100 m. When the car passes one post it has a speed of 10 m s^{-1} and when it passes the next one, its speed is 20 m s^{-1}. What is the car's acceleration?

Cambridge

A $u = 10$ m s^{-1}, $v = 20$ m s^{-1},
$s = 100$ m
Take direction to the right as positive
Use $v^2 = u^2 + 2as$
$$20^2 = 10^2 + 2a(100)$$
$$a = \frac{20^2 - 10^2}{2(100)}$$
$$= 1.5 \text{ m s}^{-2}$$

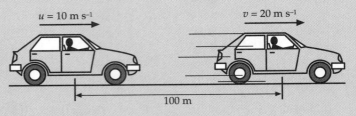

$u = 10$ m s^{-1} $v = 20$ m s^{-1} 100 m

Q The following experiment may be used to test reaction time. A new bank note, 135 mm long, is held vertically at the upper edge by the tester (Fig 3.17). You are to hold your thumb and first finger open at the bottom of the note. When the tester releases the note without warning, you must try to close your fingers in time to catch it. If you succeed, you can keep the note. What is the maximum possible value of your reaction time that will allow you to succeed?

Cambridge

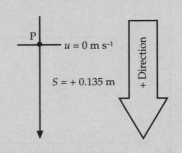

Fig 3.17

A Choose the release point P on the note to be the origin of the y-axis and take the downward direction as positive.
Initial velocity $= 0$ m s^{-1}
Gravitational acceleration $= +9.81$ m s^{-2}
Maximum distance travelled by P before it is caught by the hand
$= +135$ mm
$= +0.135$ m
Maximum reaction time $= t$

Using $s = ut + \frac{1}{2}gt^2$

$$+0.135 = (0)t + \frac{1}{2}(9.81)t^2$$

$$t = \sqrt{\frac{2 \times 0.135}{9.81}} = 0.166 \text{ s}$$

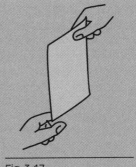

P $u = 0$ m s^{-1} $S = +0.135$ m   + Direction

72

Alternatively, choose the release point P on the note to be the origin of the y-axis and take the upward direction as positive.

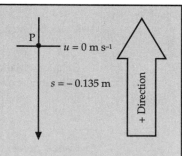

Initial velocity = 0 m s^{-1}

Gravitational acceleration = -9.81 m s^{-2}

Maximum distance travelled by P before it is caught by the hand

$= -135$ mm

$= -0.135$ m

Maximum reaction time = t

Using $s = ut + \dfrac{1}{2}gt^2$, -0.135 m $= (0)t + \dfrac{1}{2}(-9.81)t^2$

$t = \sqrt{\dfrac{2 \times 0.135}{9.81}} = 0.166$ s

Q A photographer wishes to check the time for which the shutter on a camera stays open when a photograph is being taken. To do this, a metal ball is photographed as it falls from rest. It is found that before the shutter opens, the ball falls 2.50 m from rest and during the time that shutter remains open, the ball falls a further 0.12 m, as illustrated in Fig 3.18. Assuming that air resistance is negligible, calculate

(i)   the speed of the ball after falling 2.50 m,

(ii) the time to fall the further 0.12 m.

$$\left[\text{You may wish to use an equation of the form } x = \frac{-b \pm \sqrt{b^2 - 4ac}}{2a} \right]$$

(iii) the time for which the shutter stays open is marked on the camera as $\dfrac{1}{60}$ s. Comment on whether the test confirms this time.

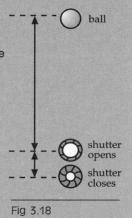

Fig 3.18

Cambridge

A

(i)   Taking downward direction as positive.

Initial velocity $u = 0$ m s^{-1}

Velocity of ball when shutter opens = v_1

Velocity of ball when shutter closes = v_2

$v^2 = u^2 + 2as$

$v_1^2 = 0 + 2(9.81)(2.50)$

$\quad\,\, = 49.05$

$v_1 = 7.00$ m s^{-1}

(ii) $s = ut + \dfrac{1}{2}at^2$

$0.12 = 7.00t + \dfrac{1}{2}(9.81)t^2$

$4.905t^2 + 7.00t - 0.12 = 0$

$t = \dfrac{-7.00 \pm \sqrt{(7.00)^2 - 4(4.905)(-0.12)}}{2(4.905)}$

$\quad = 0.01694$

$\quad = 0.017$ s

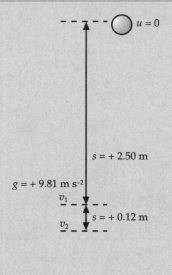

73

(iii) Marked time for which the shutter stays open, $t_1 = \dfrac{1}{60}$ s

$$= 0.01667 \text{ s}$$

Calculated time for which shutter stays open, $t_2 = 0.01694$ s

Difference between the two times $\Delta t = t_2 - t_1$

$$= 0.01694 - 0.01667$$
$$= 2.7 \times 10^{-4}$$

Hence percentage error $\left(\dfrac{\Delta t}{t_1}\right)100\% = \left(\dfrac{2.7 \times 10^{-4}}{0.01667}\right)100\%$

$$= 1.6 \text{ \%}$$

The small percentage error in the difference in time is within reasonable and acceptable limits. Hence the test confirms the time marked on the camera.

(a) Define acceleration. Explain how is it possible for a body to be undergoing acceleration although its speed remains constant.

(b) A ball is place at the top of a slope as shown in Fig 3.19.

A block is fixed rigidly to the lower end of the slope. The ball of mass 0.70 kg is released at time $t = 0$ from the top of the incline and v, the velocity of the ball down the slope, is found to vary with t as shown in Fig 3.20.

(i) Describe qualitatively the motion of the ball during the periods OA, AB and BC.

(ii) Calculate
1. the acceleration of the ball down the incline,
2. the length of the incline.

Cambridge

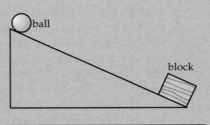

Fig 3.19

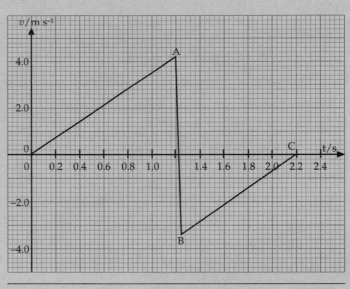

Fig 3.20

74

A (a) Acceleration is defined as the rate of change of velocity. Velocity is a vector quantity and a change in magnitude or direction or both would constitute a change in velocity. An object moving with constant speed along a circular path experiences acceleration because its direction of motion changes all the time.

(b) (i) The downward direction of the slope is chosen as the positive direction. The motion of the ball is described in the following three sections:

OA – The ball starts from rest and moves down the slope with a constant acceleration of 3.5 m s^{-2}. It strikes the block with a speed of $+4.2$ m s^{-1} at $t = 1.2$ s.

AB – The ball decelerates uniformly and is brought to rest momentarily in 0.02 s. It rebounces and accelerates uniformly to a speed of -3.4 m s^{-1} in a further time of 0.02 s. The total duration of the impact is therefore 0.04 s.

BC – The ball moves up the slope with a constant deceleration of 3.54 m s^{-2}. It will not be able to move to the top of the slope but will stop short of it at $t = 2.2$ s.

(ii) 1. Acceleration of the ball $= \dfrac{4.2 - 0.0}{1.2 - 0.0}$

$= 3.5$ m s^{-2}

2. The length of the incline $= \dfrac{1}{2}(1.2)(4.2)$

$= 2.52$

$= 2.5$ m

NON-LINEAR MOTION

Projectile Motion

- Projectile motion is a 2-dimensional curved motion of a particle subjected to constant acceleration. An example is a ball thrown obliquely into the air.

- Key terms used in projectile motion
  (a) Trajectory – the path described by a projectile
  (b) Range – the distance on the plane between the point of projection and the point of impact
  (c) Angle of projection – the angle between the direction of projection and the horizontal plane through the point of projection

Kinematics of the Motion

- The velocity along every point on the trajectory changes all the time (Fig 3.21).

- To simplify the mathematical treatment of the motion, the actual velocity at a point on the trajectory is resolved into two perpendicular velocities. These are known as the vertical component (u_y) and the horizontal component (u_x).
  From Fig 3.21,
  vertical component: $u_y = u \sin \theta$,
  horizontal component: $u_x = u \cos \theta$.

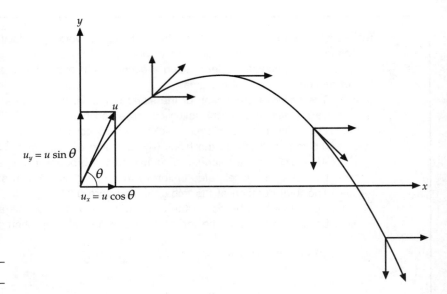

Fig 3.21 Projectile motion

- The vertical and horizontal components are independent of each other. Hence, calculations for vertical and horizontal motion are done separately. However their combined effects produce the same parabolic trajectory of a projectile motion.

- The vertical component is affected by the gravitational acceleration g directed towards the centre of the earth. The **equations of motion** for vertical motion can be written as:

  (a) $y = \dfrac{1}{2}(u_y + v_y)t$

  (b) $v_y = u_y + a_y t$ or $v_y = u \sin \theta - gt$

  (c) $y = u_y t + \dfrac{1}{2}a_y t^2$ or $y = (u \sin \theta)t - \dfrac{1}{2}gt^2$

  (d) $v_y^2 = u_y^2 + 2a_y y$ or $v_y^2 = (u \sin \theta)^2 - 2gy$

- Gravitational acceleration g has no effect on the horizontal motion of a projectile. Hence the horizontal component remains constant. The equation of motion reduces to
  $$x = u_x t \quad \text{or} \quad x = (u \cos \theta)t$$

A particle is projected with an initial velocity u directed at an angle θ to the horizontal. Find
(a) the maximum height (H) of the projectile motion;
(b) the time of flight (T);
(c) the range (X).

 (a) Vertical components:
$$a = -g, \ u_y = u \sin \theta$$
Consider the vertical motion:
$$v_y^2 = u_y^2 + 2aY$$
$$0 = (u \sin \theta)^2 - 2gH$$
$$\therefore H = \frac{u^2 \sin^2 \theta}{2g}$$

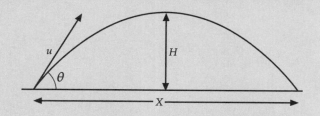

(b) $a = -g, \ y = 0, \ T = $ Time of flight

Using $y = ut + \dfrac{1}{2}at^2$

$$0 = (u \sin \theta)T - \frac{1}{2}gT^2$$

$$T = \frac{2u \sin \theta}{g}$$

(c) $u_x = u \cos \theta$
$T = $ Time of flight
$$= \frac{2u \sin \theta}{g}$$
Consider the horizontal motion:
Range $x = u_x T$
$$= (u \cos \theta)\left(\frac{2u \sin \theta}{g}\right)$$
$$= \frac{2u^2 \cos \theta \sin \theta}{g}$$
$$= \frac{u^2 \sin 2\theta}{g}$$

A ball is thrown from horizontal ground with an initial velocity of 15 m s^{-1} at an angle of 60° to the horizontal, as shown in Fig 3.22.

(a) Calculate, for this ball, the initial values of
  (i) the vertical component of the velocity,
  (ii) the horizontal component of the velocity.
(b) Assuming that air resistance can be neglected, use your answers in (a) to determine
  (i) the maximum height to which the ball rises,
  (ii) the time of flight, i.e. the time interval between the ball being thrown and returning to ground level,
  (iii) the horizontal distance between the point from which the ball was thrown and the point where it strikes the ground.
(c) Use your answers to (b) to sketch the path of the ball, assuming air resistance is negligible. Label this path N.
(d) (i) On your sketch in (c), draw the path of the ball, assuming that air resistance cannot be neglected. Label this path A.
  (ii) Suggest an explanation for any differences between the two paths N and A.

Fig 3.22

Cambridge

77

(a) (i) Vertical component of the velocity, u_y = 15 sin 60°
$= 12.99$
$= 13 \text{ m s}^{-1}$

(ii) Horizontal component of the velocity, u_x = 15 cos 60°
$= 7.5 \text{ m s}^{-1}$

(b) (i) $u_y = 12.99 \text{ m s}^{-1}$

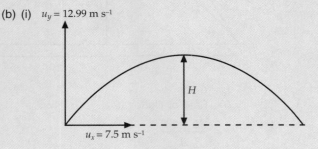

Take the upward direction as positive
H = maximum height to which the ball rises.
$v_y = 0$ (at maximum height);
$a = -g = -9.81 \text{ m s}^{-2}$
Hence $v_y^2 = u_y^2 + 2aY$
$0 = (12.99)^2 - 2\,(9.81)H$
$H = 8.6 \text{ m}$

(ii) t = time of flight
When ball returns to ground level, $y = 0$

Using $y = u_y t + \dfrac{1}{2}at^2$

$0 = (12.99)t + \dfrac{1}{2}(-9.81)t^2$

$t = 2.64$
$= 2.6 \text{ s}$

(iii) Let X be the horizontal distance between the point from which the ball was thrown and the point where it strikes the ground.
$X = u_x t$
$= 7.5\,(2.64)$
$= 19.8$
$= 20 \text{ m}$

(c) & (d)
(i)

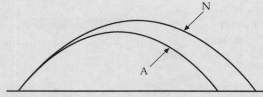

Path N – Path of ball if air resistance is negligible
Path A – Path of ball if air resistance is not negligible

(ii) Air resistance acts in the opposite direction to the motion of the ball. This reduces the vertical and horizontal component of the velocity along path N. The effect is a reduction in the range and the maximum height attained by the ball.

(a) Distinguish between the *distance moved* by an object and its *displacement* from a fixed point.

(b) An experiment was conducted on the surface of the Moon to investigate the motion of a small sphere. The sphere, mass 50 g, was projected horizontally from a point some distance above the surface of the Moon. Its subsequent motion was monitored by taking a photograph of the sphere using a series of flashes of light at intervals of 1.00 s. The first flash occurred at the instant of projection. The photograph, superimposed on a grid is illustrated in Fig 3.23.

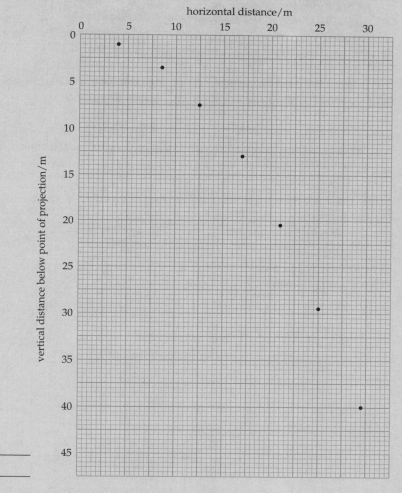

Fig 3.23

(i) By considering the horizontal distance moved, show that frictional forces opposing the motion were negligible.

(ii) Calculate the horizontal component of the velocity.

(iii) Use Fig 3.23 to determine the vertical distance travelled during the first 7.00 s of the motion.

(iv) Hence calculate a value for the acceleration of free fall on the surface of the Moon.

(c) (i) On your answer paper, sketch the path of the sphere indicated by Fig 3.23.

(ii) Add to your sketch two further lines showing the path of the sphere if
   1 the Moon had an atmosphere (Label this path A),
   2 the experiment was repeated on a planet which has no atmosphere and where the acceleration of free fall is less than that on the Moon (Label this path P).

Cambridge

79

A (a) Distance moved by an object is the length travelled by that object without taking into account the direction of its motion.
Displacement from a fixed point is the distance travelled in a specific direction.

(b) (i) The horizontal distances moved in every second are shown in the table.
As the horizontal distance moved in every second is constant, the frictional force opposing the motion is negligible.

Time /s	Horizontal distance /m	Distance moved in 1 s /m
1.00	4.2	4.2
2.00	8.4	4.2
3.00	12.6	4.2
4.00	16.8	4.2
5.00	21.0	4.2
6.00	25.2	4.2
7.00	29.4	4.2

(ii) The horizontal component of the velocity is 4.2 m s^{-1}.

(iii) The vertical distance travelled during the first 7.00 s $= 40.0$ m

(iv) Choosing the downward direction as positive and using

$$s = ut + \frac{1}{2}at^2$$

When $t = 7.00$ s, $s = 40.0$ m, $u = 0.0$ m s^{-1} and $a =$ acceleration of free fall on the surface of the Moon.

$$a = \frac{2s}{t^2}$$

$$= \frac{2(40.0)}{(7.00)^2}$$

$$= 1.63 \text{ m s}^{-2}$$

(c) (i) & (ii) Path A and path P are shown in below.

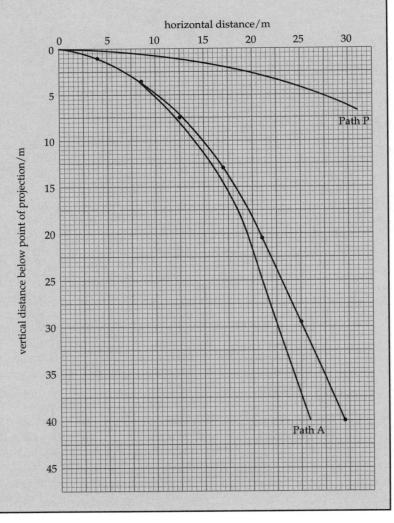

Exercise 3

Multiple Choice Questions

1. A lunar landing module is descending to the Moon's surface at a steady velocity of 10 m s^{-1}. At a height of 120 m, a small object falls from its landing gear.
   Taking the Moon's gravitational acceleration as 1.6 m s^{-2}, at what speed does the object strike the Moon?
   A 30 m s^{-1} B 22 m s^{-1}
   C 20 m s^{-1} D 17 m s^{-1}

2. The velocity of a car which is decelerating uniformly changes from 30 m s^{-1} to 15 m s^{-1} in 75 m. After what further distance will it come to rest?
   A 25 m   B 37.5 m
   C 50 m   D 75 m

3. A body starts from rest at time $t = 0$ and moves with constant acceleration. Which graph best represents how s, the displacement of the body, varies with time?

   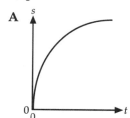
   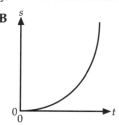
   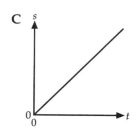
   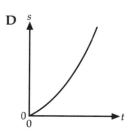

4. The acceleration of free fall is determined by timing the fall of a steel ball photo-electrically (Fig 3.24). The ball passes X and Y at times t_X and t_Y after release from P.

   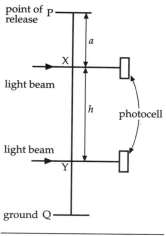

   Fig 3.24

   The acceleration of free fall is given by

   A $\dfrac{2h}{(t_X - t_Y)}$ B $\dfrac{h}{(t_Y^2 - t_X^2)}$

   C $\dfrac{h^2}{(t_X - t_Y)}$ D $\dfrac{2h}{(t_Y^2 - t_X^2)}$

5. A student measures the time t for a ball to fall from rest through a vertical distance h.

   Knowing that the equation $h = \dfrac{1}{2}at^2$ applies, the student plots the graph shown. Which of the following is an explanation for the intercept?

   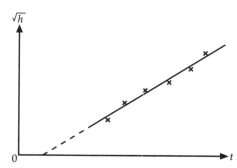

   A Air resistance should be taken into account for larger values of h.
   B There is a constant delay between starting the timer and releasing the ball.
   C There is an error in the timer which consistently makes it run fast.
   D The student should have plotted h against t^2.

6   The graph of velocity against time for a moving object is shown.

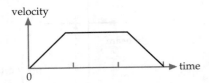

Which of the following is the corresponding graph of displacement against time?

A   displacement

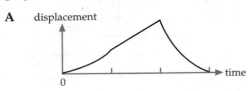

B   displacement

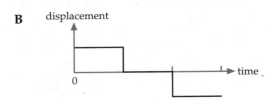

C   displacement

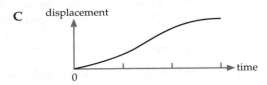

D   displacement

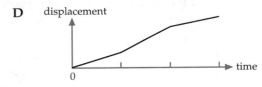

7   A parachutist steps from an aircraft, falls freely for two seconds and then opens his parachute. Which graph best represents how a, his vertical acceleration, varies with time t during the first 5 s?

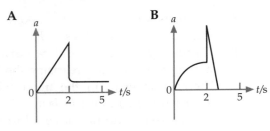

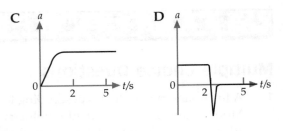

8   A tennis ball is released so that it falls vertically to the floor and bounces back again. Taking velocity upwards as positive, which one of the following graphs best represents the variation of velocity v with time t?

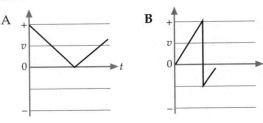

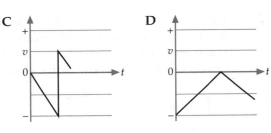

9   A motorcycle stunt rider moving horizontally takes off from a point 1.25 m above the ground, landing 10 m away as shown in the diagram.

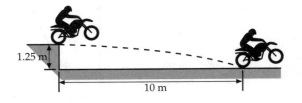

What was the speed at take-off?
A   5 m s^{-1}
B   10 m s^{-1}
C   15 m s^{-1}
D   20 m s^{-1}

82

Structured Questions

1 Fig 3.25 shows a velocity-time graph for a journey lasting 65 s. It has been divided up into six sections for ease of reference.

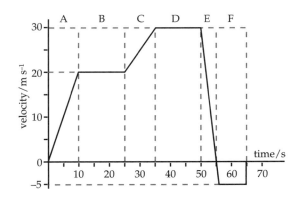

Fig 3.25

(a) Using information from the graph, obtain

   (i) the velocity 10 s after the start,

   velocity = _____ m s^{-1}

   (ii) the acceleration in section A,

   acceleration = _____ m s^{-2}

   (iii) the acceleration in section E,

   acceleration = _____ m s^{-2}

   (iv) the distance travelled in section B,

   distance = _____ m

   (v) the distance travelled in section C,

   distance = _____ m

(b) Describe qualitatively in words what happens in sections E and F of the journey.

(c) On Fig 3.26 sketch the shape of the corresponding distance-time graph. You are not expected to make detailed calculations of the distance travelled.

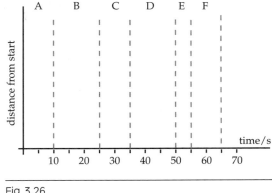

Fig 3.26

2 (a) A stone is thrown with a velocity of 15 m s^{-1} at an angle 60° to the horizontal as shown in Fig 3.27.

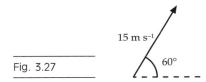

Fig. 3.27

   (i) Will the magnitude of the initial horizontal component of the velocity of the stone be greater, the same, or less than 15 m s^{-1}?

   (ii) Calculate the magnitude of the initial horizontal component of the velocity.

   (iii) Calculate the magnitude of the initial vertical component of the velocity.

(b) The stone in (a) is being thrown from the top of a cliff with the velocity of 15 m s^{-1} at 60° to the horizontal as shown in Fig 3.28.

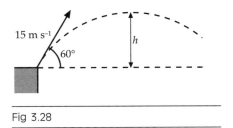

Fig 3.28

83

On the axes below (Fig 3.29), draw graphs to represent the variation with time of

(i) V_H, the horizontal component of the velocity,

(ii) V_V, the vertical component of the velocity of the stone. Ignore air resistance. Identify your graphs.

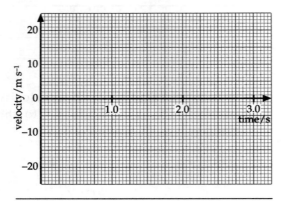

Fig 3.29

(c) Use your answer in (b) to find h, the maximum vertical height of the stone above its point of projection.

Cambridge

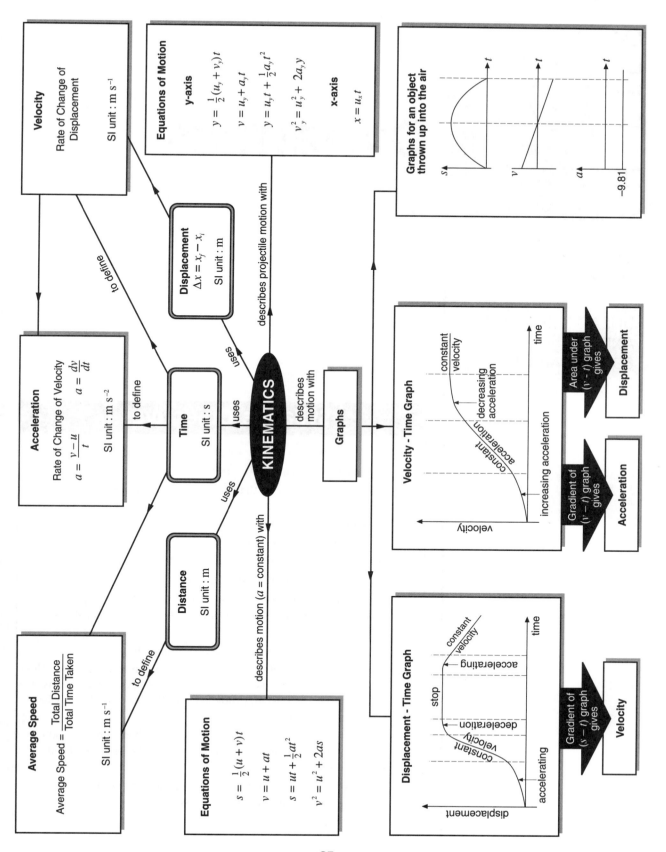

KINEMATICS

Velocity
Rate of Change of Displacement
SI unit : m s^{-1}

Equations of Motion

y-axis
$y = \frac{1}{2}(u_y + v_y)t$
$v = u_y + a_y t$
$y = u_y t + \frac{1}{2}a_y t^2$
$v_y^2 = u_y^2 + 2a_y y$

x-axis
$x = u_x t$

Graphs for an object thrown up into the air

Displacement
$\Delta x = x_f - x_i$
SI unit : m

describes projectile motion with

Acceleration
Rate of Change of Velocity
$a = \frac{v-u}{t}$ $a = \frac{dv}{dt}$
SI unit : m s^{-2}

to define

Time
SI unit : s

uses

describes motion with

Graphs

Average Speed
Average Speed = $\frac{\text{Total Distance}}{\text{Total Time Taken}}$
SI unit : m s^{-1}

to define

Distance
SI unit : m

uses

Equations of Motion
$s = \frac{1}{2}(u+v)t$
$v = u + at$
$s = ut + \frac{1}{2}at^2$
$v^2 = u^2 + 2as$

describes motion (a = constant) with

Velocity - Time Graph

constant velocity
decreasing acceleration
constant acceleration
increasing acceleration

Area under ($v-t$) graph gives → **Displacement**

Gradient of ($v-t$) graph gives → **Acceleration**

Displacement - Time Graph

constant velocity
accelerating
stop
deceleration
constant velocity
accelerating

Gradient of ($s-t$) graph gives → **Velocity**

85

4 Dynamics

NEWTON'S LAWS OF MOTION

LINEAR MOMENTUM AND ITS CONSERVATION

Syllabus Objectives

In this chapter you should be able to:

- state each of Newton's laws of motion.
- show an understanding that mass is the property of a body which resists change in motion.
- describe and use the concept of weight as the effect of a gravitational field on a mass.
- define linear momentum as the product of mass and velocity.
- define force as rate of change of momentum.
- recall and solve problems by using the relationship $F = ma$, appreciating that acceleration and force are always in the same direction.
- state the principle of conservation of momentum.
- apply the principle of conservation of momentum to solve simple problems including elastic and inelastic interactions between two bodies in one dimension. (Knowledge of the concept of coefficient of restitution is not required.)
- recognise that, for a perfectly elastic collision between two bodies, the relative speed of approach is equal to the relative speed of separation.
- show an understanding that, whilst the momentum of a system is always conserved in interactions between bodies, some change in kinetic energy usually takes place.

NEWTON'S LAWS OF MOTION

- Dynamics is the study of forces and energies that are associated with the motion of a body.

- In the seventeenth century, Sir Isaac Newton discovered three laws of motion that describes how forces affect the motion of an object. The laws are now known as Newton's laws of motion.

Newton's First Law of Motion

- An object at rest will remain at rest and an object in motion will continue in motion at constant speed in a straight line in the absence of a resultant force.

  (a) The first law implies that all matter has an in-built tendency to resist any change in its state of rest or uniform motion. This property, which is possessed by all matter, is known as inertia.

  (b) The mass of a body is a measure of its inertia. The bigger the mass, the bigger is the inertia of the body. Hence there is a great resistance to any change in velocity for a big mass. Fig 4.1 illustrates this.

Fig 4.1a Hard to change from the straight line motion

Fig 4.1b Hard to start moving

Fig 4.1c Hard to stop moving once it is in motion

  (c) Further implications of Newton's 1st law of motion are summarised in Fig 4.2

87

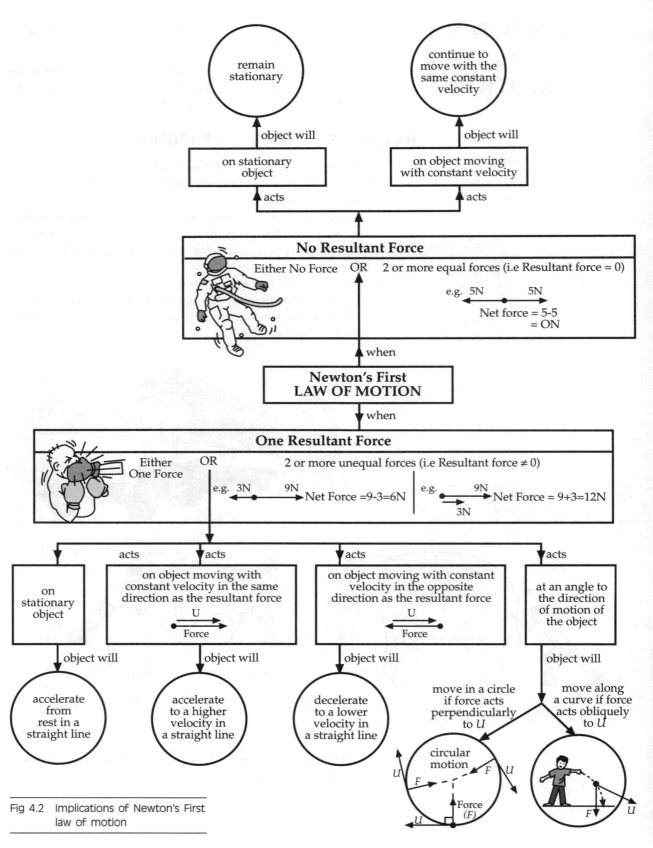

remain stationary

continue to move with the same constant velocity

object will — on stationary object — acts

object will — on object moving with constant velocity — acts

No Resultant Force

Either No Force   OR   2 or more equal forces (i.e Resultant force = 0)

e.g. 5N ←•→ 5N

Net force = 5-5
= ON

when

Newton's First LAW OF MOTION

when

One Resultant Force

Either One Force   OR   2 or more unequal forces (i.e Resultant force ≠ 0)

e.g. 3N ← • → 9N   Net Force =9-3=6N

e.g. 9N →, 3N →   Net Force = 9+3=12N

acts — on stationary object

acts — on object moving with constant velocity in the same direction as the resultant force — U → / Force

acts — on object moving with constant velocity in the opposite direction as the resultant force — U ← / Force

acts — at an angle to the direction of motion of the object

object will — accelerate from rest in a straight line

object will — accelerate to a higher velocity in a straight line

object will — decelerate to a lower velocity in a straight line

object will — move in a circle if force acts perpendicularly to U

move along a curve if force acts obliquely to U

circular motion

Fig 4.2   Implications of Newton's First law of motion

88

Newton's Second Law of Motion

- The rate of change of momentum of an object is directly proportional to the resultant force acting on that object and has the same direction as the force.

- The linear momentum of an object of mass m moving with constant speed v is defined as the product of mass and its velocity.
  Mathematically, the magnitude of the momentum is:
  momentum = mass $\times$ velocity
  $$p = m\,v$$
  It is a vector quantity and its direction is the same as the direction of the velocity. The unit of momentum is kg m s^{-1}.

- The change in momentum is given by:
  Change in momentum = final momentum $-$ initial momentum
  $$\Delta p = m\,v - m\,u$$
  where v is the final velocity and u is the initial velocity.

- Newton's second law of motion can be written as:
  $$F \propto \frac{m\,v - m\,u}{t} \qquad \text{Equation (1)}$$

  or $\quad F \propto \dfrac{\mathrm{d}}{\mathrm{d}t}(m\,v)$

  or $\quad F = k\dfrac{\mathrm{d}(m\,v)}{\mathrm{d}t} \qquad \text{Equation (2)}$

  where k is a dimensionless constant.

- If the mass and velocity changes, equation (2) can be written as:
  $$F = km\frac{\mathrm{d}v}{\mathrm{d}t} + kv\frac{\mathrm{d}m}{\mathrm{d}t} \qquad \text{Equation (3)}$$

- If the mass remains constant $\left(i.e.\ \dfrac{\mathrm{d}m}{\mathrm{d}t} = 0\right)$ and only velocity changes, equation (3) becomes:
  $$F = km\frac{\mathrm{d}v}{\mathrm{d}t}$$
  $$F = k\,m\,a \qquad \text{Equation (4)}$$
  (where a is the acceleration of the object)

- The unit for force is newton. One newton is defined as the force which produces an acceleration of 1 m s^{-2} when it is applied to a mass of 1 kg.
  1 newton = k (1 kg) (1 m s^{-2})
  $\therefore\ k = 1$
  Hence equation (4) reduces to:
  $$F = m\,a$$
  where F is the resultant force in Newton,
  $\quad m$ is the mass in kilograms and
  $\quad a$ is the acceleration in m s^{-2}.

89

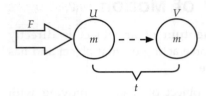

Fig 4.3a   The effect of an impulse

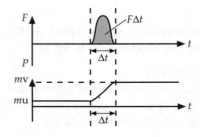

Fig 4.3b   Force against time graph and momentum-time graph

- If mass is variable and velocity is constant $\left(\dfrac{dv}{dt} = 0\right)$, equation (3) becomes:

$$F = v\,\frac{dm}{dt}$$

- Forces are vector quantities and are combined together according to the rules of vector addition. The direction of the force is the same as the direction of the acceleration.

- **Impulse**

  Consider the application of a force on a mass m which causes it to accelerate from an initial velocity u to a final velocity v in time t (Fig 4.3).

  From Newton's second law,

  $$F = \frac{d(m\,v)}{dt}$$

  Since m is constant, $F = m\,\dfrac{dv}{dt}$

  i.e. $\displaystyle\int_{t_1}^{t_2} F\,dt = \int_{u}^{v} m\,dv$

  $$\int_{t_1}^{t_2} F\,dt = m\,v - m\,u$$

  $$= \text{Area under the force-time graph}$$

  The integral of force with respect to time is known as impulse. The force is variable in size and acts for a very short time. Fig 4.3b shows the graph of force against time and the corresponding momentum-time graph.

  The area under the force-time graph gives a measure of the impulse. This is also equal to the change in momentum of the mass m.

- Table 4.1 shows some common forces encountered in mechanics.

90

Types of force	Characteristics
• The weight of a body is the gravitational force acting on the body itself. (diagram: block M with arrow $W = mg$)	• The magnitude of the weight is given by: $W = m\,g$ where g is the acceleration due to gravity. • It varies over the surface of the Earth.
• When a body is in contact with a surface, a force that is perpendicular to the surface is exerted on the body. This force is known as the reaction force (R). (diagram: block with R up, W and A down)	• Reaction varies according to the force exerted on the surface. • It is in the opposite direction to the force (Action, A) exerted on the surface (described by Newton's third law of motion).
• Friction is the force that resists the motion of a body as it slides over a rough surface. (diagram: direction of motion, block with friction F)	• The magnitude of friction is given by: $F = \mu R$ where μ is a constant known as the coefficient of friction. • Friction is always directed in the opposite direction to the motion of the body.
• Tension is the force in a cord that pulls on a body. (diagram: Tension (T), Tension (T) on hanging block)	• It is always directed away from a body and along the cord. • The tension pulls at either end of the attachment with the same magnitude.
• Compression is the force in a spring that pushes against a body. (diagram: Compression — spring — Compression)	• It is always directed towards a body and along the spring. • The compression pushes at either end of the attachment with the same magnitude.

Table 4.1

91

- When using Newton's laws, it is important to draw a free body diagram. It is a simplified diagram that shows all the forces acting on one body without showing the forces acting on the environment or other bodies. The example below illustrates this.

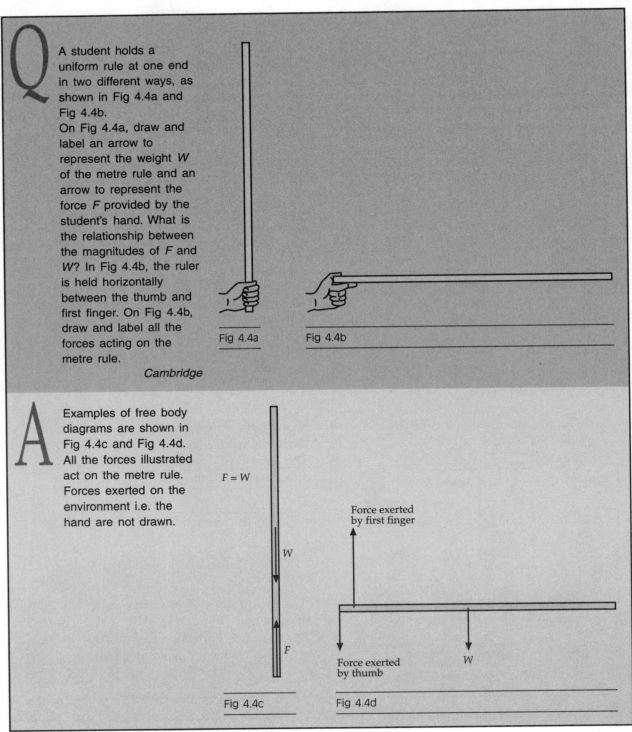

Q A student holds a uniform rule at one end in two different ways, as shown in Fig 4.4a and Fig 4.4b.
On Fig 4.4a, draw and label an arrow to represent the weight W of the metre rule and an arrow to represent the force F provided by the student's hand. What is the relationship between the magnitudes of F and W? In Fig 4.4b, the ruler is held horizontally between the thumb and first finger. On Fig 4.4b, draw and label all the forces acting on the metre rule.

Cambridge

Fig 4.4a   Fig 4.4b

A Examples of free body diagrams are shown in Fig 4.4c and Fig 4.4d. All the forces illustrated act on the metre rule. Forces exerted on the environment i.e. the hand are not drawn.

$F = W$

W

F

Force exerted by first finger

Force exerted by thumb

W

Fig 4.4c   Fig 4.4d

92

(a) Distinguish between the *mass* and the *weight* of a body. State the unit in which each is measured.

(b) Show that
  (i) the base units of acceleration of free fall are the same as the base units of gravitational field strength,
  (ii) the newton second is a unit of momentum.

(c) In the United States, plans are under consideration for launching a satellite by use of a space gun. The satellite, of mass 2000 kg, accelerates uniformly along a tube of length 1200 m and reaches a speed of 8000 m s^{-1}.
  Calculate
  (i) the momentum of the satellite as it leaves the tube,
  (ii) the time it takes to accelerate along the tube,
  (iii) the force causing the acceleration,
  (iv) the acceleration.

(d) (i) It would be impossible to use the space gun in (c) for manned space flights. Suggest a reason.
  (ii) It would be an advantage to site the gun on the Earth's equator pointing eastwards. Suggest a reason.

Cambridge

(a) The mass of a body is a measure of the inertia of the body.
  The S I unit is kg.
  The weight of a body is the gravitational force exerted on that body. The S I unit is newton (N).

(b) (i) Gravitational field strength $g = \dfrac{\text{force}}{\text{mass}}$

  Base units of $g = \dfrac{\text{kg m s}^{-2}}{\text{kg}}$

  $= \text{m s}^{-2}$

  $= $ Base units of acceleration

  (ii) momentum $(p) = $ mass $(m) \times$ velocity (v)
  Units of momentum $= $ kg m s^{-1}
  $= $ (kg m s^{-2}) s
  $= $ N s

(c) (i) $p = m v$
  $= (2000)\,(8000)$
  $= 1.6 \times 10^7$ N s

  (ii) If $t = $ time taken by the satellite to accelerate along the tube

  $$s = \frac{1}{2}(u + v)\, t$$

  where $s = 1200$ m, $u = 0$ m s^{-1}, $v = 8000$ m s^{-1}

  i.e. $1200 = \dfrac{1}{2}(0 + 8000)\, t$

  $\therefore t = 0.30$ s

93

(iii) $F \Delta t = \Delta p$ where F is the force causing the acceleration

$$\therefore F = \frac{\Delta p}{\Delta t} = \frac{1.6 \times 10^7}{0.30}$$
$$= 5.33 \times 10^7$$
$$= 5.3 \times 10^7 \text{ N}$$

(iv) acceleration $a = \frac{F}{m} = \frac{5.33 \times 10^7}{2000}$
$$= 26\ 650$$
$$= 27\ 000 \text{ m s}^{-2}$$

(d) (i) The enormous force that is required to produce the high acceleration will kill any astronaut in the space vehicle.

(ii) As the Earth rotates eastward, the speed of the satellite will be enhanced.

Q The graph shows how the force acting on a body varies with time.
Assuming that the body is moving in a straight line, by how much does its momentum change?

Cambridge

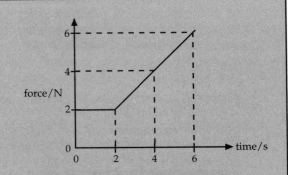

A Change in momentum = Area under the force-time graph

$$= (2 \times 6) + \frac{1}{2}(4)(4)$$
$$= 20 \text{ kg m s}^{-1}$$

Q A model helicopter of mass 5.0 kg rises with constant acceleration from rest to a height of 60 m in 10 s. Find the thrust exerted by the rotor blades during the ascent.

Cambridge

A Using $s = u\,t + \frac{1}{2}a\,t^2$, acceleration of helicopter $a = \frac{2\,s}{t^2}$

$$= \frac{2 \times 60}{10^2}$$
$$= 1.2 \text{ m s}^{-2}$$

If T is the thrust exerted by the rotor blades during the ascent,

$T - mg = ma$
$T - (5.0)(9.81) = 5(1.2)$
$T = 55 \text{ N}$

94

 A conveyor belt is used to transfer luggage at an airport. It consists of a horizontal endless belt running over driving rollers, moving at a constant speed of 1.5 m s^{-1}. To keep the belt moving when it is transporting luggage requires a greater driving force than for an empty belt. On average, the rate at which baggage is placed on one end of the belt and lifted off at the other end is 20 kg per second. Why is an additional driving force required, and what is its value?

Cambridge

 An additional driving force is required to accelerate the baggage to a constant speed of 1.5 m s^{-1}. The magnitude of this force is given by:

$$F = v\frac{dm}{dt} = (1.5)\ (20)$$
$$= 30\ N$$

 The rotating rotor of a hovering helicopter imparts a downward velocity v to a cylindrical column of air of cross-sectional area A. The density of the air column is ρ. Show that the force exerted by the helicopter on the air mass is given by: $F = \rho\ A\ v^2$.

 The magnitude of the downward force exerted by the helicopter on the air is given by $F = v\frac{dm}{dt}$.

A cylindrical column of air of cross sectional area A and volume V' is pushed down by the rotor every second.

$$\frac{dV'}{dt} = A\frac{dl}{dt} = A\ v$$

Hence $\dfrac{dm}{dt} = \rho\dfrac{dV'}{dt} = \rho\ A\ v$

$$F = v\frac{dm}{dt} = \rho\ A\ v^2$$

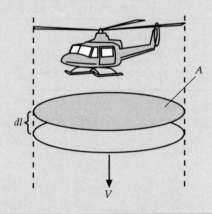

Newton's Third law of Motion

- Action and reaction are always equal but oppositely directed on two different bodies.

  (a) Action and reaction forces always occur in pairs. Fig 4.6 shows several examples of action-reaction pairs.

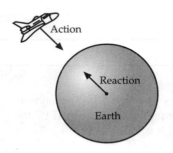

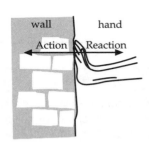

Fig 4.6   Examples of action and reaction

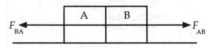

(b) When body A exerts a force of $\mathbf{F}_{AB}$ on body B, body B will exert an equal and opposite force $\mathbf{F}_{BA}$ on body A but directed in the opposite direction. Mathematically it is written as: $\mathbf{F}_{AB} = -\mathbf{F}_{BA}$.

(c) Action and reaction forces always act on different bodies. In Fig 4.7a, only $\mathbf{A}$ and $\mathbf{R}$ is an action-reaction pair. The weight mg and $\mathbf{R}$ do not constitute an action-reaction pair because they are exerted on the same box.

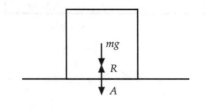

Fig 4.7a

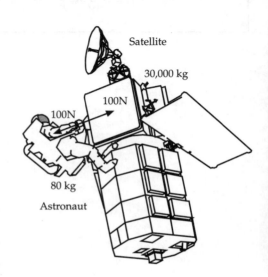

Fig 4.7b

96

Fig 4.7 also shows an astronaut of mass 80 kg pushing against a satellite of mass 30 000 kg. If the forces acting on both bodies are 100 N, the magnitude of acceleration of the astronaut is given by:

$$a = \frac{F}{m} = \frac{100}{80}$$
$$= 1.25 \text{ m s}^{-2}$$

The acceleration of the satellite is given by:

$$a = \frac{F}{M} = \frac{100}{30\,000}$$
$$= 3.3 \times 10^{-3} \text{ m s}^{-2}$$

As the forces are directed in the opposite direction on two different bodies, the astronaut and satellite will move away from each other at different speeds.

Q

Two blocks, X and Y, of masses m and $2m$ respectively, are accelerated along a smooth horizontal surface by a force F applied to block X, as shown.
What is the magnitude of the force exerted by block Y on block X during this acceleration?

Cambridge

A

The free body diagram of forces acting on X is as shown.
From the figure above, $F = 3ma$

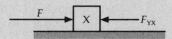

$$\therefore ma = \frac{1}{3}F$$

From the figure, $F - F_{YX} = ma$
$$\therefore F_{YX} = F - ma$$
$$= F - \frac{1}{3}F$$
$$= \frac{2}{3}F$$

Q

The figure shows a man of weight 800 N pulling a wooden crate of weight 600 N with a frictionless pulley system. The force exerted by the man on the floor is 400 N as the crate moves upwards. Find the acceleration of the crate and the man.

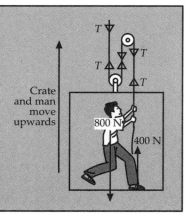

Crate and man move upwards

97

A

Consider the forces acting on the man

$$T + 400 - 800 = 80a$$
$$T - 400 = 80a \quad\text{————————} \quad (1)$$

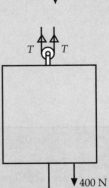

Consider the forces acting on the crate

$$2T - 600 - 400 = 60a$$
$$T - 500 = 30a \quad\text{————————} \quad (2)$$

equation (1) − equation (2)

$$50a = 100$$
$$\therefore \ a = \frac{100}{50}$$
$$= 2 \text{ m s}^{-2}$$

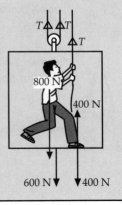

Alternatively, we can consider forces acting on the crate and the man.

$$3T - 800 - 600 = 140a$$
$$3T - 1400 = 140a \quad\text{————————} \quad (3)$$

Multiply equation (1) by 3

$$3T - 1200 = 240a \quad\text{————————} \quad (4)$$

equation (4) − equation (3)

$$100a = 200$$
$$\therefore \ a = 2 \text{ m s}^{-2}$$

CONSERVATION OF MOMENTUM

Before collision:

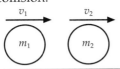

During collision:

After collision:

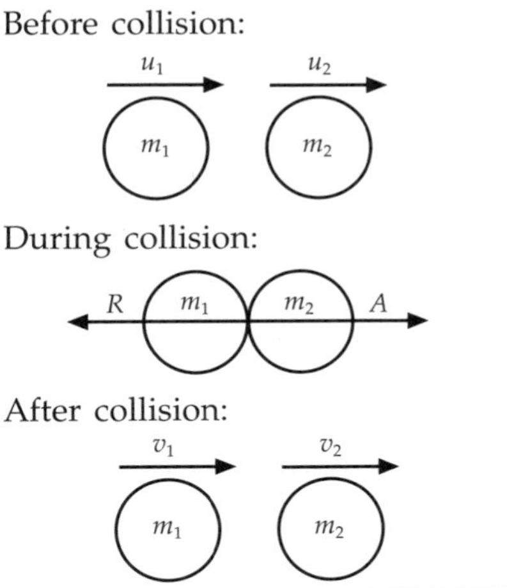

Fig 4.8   Momentum is conserved

• Consider two bodies of masses m_1 and m_2 colliding linearly with each other. The velocities before and after the impact are shown in Fig 4.8.

From Newton's second law of motion,

for mass m_1: $\int R dt = m_1 v_1 - m_1 u_1$

for mass m_2: $\int A dt = m_2 v_2 - m_2 u_2$

From Newton's third law of motion,

$$\int R dt = - \int A dt$$
$$m_1 v_1 - m_1 u_1 = -(m_2 v_2 - m_2 u_2)$$
$$m_1 v_1 + m_2 v_2 = m_1 u_1 + m_2 u_2$$

The principle of **conservation of linear momentum** states that the total momentum of a closed system of colliding objects remains constant if no external forces act on that system.

Q

(a) State Newton's first law of motion and show that it leads to the concept of force.

(b) Newton's second law states that 'the rate of change of momentum of a body is proportional to the resultant force acting on it'. Show how this law, together with a suitable definition of the unit of force, leads to the relationship force = mass × acceleration for a body of constant mass.

(c) Together with these two laws, Newton's third law can be used to derive the principle of conservation of momentum. State the third law and show this derivation.

A

(a) An object at rest will remain at rest and an object in motion will continue in motion at constant speed in a straight line in the absence of a resultant force.
According to Newtons first law of motion:
If the resultant force is zero, the change in velocity, $\Delta v = 0$ and the object remains at rest or move with constant speed in a straight line. Conversely, if $\Delta v \neq 0$, the object accelerates.
This leads to the concept of force that causes the change in velocity.

(b) The magnitude of the resultant force F is given by

$$F \propto \frac{d(mv)}{dt}$$

$$F = k \frac{d(mv)}{dt} \quad \text{where } k \text{ is a constant}$$

For a body with constant mass,

$$F = km \frac{dv}{dt}$$
$$F = k\, m\, a$$

Define the unit of force 1 N as that force that will produce an acceleration of 1 m s^{-2} when it is applied to a mass of 1 kg i.e. $1 \text{ N} = k\,(1 \text{ kg})\,(1 \text{ m s}^{-2})$

$\therefore k = 1$

Hence $F = m\, a$

99

(c) Take the direction to the right as positive

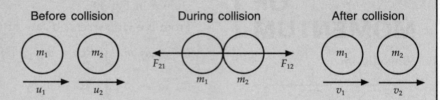

If F_{12} is the force acting on m_2 by m_1 and F_{21} is the force acting on m_1 by m_2, by Newton's third law of motion: During the time of collision $F_{12} = -F_{21}$

By Newton's first and second laws of motion

$$\frac{m_1v_1 - m_1u_1}{\Delta t} = -\left(\frac{m_2v_2 - m_2u_2}{\Delta t}\right)$$

$m_1 v_1 - m_1 u_1 = -m_2 v_2 + m_2 u_2$

Hence $m_1 u_1 + m_2 u_2 = m_1 v_1 + m_2 v_2$

The total linear momentum before collision is equal to the total linear momentum after the collision.

Elastic Collision

- The characteristics of an elastic collision are:
  (a) The total momentum of the colliding objects is always conserved.
  (b) The total kinetic energy is conserved.

- Consider the head-on elastic collision of two objects in one dimension. Take the direction to the right as positive.

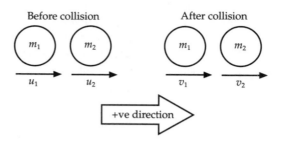

Fig 4.9   Elastic Collision

Fig 4.9 shows an object of mass m_1 and velocity u_1 colliding linearly with another mass m_2 travelling with velocity u_2. After the collision, the velocities of m_1 and m_2 are v_1 and v_2 respectively.

By conservation of momentum,

$$m_1 u_1 + m_2 u_2 = m_1 v_1 + m_2 v_2 \qquad\qquad (1)$$

100

Rearranging:

$$m_1 (u_1 - v_1) = m_2 (v_2 - u_2) \text{————————————} (2)$$

Since the collision is elastic, the kinetic energy is conserved.

$$\frac{1}{2} m_1 u_1{}^2 + \frac{1}{2} m_2 u_2{}^2 = \frac{1}{2} m_1 v_1{}^2 + \frac{1}{2} m_2 v_2{}^2 \text{————————} (3)$$

Rearranging:

$$m_1 (u_1{}^2 - v_1{}^2) = m_2 (v_2{}^2 - u_2{}^2) \text{————————————} (4)$$

Divide equation (4) by equation (2):

$$\frac{m_1(u_1{}^2 - v_1{}^2)}{m_1(u_1 - v_1)} = \frac{m_2(v_2{}^2 - u_2{}^2)}{m_2(v_2 - u_2)}$$

$$\frac{m_1(u_1 - v_1)(u_1 + v_1)}{m_1(u_1 - v_1)} = \frac{m_2(v_2 - u_2)(v_2 + u_2)}{m_2(v_2 - u_2)}$$

$$u_1 + v_1 = v_2 + u_2$$

$$u_1 - u_2 = v_2 - v_1 \text{————————} (5)$$

Equation (5) tells us that the relative speed of approach is equal to the relative speed of separation.

From equation (5)

$$v_2 = u_1 - u_2 + v_1$$

Substituting for v_2 in equation (2), we have

$$m_1(u_1 - v_1) = m_2 ((u_1 - u_2 + v_1) - u_2)$$

Simplifying,

$$m_1 u_1 - m_1 v_1 = m_2 u_1 - 2 m_2 u_2 + m_2 v_1$$

$$(m_1 + m_2) v_1 = (m_1 - m_2) u_1 + 2 m_2 u_2$$

$$\therefore v_1 = \left(\frac{m_1 - m_2}{m_1 + m_2} \right) u_1 + \left(\frac{2m_2}{m_1 + m_2} \right) u_2 \text{————————} (6)$$

Through a similar derivation, v_2 is obtained, i.e.

$$v_2 = \left(\frac{2m_1}{m_1 + m_2} \right) u_1 + \left(\frac{m_2 - m_1}{m_1 + m_2} \right) u_2 \text{————————} (7)$$

With reference to equations (6) and (7), consider the following situations.

(a) If $m_1 << m_2$ and $u_2 = 0$, we have $v_1 \approx -u_1$ and $v_2 \approx 0$. When a very small mass collides with a massive object, the small mass will rebound in the opposite direction with almost the same speed as its initial speed.

(b) If $m_1 = m_2$ and $u_2 = 0$, we have $v_1 = 0$ and $v_2 = u_1$. When a mass collides with another identical mass at rest, a complete transfer of velocity will occur. m_1 will be stopped dead in its track and its velocity will be transferred completely to m_2.

(c) If $m_1 >> m_2$ and $u_2 = 0$, we have $v_2 \approx 2u_1$ and $v_1 \approx u_1$. When a very massive object collides with a very small mass at rest, the velocity of the massive object remains practically unchanged while the small mass almost double u_1.

101

Inelastic Collision

- The characteristics of inelastic collision are:
  - (a) The total momentum of the colliding objects is always conserved.
  - (b) The total kinetic energy is not conserved.

- In most collisions, some change in kinetic energy usually takes place although the momentum of the system is always conserved. The loss of kinetic energy is due to the increase in internal energy and heat loss dissipated to the surroundings. In some cases, sound and light energy may be produced.

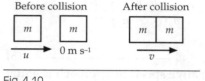

Fig 4.10

- Consider a perfectly inelastic collision whereby a particle of mass m travelling with velocity u collides with an identical particle at rest (Fig 4.10). After impact, the two particles coalesce and move off together with a velocity v.

By the principle of conservation of momentum,
$$m u + 0 = (m + m)v$$

$$v = \frac{1}{2}u$$

Kinetic energy before collision $= \frac{1}{2}m u^2$

Kinetic energy after collision $= \frac{1}{4}m u^2$

For a perfectly inelastic collision, the kinetic energy after collision is half the initial kinetic energy of the first particle. The loss in energy is due to the change in the internal energy and heat loss.

The figure shows two trolleys X and Y about to collide. The momentum of each trolley before the impact is given.
After the collision, the trolleys travel in opposite directions and the momentum of X is 2 kg m s^{-1}. What is the magnitude of the momentum of trolley Y?

Cambridge

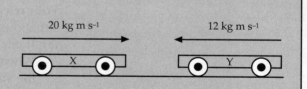

Let the magnitude of the momentum of trolley Y after collision be p. The direction to the right is taken as positive. By the conservation of momentum, $20 - 12 = -2 + p$
∴ $p = 10$ kg m s^{-1} moving to the right

 Two spheres of masses m_1 and m_2 are moving towards one another along the same straight line.
The spheres have velocities u_1 and u_2, as illustrated in Fig 4.11.

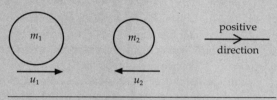

Fig 4.11

During impact, the spheres stick together and then move off with velocity V, as illustrated in Fig 4.12.

(i) State and explain whether the collision is elastic or inelastic.

(ii) Taking the direction of the final velocity V as being positive, write down equations, in terms of m_1, m_2, u_1, u_2 and V, to represent the change in momentum of
   1. the sphere of mass m_1,
   2. the sphere of mass m_2.

(iii) Using your answers to (ii), write down, for this collision, an equation to represent conservation of linear momentum.

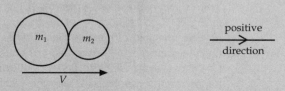

Fig 4.12

(i) Collision is inelastic as the spheres stick together during impact.

(ii) Change in momentum of sphere $m_1 = m_1 V - m_1 u_1$
Change in momentum of sphere $m_2 = -m_2 u_2 + m_2 V$
Force exerted on m_2 by $m_1 = \boldsymbol{F}_{12}$
Force exerted on m_1 by $m_2 = \boldsymbol{F}_{21}$
During the impact $\boldsymbol{F}_{12} = -\boldsymbol{F}_{21}$

$$\frac{m_1 V - m_1 u_1}{t} = -\left(\frac{-m_2 u_2 + m_2 V}{t}\right)$$

$$m_1 V - m_1 u_1 = m_2 u_2 - m_2 V$$
$$m_1 V + m_2 V = m_1 u_1 + m_2 u_2$$
$$(m_1 + m_2) V = m_1 u_1 + m_2 u_2$$

Total momentum after impact = Total momentum before impact

(a) (i) State the principle of conservation of linear momentum.

(ii) Explain what is meant by a perfectly elastic collision between two bodies.

(b) A sphere of mass m travelling in a straight line with speed u collides head-on with a stationary sphere, also of mass m. The collision is perfectly elastic. The final speeds are v_1 and v_2 respectively, as shown in Fig 4.13. Write down expressions in terms of the quantities shown in Fig 4.13, to illustrate

(i) the principle of conservation of linear momentum,
(ii) the principle of conservation of energy.

Use these expressions to find v_2 in terms of u. What happens after the collision with the incoming sphere?

(c) The collision experiment in (b) is repeated but this time the second sphere is not stationary but has speed u_2. The speed u of the incoming sphere is greater than u_2 (See Fig 4.14).

The incoming sphere of kinetic energy E may lose an amount of kinetic energy W. Fig 4.15 shows how $\dfrac{W}{E}$, the fractional energy lost by the incoming sphere, depends on the ratio $\dfrac{u_2}{u}$.

(i) What happens to the kinetic energy lost by the incoming sphere?

(ii) Given that the initial energy of the incoming sphere is 1.6×10^{-13} J, calculate the energy lost by this sphere in a perfectly elastic collision when

$$\frac{u_2}{u} = 0.40.$$

(iii) Use the graph of Fig 4.15 to suggest why paraffin wax, which has a high number density of protons, is a good absorber of high-speed neutrons.

Cambridge

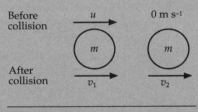

Fig 4.13

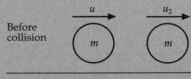

Fig 4.14

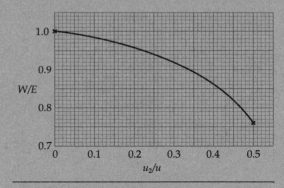

Fig 4.15

(a) (i) The principle of conservation of linear momentum states that the total momentum of a closed system of colliding objects remains constant if no external forces act on that system.

(ii) A perfectly elastic collision between two bodies is one where the total momentum and total kinetic energy of the colliding bodies are conserved.

(b) (i) By the principle of conservation of linear momentum

$$m\,u = m\,v_1 + m\,v_2$$
$$\therefore v_1 = u - v_2 \quad\text{————————————— (1)}$$

104

(ii) By the principle of conservation of kinetic energy

$$\frac{1}{2}m\,u^2 = \frac{1}{2}m\,v_1^2 + \frac{1}{2}m\,v_2^2$$

$$\therefore v_1^2 = u^2 - v_2^2 \rule{4cm}{0.4pt} (2)$$

To obtain v_2 in terms of u, we substitute equation (1) into equation (2)

$$(u - v_2)^2 = u^2 - v_2^2$$
$$u^2 - 2u\,v_2 + v_2^2 = u^2 - v_2^2$$
$$2v_2^2 - 2u\,v_2 = 0$$
$$2\,v_2\,(v_2 - u) = 0$$

i.e. $v_2 = 0$ and $v_2 - u = 0$

As $v_2 = 0$ is inadmissible, $v_2 = u$

From equation (1), $v_1 = 0$. The incoming sphere is brought to rest on impact.

(c) (i) The kinetic energy lost by the incoming sphere is transmitted to the second sphere.

(ii) When $\dfrac{u_2}{u} = 0.40$, $\dfrac{W}{E} = 0.855$

$$\therefore \text{ The energy lost is, } W = 1.6 \times 10^{-13} \times 0.855$$
$$= 1.4 \times 10^{-13} \text{ J}$$

(iii) Since the proton and neutron have approximately the same mass, the variation of $\dfrac{W}{E}$ with

$\dfrac{u_2}{u}$ is described by Fig 4.15. The ratio $\dfrac{u_2}{u}$ is small because the speed of the neutrons

used is high while the speed of protons in paraffin wax is relatively small. This means that

the ratio $\dfrac{W}{E}$, as obtained from Fig 4.15, has a value that is close to the maximum value

of 1.0. Hence, loss in kinetic energy W is large and incoming neutrons are slowed down.

Exercise 4

Multiple Choice Questions

1 A force applied horizontally to a certain mass near the Earth's surface produces an acceleration a. If an equal force were applied to the same mass near the surface of the Moon, where the acceleration of free fall is one sixth of its value at the Earth's surface, the acceleration produced would be

   A $\dfrac{a}{36}$ B $\dfrac{a}{6}$
   C a D $6a$

2 A body of mass 3 kg is acted on by a force which varies as shown in Fig 4.16. The momentum acquired is

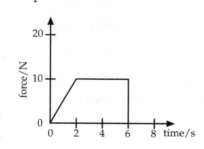

Fig 4.16

   A 0 N s   B 5 N s
   C 30 N s   D 50 N s

3 A pendulum bob hangs from the ceiling in a carriage in a train and is just above a certain mark on the floor when the train is at rest. When the train is moving with constant velocity forward, the bob

   A is behind the mark, so that the pendulum thread is along the resultant of the forces due to the motion of the train and gravity.

   B remains over the mark because the force due to the motion of the train is balanced by the reaction of the thread on the support.

   C oscillates with simple harmonic motion about its former position because of the unbalanced force due to the motion of the train.

   D remains over the mark because the motion of the train produces no additional force on the bob.

4 A helicopter of mass 3.0×10^3 kg rises vertically with a constant speed of 25 m s^{-1}. Taking the acceleration of free fall as 10 m s^{-2}, what resultant force acts on helicopter?

   A zero
   B 3.0×10^4 N downwards
   C 4.5×10^4 N upwards
   D 7.5×10^4 N upwards

5 Two bodies P and Q, having masses M_P and M_Q respectively, exert forces on each other and have no other forces acting on them. The force acting on P is F, which gives P an acceleration a. Which of the following pairs is correct?

	magnitude of force on Q	*magnitude of acceleration of* Q
A	$\dfrac{M_Q}{M_P}F$	a
B	$\dfrac{M_P}{M_Q}F$	a
C	F	a
D	F	$\dfrac{M_P}{M_Q}a$

6 A man is parachuting at constant speed towards the surface of the Earth. The force which, according to Newton's third law, makes an action-reaction pair with the gravitational force on the man is

   A the tension in the harness of the parachute.

   B the viscous force of the man and his parachute or the air.

   C the gravitational force on the Earth due to the man.

   D the viscous force of the air on the man and his parachute.

106

7 Which statement is correct with reference to perfectly elastic collisions between two bodies?

 A Neither total momentum nor total kinetic energy need be conserved but total energy must be conserved.
 B Total momentum and total energy are conserved but total kinetic energy may be changed into some other form of energy.
 C Total kinetic energy and total energy are both conserved but total momentum is conserved only if the two bodies have equal masses.
 D Total momentum, total kinetic energy and total energy are all conserved.

8 Three identical stationary discs, **P**, **Q** and **R** are placed in a line on a horizontal, flat, frictionless surface. Disc **P** is projected straight towards disc **Q**.

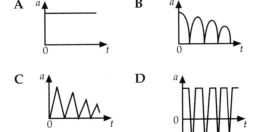

If all consequent collisions are perfectly elastic, what will be the final motion of the three discs?

	P	Q	R
A	moving left	moving left	moving right
B	stationary	stationary	moving right
C	moving right	moving right	moving right
D	moving left	stationary	moving right

9 A positron, a positively-charged particle of mass 10^{-30} kg, is moving at a speed v, which is much less than the speed of light. It makes a head-on elastic collision with a stationary proton of mass 10^{-27} kg. Which one of the following correctly describes the outcome of the collision?

 A the positron rebounds at speed $\frac{v}{2}$ and the proton moves on at speed $\frac{v}{2}$.
 B The positron rebounds at a speed nearly equal to v, and the proton moves on at a a speed much less than v.
 C The positron comes to rest and the proton moves on at speed v.
 D The positron rebounds at speed v and the proton moves on at speed v.

10 The rate of change of momentum of a body falling freely under gravity is equal to its
 A impulse.   B kinetic energy.
 C power.   D weight.

11 A steel ball is held above a horizontal table and released so that it falls on to the table and rebounds several times.
 If the collisions are inelastic, which graph best represents the variation of the ball's acceleration a with time t?

A ![graph A] B ![graph B]

C ![graph C] D ![graph D]

Structured Questions

1 (a) Define linear momentum.
 (b) Use your definition of momentum to define force.
 (c) Show that this definition leads to the equation $F = ma$.
 (d) State the principle of conservation of momentum.

2   A particle of mass m moving with speed u makes a head-on collision wth an identical particle which is initially at rest. The particles coalesce and move off with a common velocity.
    (a) Find the common speed of the particles after the collision.
    (b) Find the ratio of the kinetic energy of the system after the collision to that before it.
    (c) What happens to the kinetic energy that is 'lost'?

    Cambridge

3   A stone is dropped from a point a few metres above the Earth's surface. Considering the system of stone and Earth, discuss briefly how the principle of conservation of momentum applies *before* the impact of the stone with the Earth.

    Cambridge

4   (a) Show that E_k, the kinetic energy of a body of mass m moving with speed v is given by the expression

$$E_k = \frac{1}{2} mv^2.$$

    (b) A particle A of mass M moving with velocity U in the direction shown in Fig 4.17 collides head-on with a particle B of mass m which is originally at rest.

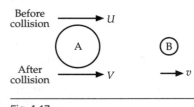

Fig 4.17

    The collision is perfectly elastic. After the collision, A and B move off with velocities V and v as shown.
    (i) Write down equations which summarise the application of the principles of conservation of energy and momentum to this collision.

    (ii) What is the ratio m/M such that all the kinetic energy of A is transferred to B during the collision (i.e. $V = 0$)?
(c) An executive toy consists of two identical steel spheres suspended so that they are free to move in a vertical plane as shown in fig 4.18.

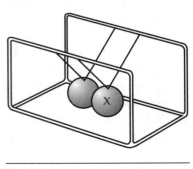

Fig 4.18

The separation of the pairs of suspension threads is equal to the diameter of a sphere. Sphere X is displaced to the right and then released. With reference to your answer to *(b)*, discuss the subsequent motion of the spheres.

    Cambridge

5   (a) Collisions between objects are said to be either *elastic* or *inelastic*. Complete Fig 4.19 by placing a tick (✓) in the relevant boxes to indicate which quantities are conserved in these collisions.

collision	momentum	kinetic energy	total energy
elastic			
inelastic			

Fig 4.19

(b) (i) A fast-moving neutron of mass m collides head-on with a stationary atom of hydrogen, also of mass m, as illustrated in Fig 4.20.

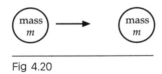

Fig 4.20

The neutron is captured by the atom to form a 'heavy' isotope of hydrogen of mass $2m$ which moves off with a speed of 3.0×10^7 m s^{-1}.

1. State whether the collision process whereby the neutron is captured is elastic or inelastic.

2. Calculate the speed of the neutron before capture.

   Speed = ... m s^{-1}

(ii) A similar neutron to that in (i) now collides head-on with a stationary nitrogen atom of mass $14\,m$ to form a 'heavy' isotope of nitrogen. Calculate the speed of this 'heavy' nitrogen atom.

   Speed = ... m s^{-1}

109

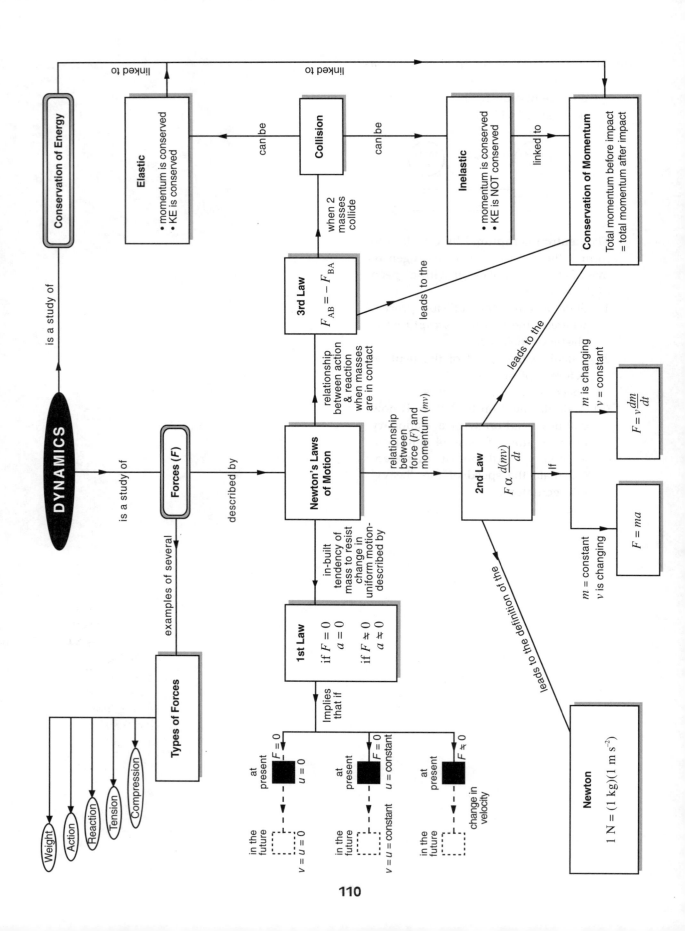

DYNAMICS

is a study of → **Conservation of Energy**

is a study of → **Forces (F)**

examples of several → **Types of Forces**: Weight, Action, Reaction, Tension, Compression

described by → **Newton's Laws of Motion**

in-built tendency of mass to resist change in uniform motion-described by → **1st Law**
if $F = 0$, $a = 0$
if $F \neq 0$, $a \neq 0$

Implies that if:
- at present $F = 0$, $u = 0$ → in the future $v = u = 0$
- at present $F = 0$, $u = $ constant → in the future $v = u = $ constant
- at present $F \neq 0$ → in the future change in velocity

relationship between action & reaction when masses are in contact → **3rd Law** $F_{AB} = -F_{BA}$

when 2 masses collide → **Collision**

Collision can be → **Elastic**: momentum is conserved; KE is conserved

Collision can be → **Inelastic**: momentum is conserved; KE is NOT conserved

Inelastic linked to → **Conservation of Momentum**: Total momentum before impact = total momentum after impact

3rd Law leads to the → Conservation of Momentum

relationship between force (F) and momentum (mv) → **2nd Law** $F \propto \dfrac{d(mv)}{dt}$

2nd Law leads to → Conservation of Momentum

If:
- m is changing, $v = $ constant → $F = v\dfrac{dm}{dt}$
- $m = $ constant, v is changing → $F = ma$

leads to the definition of the → **Newton** $1\ N = (1\ kg)(1\ m\ s^{-2})$

linked to (Conservation of Energy ↔ Elastic)

linked to (Conservation of Momentum)

110

CHAPTER

5

Forces

TYPES OF FORCE

CENTRE OF GRAVITY

TURNING EFFECTS OF FORCES

EQUILIBRIUM OF FORCES

Syllabus Objectives

In this chapter you should be able to:

- describe the forces on mass, charge and current in gravitational, electric and magnetic fields, as appropriate.
- show an understanding of the origin of the upthrust acting on a body in a fluid.
- show a qualitative understanding of frictional forces and viscous forces, including air resistance. (No treatment of the coefficients of friction and viscosity is required.)
- recall and apply Hooke's law in problem solving.
- use a vector triangle to represent forces in equilibrium.
- show an understanding that the weight of a body may be taken as acting at a single point known as its centre of gravity.
- show an understanding that a couple is a pair of forces which tends to produce rotation only.
- define and apply the moment of a force and the torque of a couple.
- show an understanding that, when there is no resultant force and no resultant torque, a system is in equilibrium.
- apply the principle of moments.

TYPES OF FORCE

- Four types of fundamental forces govern the physical universe. These forces are listed in Table 5.1.

Force	Effects	Strength/N	Range/m
Strong	Binds protons and neutrons in the nucleus	10^4	10^{-15}
Electromagnetic force	Acts on electric charges	10^2	Infinite
Weak	Causes radioactive decay in some atoms	10^{-2}	Less than 10^{-17}
Gravitational	Acts on all masses	10^{-34}	Infinite

Table 5.1 Fundamental forces of the universe

- This chapter describes in detail only the gravitational and electromagnetic forces.

- The **gravitational force** is the mutual attraction between all masses. It is the weakest force in the universe. A proton exerts an insignificant gravitational force of 10^{-34} N on another proton. However, if the masses concerned are as big as the earth and the moon, the gravitational force of attraction between them becomes significant.

- The **electromagnetic force** is the mutual attraction or repulsion between electric charges. It consists of two forces: an electric force and a magnetic force. They were once considered as separate forces but were unified into a single electromagnetic force by James Clarke Maxwell in the nineteenth century. In this book, the electric and magnetic force are treated separately in accordance to the A-level syllabus.

- The electromagnetic force is very pervasive in the universe. Most of the forces described in this book can be traced at the fundamental level to the electromagnetic force. Action, reaction, friction, tension, compression, upthrust, elastic force and so on can be explained in terms of electric forces between atoms of one body and another.

- Table 5.2 shows how forces affect mass, charge and current in gravitational, electric and magnetic forces.

112

Force	Nature of force	Law/formula
Gravitational force	• Acts on all masses • Attracts only *(diagram: mass m attracted to mass M, force F on each, distance r between them)*	Newton's Law of Universal Gravitation $$F = G \frac{mM}{r^2}$$ m, M — masses r — distance between masses G — Gravitational constant
Electric force	• Acts on electric charges • Forces are either attractive or repulsive *(diagram: Repulsion between $Q_1(+)$ and $Q_2(+)$; Repulsion between $Q_1(-)$ and $Q_2(-)$; Attraction between $Q_1(+)$ and $Q_2(-)$)*	Coulomb's Law $$F = \frac{Q_1 Q_2}{4\pi\varepsilon_0 r^2}$$ Q_1, Q_2 — electric charges ε_0 — permittivity of free space r — distance between charges
Magnetic force	Acts on moving charges *(diagram: charge $q(+)$ with force F_B, field B, velocity v, angle θ)* A magnetic force acts on a positive charge when it moves through a magnetic field with speed v. • Acts on a current carrying conductor *(diagram: wire of length L with current I, force F_B, field B, angle θ)* A magnetic force acts on a wire segment of length L which makes an angle θ with the magnetic field	$F_B = B\, q\, v \sin\theta$ B — magnetic field q — charge v — velocity θ — angle of inclination between B and v $F_B = B\, I\, L \sin\theta$ B — magnetic field I — electric current (conventional) L — length of wire carrying the current θ — angle of inclination between B and L

Table 5.2

113

Upthrust

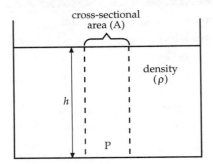

Fig 5.1   Pressure in a fluid

- Consider the pressure of a point P at depth h below the surface of a liquid of density ρ (Fig 5.1). The pressure at point P due to the liquid is equal to the weight of a column of liquid of depth h.

$$\text{Pressure} = \frac{\text{force}}{\text{area}} = \frac{mg}{A}$$
$$= \frac{(Ah\rho)g}{A}$$
$$= h \rho g$$

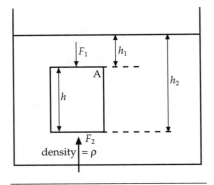

Fig 5.2   Upthrust on cylinder

- Consider a uniform cylinder of cross-sectional area A and height h totally immersed in a liquid as shown in Fig 5.2. The top and bottom face of the cylinder are at depth of h_1 and h_2 respectively from the surface of the liquid.

  Pressure at the top face $= h_1\rho\, g$
  Force at the top face $= h_1\rho\, gA$
  Pressure at the bottom face $= h_2\rho\, g$
  Force at the bottom face $= h_2\rho\, gA$

As different forces act on the two faces, a resultant force known as the upthrust is exerted on the cylinder.

Hence upthrust $= F_2 - F_1$
$$= h_2\rho\, gA - h_1\rho\, gA$$
$$= \rho\, g\, A\, (h_2 - h_1)$$
$$= \rho\, g\, V \text{ where } V \text{ is the volume of the cylinder}$$
$$= mg \text{ where } m \text{ is the mass of liquid displaced by volume } V$$

The upthrust on an object immersed in a liquid is equal to the weight of the liquid displaced by that object. This statement is commonly remembered as **Archimedes' Principle**.

- If the weight of an object is greater than the upthrust, it will sink (Fig 5.3a).

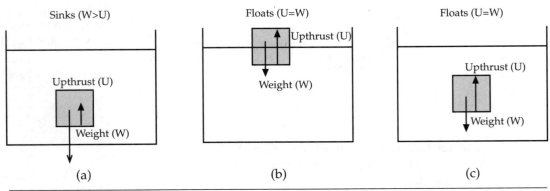

Fig 5.3   Object remains in equilibrium (floats) only when U = W

114

- If the weight of an object is equal to the upthrust, it will float (Fig 5.3b and c). This is known as the **principle of floatation**. A ship made of steel can float because its internal hollow volume displaces a large amount of water which in turn generates sufficient upthrust to keep the ship in equilibrium. A submarine can rise or sink at will because it contains ballast tanks that can expel or take in water. The variable upthrust produced controls the up and down motion of the submarine.

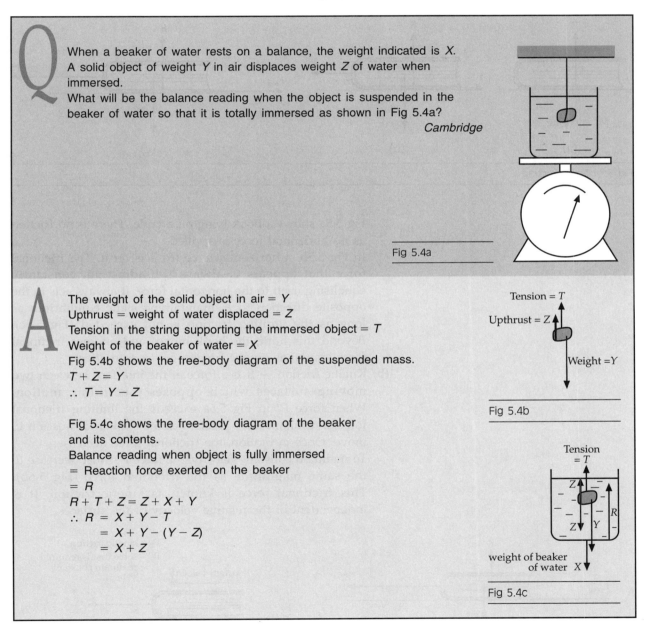

Q

When a beaker of water rests on a balance, the weight indicated is X. A solid object of weight Y in air displaces weight Z of water when immersed.
What will be the balance reading when the object is suspended in the beaker of water so that it is totally immersed as shown in Fig 5.4a?

Cambridge

Fig 5.4a

A

The weight of the solid object in air $= Y$
Upthrust $=$ weight of water displaced $= Z$
Tension in the string supporting the immersed object $= T$
Weight of the beaker of water $= X$
Fig 5.4b shows the free-body diagram of the suspended mass.
$T + Z = Y$
$\therefore T = Y - Z$

Tension $= T$

Upthrust $= Z$

Weight $= Y$

Fig 5.4b

Fig 5.4c shows the free-body diagram of the beaker and its contents.
Balance reading when object is fully immersed
$=$ Reaction force exerted on the beaker
$= R$
$R + T + Z = Z + X + Y$
$\therefore R = X + Y - T$
$\quad = X + Y - (Y - Z)$
$\quad = X + Z$

Tension $= T$

weight of beaker of water X

Fig 5.4c

115

Friction

- Frictional forces are produced when two surfaces move or try to move in opposition to each other.

- There are two kinds of frictional forces:
  - (a) Static friction — It is a force at the interface between two stationary surfaces which prevents the surfaces from sliding over each other.

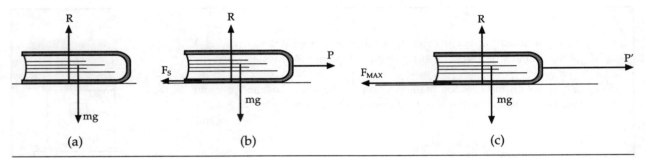

(a)　　　　(b)　　　　(c)

Fig 5.5　Static friction

Fig 5.5a shows a book lying on a table. There is no friction as no horizontal force is applied.

In Fig 5.5b, a horizontal force (P) acts on it. The frictional force that appears is always self-adjusting, constantly equalising itself to the horizontal force. It always acts in the opposite direction to P, maintaining static equilibrium as long as the limiting friction is not exceeded (Fig 5.5c). Beyond this limit, the book moves and another frictional force known as kinetic friction comes into effect.

- (b) Kinetic friction — It is a force at the interface between two moving surfaces which opposes the sliding motion. When force P'' in Fig 5.6a exceeds the limiting frictional force, a resultant force accelerates the book and causes it to move. Once in motion, the frictional force decreases.

To maintain constant velocity, the force P'' must decrease to the same magnitude as the frictional force (Fig 5.6b). This frictional force is known as kinetic friction. It is independent of the relative velocity of the surfaces.

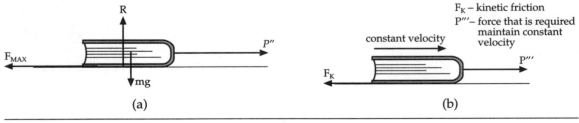

(a)　　　　(b)

Fig 5.6　Kinetic friction

116

- Fig 5.7 shows a graph of the magnitude of the frictional force against time when P acts on the book.

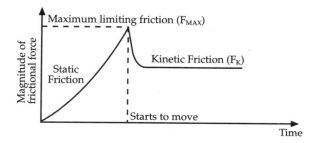

Fig 5.7 Graph of frictional forces against time

- Static and kinetic friction share the following common characteristics:
  (a) It depends on the nature of the surfaces.
  (b) It is independent of the area of contact.
  (c) It is proportional to the normal reaction.
  (d) It always opposes the relative velocity of the two surfaces.

Viscous Force

- Viscous force is the frictional force exerted on a body when it moves through a fluid.

- A fluid is generally a gas or a liquid that flows. The characteristics of fluid flow are summarised in Fig 5.8.

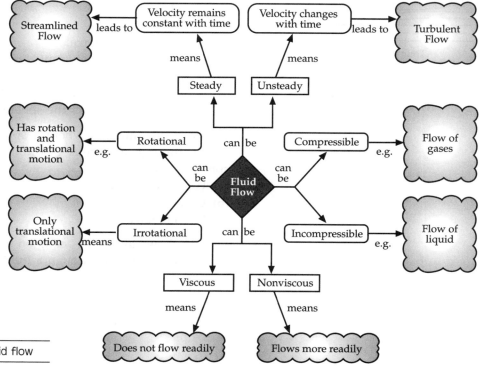

Fig 5.8 Concept map of fluid flow

117

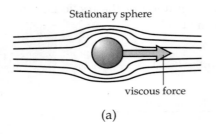

Stationary sphere

viscous force

(a)

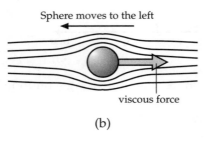

Sphere moves to the left

viscous force

(b)

Fig 5.9   Streamline flow

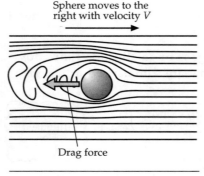

Sphere moves to the right with velocity V

Drag force

Fig 5.10   Turbulent flow

- Fluid flow can be thought of as consisting of fluid elements. They form the smallest volume of fluid whose motion can be traced. The paths they travel on are called flow lines.

- Consider the situation where the fluid flows past an immovable sphere (Fig 5.9a). Several layers of flow lines can be drawn to represent the motion of the fluid.

- As different layers of the fluid are pushed aside and displaced over each other, a streamline flow is produced. This means that the velocity of the fluid at a point is constant in time. In addition, a viscous force acts on the sphere in the opposite direction to the streamline flow. The pattern will be the same if the sphere moves slowly through the fluid (Fig 5.9b). The magnitude of the viscous force is given by Stokes law:

$$F = 6\,\pi\,\eta\,v\,r$$

where η is the coefficient of viscosity,
v is the velocity of the sphere and
r is the radius of the sphere.

Drag Force

- Fig 5.10 shows a sphere moving through a fluid with velocity v. As this velocity exceeds a certain critical value, the streamline motion of the fluid changes into turbulent motion (Fig 5.10). The frictional force exerted is known as the drag force and it is directly proportional to the square of the velocity:

$$D \propto v^2$$

or $D = \dfrac{1}{2}\rho\,A\,C\,v^2$

where D is the drag force,
C is the drag coefficient,
ρ is the density of liquid,
A is the cross-sectional area of the sphere and
v is the velocity of the sphere.

- Consider the situation where a sphere (radius r) is moving slowly through a viscous medium. Three forces act on the sphere. They are:
(a) Weight of the sphere
(b) Upthrust
(c) Viscous force

- Fig 5.11 shows the forces acting on a sphere at different stages of its free-fall motion through a fluid.

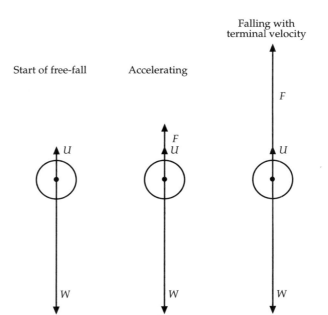

Start of free-fall   Accelerating   Falling with terminal velocity

Fig 5.11 Free fall motion of a sphere through a fluid

- At the moment of release the sphere is stationary and the viscous force is zero. The resultant force is a maximum at this point and acts downwards in the direction of the weight. Its acceleration is also at its maximum. As the sphere moves, the viscous force increases until the total upward force is equal to the weight. This means that the resultant force and the acceleration decrease to zero. At this point, the sphere moves with constant terminal velocity (v_T). The forces acting on the sphere can be described by the equation:

$$U + F = W$$
$$F = W - U$$

Now, $U = \rho_f \, g \left(\dfrac{4}{3}\, \pi r^3\right)$ where ρ_f is the density of the fluid

$W = \rho \, g \left(\dfrac{4}{3}\, \pi r^3\right)$ where ρ is the density of the sphere

$$F = 6 \, \pi \, \eta \, r \, v_T$$

where v_T is the terminal velocity of the sphere

Hence $\rho_f \, g \left(\dfrac{4}{3}\, \pi r^3\right) + 6 \, \pi \, \eta \, r \, v_T = \rho \, g \left(\dfrac{4}{3}\, \pi r^3\right)$

$$v_T = \frac{2r^2 g}{9\eta}(\rho - \rho_f)$$

119

- When a small sphere of radius r falls freely through the air, the upthrust acting on it is negligible. The forces acting on the sphere are the drag force and the weight. When the sphere attains terminal velocity v_T,

  drag force = weight

  $$\frac{1}{2}\rho A C v_T^2 = mg$$

  $$\therefore v_T = \sqrt{\frac{2\, m\, g}{\rho\, A\, C}}$$

(a) An object has a mass of 2.3 kg. What is its weight?

(b) When the object in (a) falls in air, the air resistance F is given by the equation
$$F = k\, v^2$$
where v is the velocity of the object and k has the value of 0.042 N s^2 m^{-2}.

  (i) Explain why the object eventually falls with uniform velocity (the terminal velocity).

  (ii) Calculate the terminal velocity of the object.

(c) Calculate the acceleration of the object when it is falling with a velocity of 12 m s^{-1}.

Cambridge

(a) Weight $= m\, g = (2.3)\,(9.81)$
$= 22.56$ N
≈ 23 N

(b) (i) As the velocity of the falling object increases, the air resistance acting on it will also increase. This means that the resultant force acting on the object decreases to zero. At this stage, the upward air resistance and upthrust balances the weight. The object will fall freely to the ground with constant or terminal velocity.

  (ii) Assuming the upthrust to be small enough to be neglected, the object will reach terminal velocity when
  $$F = m\, g$$
  i.e. $k\, v^2 = 22.56$

  $$v = \sqrt{\frac{22.56}{0.042}}$$
  $= 23.18$ m s^{-1}
  ≈ 23 m s^{-1}

(c) If acceleration is a,
$$m a = m g - k\, v^2$$

$$\therefore a = \frac{mg - kv^2}{m}$$

$$= \frac{22.56 - (0.042)(12^2)}{2.3}$$
$= 7.2$ m s^{-2}

CENTRE OF GRAVITY

- The weights of individual particles of an object in a gravitational field are effectively parallel to each other (Fig 5.12).

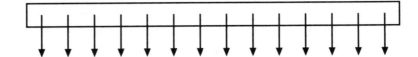

Fig 5.12   Weight of an object

- The weight of an object is the resultant force of all the individual weights of particles in the object. It is always directed towards the centre of the Earth. It's magnitude is given by $W = mg$.

- The centre of gravity of a rigid body is the single point through which the weight of the object appears to act.

- The position of the centre of gravity $(\bar{x}, \bar{y})$ of a system of particles of weights $m_1 g$, $m_2 g$, and so on (Fig 5.13), is given by

$$\bar{x} = \frac{m_1 g x_1 + m_2 g x_2 + \ldots m_n g x_n}{m_1 g + m_2 g + \ldots m_n g}$$

$$\bar{x} = \sum \frac{m_i g x_i}{m_i g}$$

$$\bar{y} = \frac{m_1 g y_1 + m_2 g y_2 + \ldots m_n g y_n}{m_1 g + m_2 g + \ldots m_n g}$$

$$\bar{y} = \sum \frac{m_i g y_i}{m_i g}$$

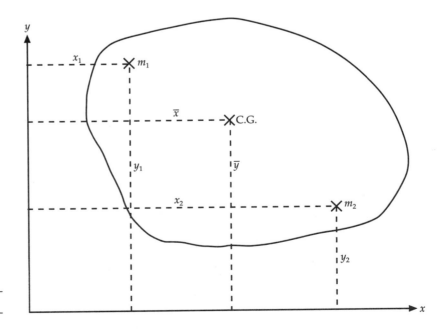

Fig 5.13   Centre of gravity

121

- From the above example, it can be seen that the centre of gravity is dependent on:
  (a) the distribution of the masses,
  (b) the gravitational acceleration g.

- If the distribution of masses and gravitational acceleration remain constant on all parts of the object, the centre of gravity will coincide with the centre of mass of the object.

Hooke's Law

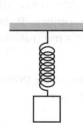

(a) A spring under load

- Hooke's Law states that the force is directly proportional to the extension in a spring or wire if the limit of proportionality is not exceeded.
  Mathematically, it is written as
  $$F \propto x$$
  or $F = k\, x$
  where F is the force or tension in the spring,
  x is the extension of the spring and
  k is known as the stiffness or spring constant. The unit of k is Newton per metre ($N\ m^{-1}$).

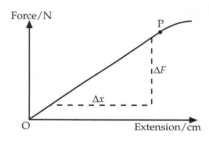

(b) Graph of force against extension

Fig 5.14 Elastic behaviour of spring

- The graph of force plotted against extension for a helical spring or wire under load is illustrated in Fig 5.14.

- The following points should be noted:
  (a) The force or load is directly proportional to the extension between O and P.
  (b) The gradient of the line is the spring constant. The larger the value, the greater the stiffness of the spring.
  $$\text{Gradient} = \frac{\Delta F}{\Delta x}$$
  $$= \text{spring constant } k$$
  (c) P is known as the limit of proportionality. Beyond this point, force is no longer proportional to extension.

The force constant k of a spring is the constant of proportionality in the Hooke's law relation $T = k\, e$ between tension T and extension e. A spring A of force constant $6\ N\ m^{-1}$ is connected in series with a spring B of force constant $3\ N\ m^{-1}$, as shown in Fig 5.15. One end of the combination is securely anchored and a force of 0.6 N is applied to the other end.
(a) By how much does each spring extend?
(b) What is the force constant of the combination?

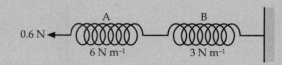

Fig 5.15

Cambridge

122

A (a) For spring A, extension $e_A = \dfrac{F}{k_B}$

$$= \dfrac{0.6\ \text{N}}{6\ \text{N m}^{-1}}$$

$$= 0.1\ \text{m}$$

For spring B, extension $e_B = \dfrac{F}{k_B}$

$$= \dfrac{0.6\ \text{N}}{3\ \text{N m}^{-1}}$$

$$= 0.2\ \text{m}$$

(b) Let e be the total extension of the two springs and k be the force constant of the combination. Since the two springs are connected in series,

total extension $e = e_A + e_B$

$$\frac{F}{k} = \frac{F}{k_A} + \frac{F}{k_B}$$

i.e. $\dfrac{1}{k} = \dfrac{1}{k_A} + \dfrac{1}{k_B}$

or $k = \dfrac{k_A k_B}{k_A + k_B}$

$$= \frac{(6)(3)}{6 + 3}$$

$$= 2\ \text{N m}^{-1}$$

Q A light platform is supported by two identical springs, each having spring constant 20 N m^{-1}, as shown in Fig 5.16.
Calculate the weight which must be placed on the centre of the platform in order to produce a displacement of 3.0 cm.

Cambridge

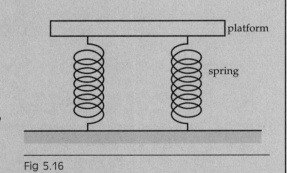

Fig 5.16

A *If* W is the weight and T is the tension in each spring, then

$W = 2T$

$\quad = 2\ k\ x$

where k is the spring constant and x is the displacement.

$\therefore\ W = 2(20 \times 0.03)$

$\quad\quad = 1.2\ \text{N}$

123

 In a dynamics experiment, a trolley is accelerated from rest along a horizontal runway as shown in Fig 5.17.

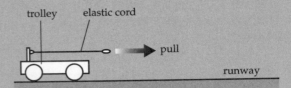

Fig 5.17

The accelerating force is provided by an elastic cord. One end of the cord is attached to the trolley and the other end is pulled so that the extension of the cord remains constant as the trolley moves along the runway. The acceleration a of the trolley varies with the extension x of the elastic cord as shown in Fig 5.18.

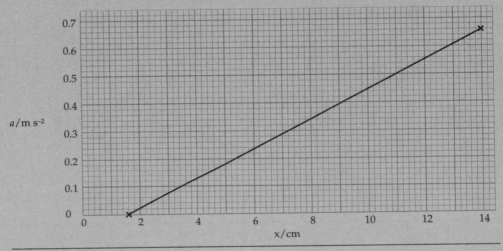

Fig 5.18

The trolley experiences a constant frictional force when in motion.

(a) Use Fig 5.18 to
   (i) determine the extension of the cord required to maintain constant speed of the trolley, giving a brief explanation for your answer,
   (ii) show that the increase in extension, beyond that found in (i), to produce an acceleration of 0.6 m s^{-2} is 11.2 cm.

(b) (i) Calculate the force required, in the absence of friction, to cause the trolley of mass 800 g to have an acceleration of 0.60 m s^{-2}.
   (ii) Using your answer to (b)(i) and (a)(ii), determine the spring constant of the elastic cord. Assume that the cord obeys Hooke's law.
   (iii) Calculate the frictional force on the trolley.

(c) In one particular experiment, the extension of the cord is kept constant at 3.5 cm. Calculate
   (i) the speed of the trolley after it has travelled 1.2 m from rest along the runway,
   (ii) the time taken to travel a further 30 cm along the runway.

(d) By reference to Fig 5.18, state and explain
   (i) whether the acceleration of the trolley is proportional to the extension of the cord,
   (ii) how it may be concluded that the Hooke's law limit of the cord has not been exceeded.

Cambridge

124

A

(a) (i) When trolley is moving with constant speed, its acceleration a is zero.
From the graph, when $a = 0$, extension $x_1 = 1.6$ cm

(ii) When $a = 0.60$ m s^{-2}, extension $x_2 = 12.8$ cm
∴ Increase in extension, $\Delta x = x_2 - x_1$
$$= 12.8 - 1.6$$
$$= 11.2 \text{ cm}$$

(b) (i) Force required $F = m\,a$
$$= (0.800)\,(0.60)$$
$$= 0.48 \text{ N}$$

(ii) $F = k\,x$ where k is the spring constant of the elastic cord

$$k = \frac{F}{x}$$

$$= \frac{0.48}{0.112}$$

$$= 4.29 \text{ N m}^{-1} = 4.3 \text{ N m}^{-1}$$

(iii) When $a = 0$, $x_1 = 1.6$ cm $= 0.016$ m
Frictional force $= kx_1$
$$= (4.29)(0.016)$$
$$= 0.0686 \text{ N} = 0.069 \text{ N}$$

(c) (i) When extension $x_3 = 0.035$ m, the resultant force acting on the trolley is
$k\,x_3$ − frictional force $= m\,a$
$(4.29)\,(0.035) - 0.0686 = 0.800\,a$
$$a = 0.1019 \text{ m s}^{-2}$$
Using $v^2 = u^2 + 2\,a\,s$, where $v =$ speed of trolley after travelling 1.2 m,
$u = 0$ m s^{-1} and $s = 1.2$ m
$v^2 = 0 + 2\,(0.1019)(1.2)$
$v = 0.4945$ m s^{-1}
$\;\;\; = 0.49$ m s^{-1}

(ii) Using $s = u\,t + \dfrac{1}{2}\,a\,t^2$ where $t =$ time taken to travel a further 30 cm,
$u = 0.4945$ m s^{-1} and $a = 0.1019$ m s^{-2}

$0.30 = 0.4945\,t + \dfrac{1}{2}(0.1019)\,t^2$

$t^2 + 9.706\,t - 5.888 = 0$

$$t = \frac{-9.706 \pm \sqrt{(9.706)^2 - 4(1)(-5.888)}}{2(1)}$$

$$= \frac{-9.706 \pm \sqrt{117.76}}{2}$$

$t = +0.573$ s and -10.3 s
As $t = -10.3$ s is inadmissible, the time taken to travel a further 30 cm along the runway is 0.573 s.

(d) (i) From Fig 5.18 the acceleration of the trolley is not proportional to the extension of the cord as the straight line graph did not pass through the origin.

(ii) The force pulling on the trolley is directly proportional to the acceleration. Hence a graph of force (F) plotted against extension (x) would yield a similar straight line as that in Fig 5.18. This indicates that the extension of the cord has not exceeded the limit of proportionality.

TURNING EFFECTS OF FORCES

Moment of a Force

- Torque or the moment of a force about a point is the product of that force and the perpendicular distance from the line of action of the force to the point.

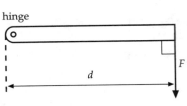
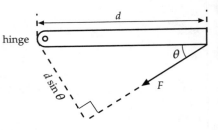

Fig 5.19 Moment of a force

(a) Torque $\tau = F \times d$

(b) Torque $\tau = F \, d \, \sin \theta$

- **Characteristics of a torque:**
  (a) It is a vector. The direction of a torque is given by the right hand grip rule.
  (b) A torque can turn in a clockwise direction (positive) or an anticlockwise direction (negative).
  (c) The S. I. unit for a torque is N m (Newton metre).

- A couple is a pair of forces which tends to produce rotation only. This is illustrated in Fig 5.20.

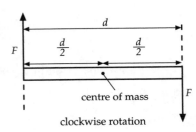
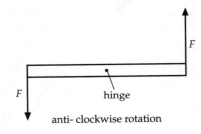

Fig 5.20 A couple

clockwise rotation

anti- clockwise rotation

- Essentially a couple consists of two equal but opposite forces whose lines of action do not meet. The moment of these two forces about the centre of mass is given by:

$$\tau = F \left(\frac{d}{2} \right) + F \left(\frac{d}{2} \right)$$
$$= F \, d$$

- The moment of a couple is the product of one of the forces and the perpendicular distance between the two forces. Its S. I. unit is the newton metre (N m).

126

EQUILIBRIUM OF FORCES

Conditions for equilibrium

- There are two conditions for the equilibrium of forces acting on a rigid body.

  (1) The vector sum of all forces acting on a rigid body must be zero. This ensures translational equilibrium.

  $$\Sigma F = 0$$

  This is equivalent to the three independent scalar equations along the direction of the coordinate axes.

  $$\Sigma F_x = 0, \qquad \Sigma F_y = 0, \qquad \Sigma F_z = 0$$

- Table 5.3 shows some examples of forces in equilibrium.

Two forces in equilibrium along the x-axis 	They are equal and opposite along the x-axis. $$F_1 - F_2 = 0$$ Resultant $= 0$ i.e. $\Sigma F_x = 0$
Three forces in equilibrium on the x, y plane 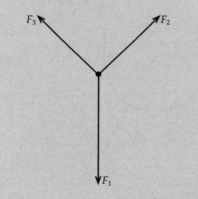	They will form a closed triangle. 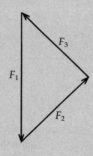 Resultant $= 0$ i.e. $\Sigma F_x = 0$ and $\Sigma F_y = 0$
Four forces in equilibrium on the x, y plane 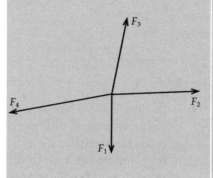	They will form a closed polygon. 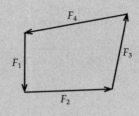 Resultant $= 0$ i.e. $\Sigma F_x = 0$ and $\Sigma F_y = 0$

Table 5.3   Forces in equilibrium

(2) The vector sum of all external torques acting on a rigid body must be zero. This ensures rotational equilibrium.

$$\Sigma \tau = 0$$

This is equivalent to the three independent scalar equations along the direction of the coordinate axes.

$$\Sigma \tau_x = 0, \qquad \Sigma \tau_y = 0, \qquad \Sigma \tau_z = 0$$

Alternatively, we can say that the sum of the clockwise moments about a point must be equal to the sum of the anticlockwise moments about that point when a body is in equilibrium. This is known as the **principle of moment**.

Equilibrium of Rigid Body Under Concurrent Forces

- Concurrent forces are forces whose lines of action pass through a single common point.

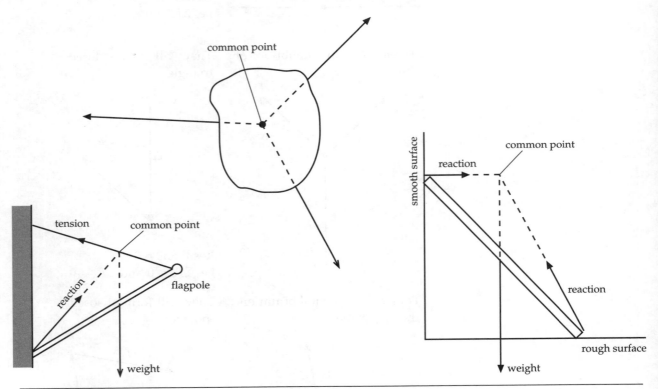

Fig 5.21   Examples of concurrent forces

- To determine whether concurrent forces acting on a rigid body has translational and rotational equilibrium, all that is required is to check whether condition (1) is satisfied. If the resultant is zero, the vector sum of all torques acting on the body must be zero. Condition (2) is presumed to hold.

128

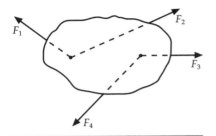

Fig 5.22   Non-concurrent forces

Equilibrium of Rigid Body Under Non-Concurrent Forces

Non-concurrent forces are forces whose lines of action do not pass through a single common point. An example of non-concurrent forces is shown in Fig 5.22.

- In Fig 5.23, F_1 and F_2 produces the resultant R_1 and F_3 and F_4 produces the resultant R_2. Both R_1 and R_2 are equal in magnitude and oppositely directed. They produce a torque which causes rotation of the body.

- To determine whether non-concurrent forces acting on a rigid body has translational and rotational equilibrium, it is necessary to check whether condition(1) as well as condition (2) are satisfied.

- In Fig 5.23, the rigid body do not have translational motion as there is no resultant force. However the body rotates and do not have rotational equilibrium as the vector sum of torque is not zero.

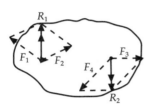

Fig 5.23   Couple causing rotation

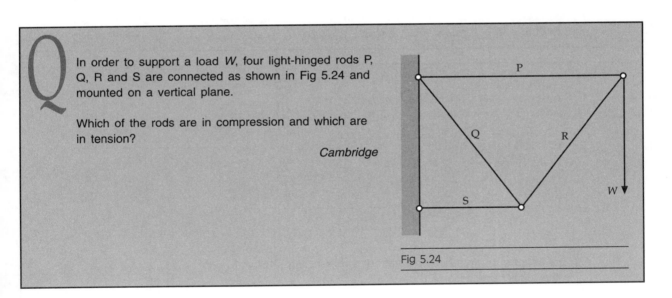

In order to support a load W, four light-hinged rods P, Q, R and S are connected as shown in Fig 5.24 and mounted on a vertical plane.

Which of the rods are in compression and which are in tension?

Cambridge

Fig 5.24

129

In order for the four light rods to remain in equilibrium, the forces acting at hinge 1 and 2 must form a closed triangle. Fig 5.25 shows two free-body diagrams of forces acting at the two hinges.

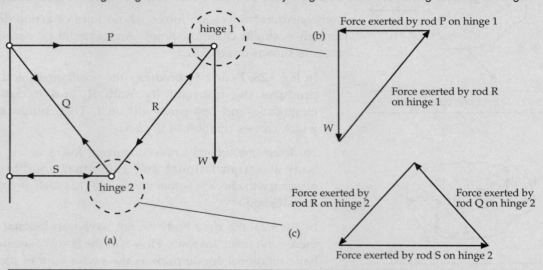

Fig 5.25

Forces acting on the connected rods are shown above. Hence the rods in compression are R and S. The rods in tension are P and Q.

In the diagram below (Fig 5.26), a body S of weight W hangs vertically by a thread tied at Q to the string PQR.

If the system is in equilibrium, what is the tension in the section PQ?

Cambridge

Fig 5.26

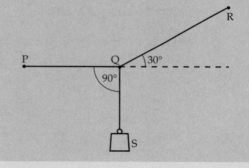

Fig 5.27 shows the free-body diagram of forces acting at Q.
T_1 is the tension in section PQ.
T_2 is the tension in section QR.
For Q to be in equilibrium,

$$\Sigma F_y = T_2 \sin 30° - W = 0$$

i.e. $$T_2 \sin 30° = W$$

$$T_2 = \frac{W}{\sin 30°}$$

and $$\Sigma F_x = T_2 \cos 30° - T_1 = 0$$

i.e. $$T_1 = T_2 \cos 30°$$

$$= \left(\frac{W}{\sin 30°} \right) \cos 30°$$

$$= W \cot 30°$$

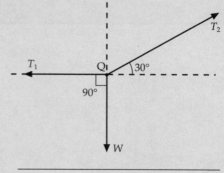

Fig 5.27

Q A picture of weight 5.0 N is suspended from a hook on a wall by a cord which has a breaking strength of 25.0 N. Initially (Fig 5.28a) the picture is found to be too low; the cord is shortened,
with the intention of hanging the picture as in Fig 5.28b. However, when the picture is replaced the cord breaks immediately. Explain why the cord broke when supporting a load so much less than its breaking strength.

Cambridge

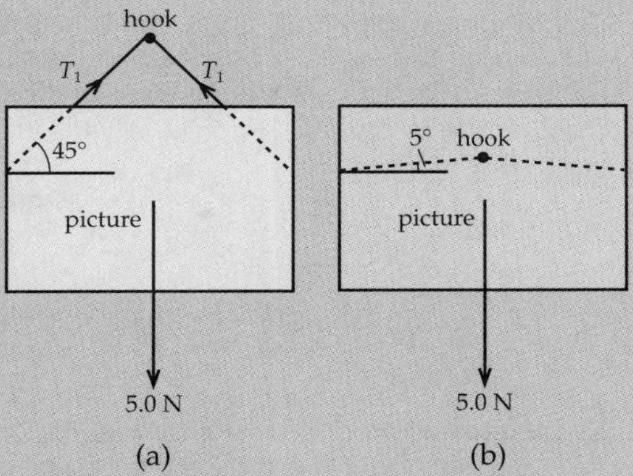

Fig 5.28

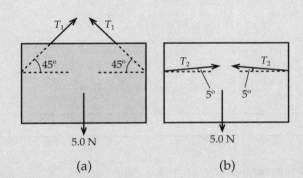

(a)

(b)

A

Fig 5.29

(a)

(b)

In Fig 5.29(a), the tension in the cord is T_1. For the picture to be in equilibrium,
$$\Sigma F_y = T_1 \sin 45° + T_1 \sin 45° - 5.0 = 0$$
i.e. $T_1 = \dfrac{5.0}{2 \sin 45°}$
$= 3.5$ N

In Fig 5.29(b), the tension in the cord is T_2. For the picture to be in equilibrium,
$$\Sigma F_y = T_2 \sin 5° + T_2 \sin 5° - 5.0 = 0$$
i.e. $T_2 = \dfrac{5.0}{2 \sin 5°}$
$= 28.7$ N
$= 29$ N

The tension of the cord in Fig 5.29(b) is greater than the breaking strength of 25.0 N. The cord will not be able to support the picture.

Q A uniform rod XY of weight 10.0 N is freely hinged to a wall at X. It is held horizontal by a force F acting from Y at an angle of 60° to the vertical as shown in Fig 5.30. What is the value of F?

Cambridge

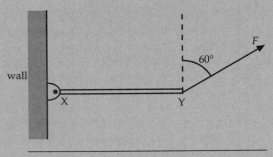

Fig 5.30

A Forces acting on XY are shown in Fig 5.31. F is resolved into vertical and horizontal components. Let the length of the rod be ℓ.
Take moments about X,

$$\Sigma\tau = (F \cos 60°)\, \ell - 10.0 \left(\frac{\ell}{2}\right) = 0$$

i.e. $F = \dfrac{5.0}{\cos 60°}$

$\quad = 10.0$ N

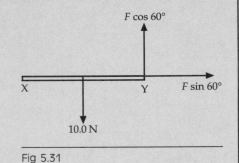

Fig 5.31

Q A heavy uniform beam of length I is supported by two vertical cords as shown in Fig 5.32.

What is the ratio $\dfrac{T_1}{T_2}$ of the tensions in these cords?

Cambridge

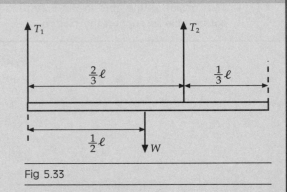

Fig 5.32

A Let the weight of the uniform beam be W.
Forces acting on the beam are shown in Fig 5.33.
Take moments about the centre of gravity

$$\Sigma\tau = T_1 \left(\frac{1}{2}\, \ell\right) - T_2 \left(\frac{2}{3}\, \ell - \frac{1}{2}\, \ell\right) = 0$$

i.e. $T_1 \left(\dfrac{1}{2}\, \ell\right) = T_2 \left(\dfrac{1}{6}\, \ell\right)$

$\dfrac{T_1}{T_2} = \dfrac{1}{3}$

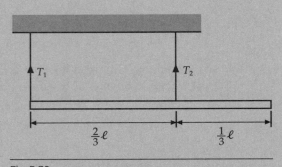

Fig 5.33

Q A ruler of length 0.30 m is pivoted at its centre. Equal and opposite forces of magnitude 2.0 N are applied to the ends of the ruler, creating a couple as shown in Fig 5.34.
What is the magnitude of the torque of the couple on the ruler when it is in the position shown?

Cambridge

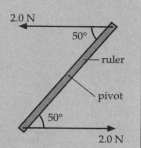

Fig 5.34

A
$$\tau = (2.0)\ (0.30\ \sin 50°)$$
$$= 0.46\ \text{N m}$$

Q A desk lamp is illustrated in Fig 5.35.
The lamp must be constructed so that it does not topple over when fully extended as shown in Fig 5.36. The base of the lamp is circular and has a radius of 10 cm. Other dimensions are shown on the figure. The total weight of the light bulb and shade is 6.0 N and each of the two uniform arms has weight 2.0 N.

(a) On Fig 5.36, draw an arrow to represent the weight of the base.

(b) The lamp will rotate about a point if the base is not heavy enough. On Fig 5.36, mark this point and label it P.

(c) Calculate the following moments about P.
　1. moment of first arm.

　　moment = _____ N m

　2. moment of second arm

　　moment = _____ N m

　3. moment of light bulb and shade

　　moment = _____ N m

(d) Use the principle of moments to calculate the minimum weight of base required to prevent toppling.

　weight = _____ N

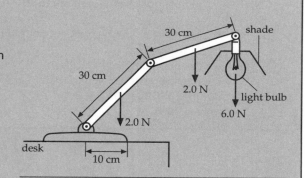

Fig 5.35

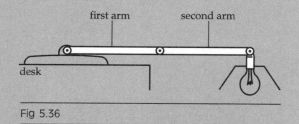

Fig 5.36

Cambridge

A (a), (b)

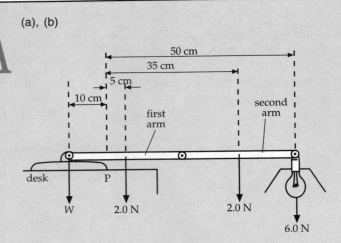

(c)

1. Moment of first arm about P = (2.0) (0.05)
   = 0.10 N m
2. Moment of second arm about P = (2.0) (0.35)
   = 0.70 N m
3. Moment of light bulb and shade about P = (6.0) (0.50)
   = 3.0 N m

(d) Let the minimum weight of base be W.
Total anticlockwise moment = total clockwise moment
W (0.10) = 0.10 + 0.70 + 3.0
∴ W = 38 N

Exercise 5

Multiple Choice Questions

1   A ball falls vertically and bounces on the ground. The following statements are about the forces acting while the ball is in contact with the ground. Which statement is correct?

   A The force that the ball exerts on the ground is always equal to the weight of the ball.

   B The force that the ball exerts on the ground is always equal in magnitude and opposite in direction to the force the ground exerts on the ball.

   C The force that the ball exerts on the ground is always greater than the weight of the ball.

   D The weight of the ball is always equal and opposite to the force that the ground exerts on the ball.

2   A body is thrown vertically upwards in a medium in which the viscous drag cannot be neglected. If the times of flight for the upward motion t_u and the downward motion t_d (to return to the same level) are compared, then

   A $t_d > t_u$, because the body moves faster on its downward flight and therefore the viscous force is greater.

   B $t_d < t_u$, because the effect of the viscous force is greatest at the moment of projection.

   C $t_d < t_u$, because at a given speed the net accelerating force when the body is moving downwards is greater than the retarding force when it is moving upwards.

   D $t_d > t_u$, because at a given speed the net accelerating force when the body is moving downwards is smaller than the retarding force when it is moving upwards.

3   The diagram below shows a heavy flagpole PQ hinged at a vertical wall at end P and held by a wire connected between end Q and a point R on the wall. The weight of the flagpole is W and the tension in the wire is T.

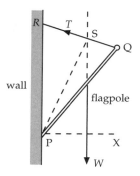

What is the direction of the force exerted by the wall on the flagpole?

   A PQ   B PS
   C PX   D SP

4   The diagrams show spring balances joined to demonstrate a system of three coplanar forces acting at a point. The readings represent the magnitude of the forces. Which system of forces could be in equilibrium?

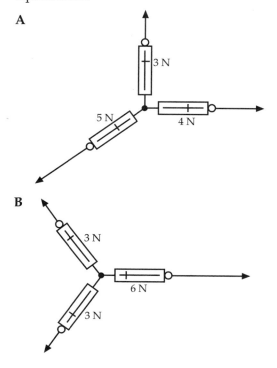

C

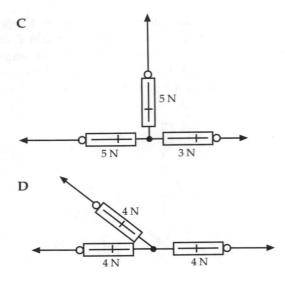

5 N

5 N   3 N

D

4 N

4 N   4 N

5   Two forces **P** and **Q** act at a point X as shown in the vector diagram below.

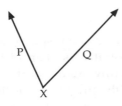

In which of the following diagrams does the vector **F** represent the force which must be applied at X to maintain equilibrium?

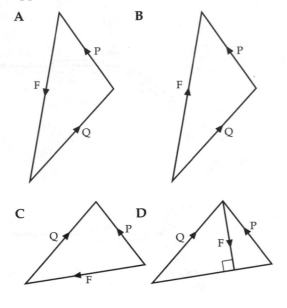

6   A small ball of weight W is suspended by a light thread. When a strong wind blows horizontally exerting a constant force F on the ball, the thread makes an angle θ to the vertical as shown in the diagram.

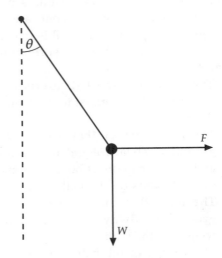

Which of the following equations correctly relates θ, F and W?

A $\cos\theta = \dfrac{W}{F}$ **B** $\sin\theta = \dfrac{F}{W}$

C $\tan\theta = \dfrac{F}{W}$ **D** $\tan\theta = \dfrac{W}{F}$

7   A trailer of weight 30 kN is hitched to a cab at the point X as shown in the diagram below.

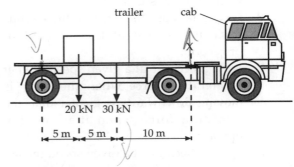

If the trailer carries a weight of 20 kN at the position shown in the diagram, what upward force is exerted by the cab on the trailer at the point X?

A 15 kN   **B** 20 kN
C 30 kN   **D** 40 kN

8   A heavy uniform plank of length L is supported by forces F_1 and F_2 at points distant $\frac{L}{8}$ and $\frac{L}{4}$ from the ends as shown in the diagram.

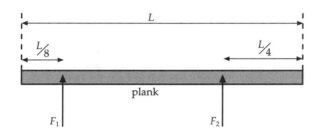

What is the ratio of F_1 to F_2?

A $2 : 5$ B $3 : 5$
C $5 : 8$ D $2 : 3$

9   A rod of length 1 metre has non-uniform composition, so that the centre of gravity is not at its geometrical centre.
The rod is laid on supports across two top-pan balances as shown in the diagram. The balances (previously set at zero) give readings of 360 g and 240 g.

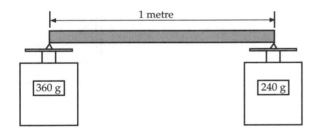

Where is the centre of gravity of the rod relative to its geometrical centre?

A $\frac{1}{10}$ metre to the left

B $\frac{1}{10}$ metre to the right

C $\frac{1}{6}$ metre to the left

D $\frac{1}{5}$ metre to the right

10 Diagram 1 show two parallel forces F acting on a bar of length ℓ pivoted at P. The forces give rise to a couple of torque M.
Diagram 1

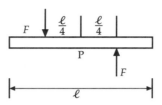

In diagram 2, the lines of action of the forces are moved a distance $\frac{\ell}{4}$ to the left.
Diagram 2

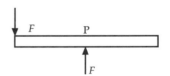

What is now the torque of the couples?

A   0   B $\frac{M}{2}$
C M D $2M$

11 A light rod is acted upon by three forces P, Q and R. Which diagram could show the position and direction of each of the forces when the rod is in equilibrium?

A

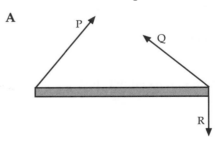

B

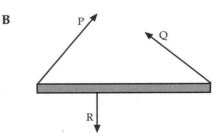

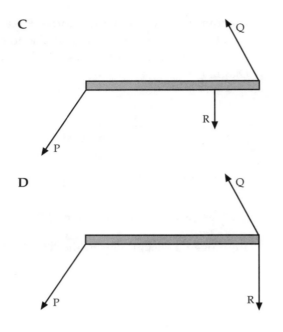

C

D

12 A uniform plank of weight 60 N is 2000 mm long and rests on support that is 600 mm from end E. At what distance from E must a 160 N weight be placed in order to balance the plank?

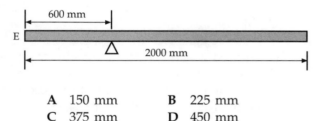

A	150 mm	**B**	225 mm
C	375 mm	**D**	450 mm

Structured Questions

1 (a) Coplanar forces, F_1, F_2, F_3 act on a point mass A, as shown in Fig 5.37.

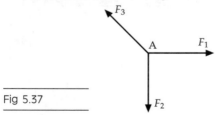

Fig 5.37

State, or show on a labelled diagram, the condition for the mass to be in equilibrium.

(b) Coplanar forces, F_4, F_5, F_6, F_7, which do not all pass through the same point, act on a body B, as shown in Fig 5.38.

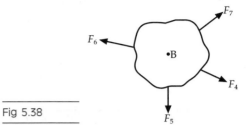

Fig 5.38

State, or show on labelled diagrams, the conditions for the body to be in equilibrium.

2 The cables of a suspension bridge are anchored into large free-standing blocks of concrete as shown in Fig 5.39. One of these blocks is shown on a larger scale in Fig 5.40; it has a length of 30 m and its cross-section and density are uniform. The maximum force which the cables could exert on this block is 5.5×10^8 N for a particular bridge. The force acts in the direction shown so that its line of action is 26 m from the point about which the block might possibly rotate.

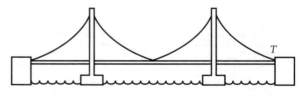

Fig 5.39

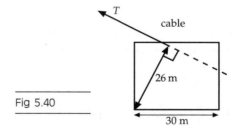

Fig 5.40

(i) Sketch Fig 5.40 and show the forces which would be acting on the block if it were just about to rotate.

(ii) Calculate the minimum mass of the block needed to prevent rotation when the force exerted by the cable has its maximum value.

138

(iii) Show on a second sketch the forces which would be acting under normal operating conditions.

3   A water wheel has eight buckets equally spaced around its circumference, as illustrated in Fig 5.41.

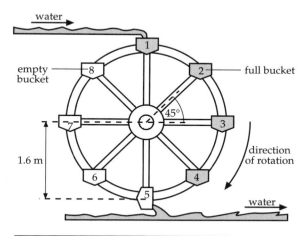

Fig 5.41

The distance between the centre of each bucket and the centre of the wheel is 1.6 m. When a bucket is at its highest point, the bucket is filled with a mass of 40 kg of water. The wheel rotates and the bucket is emptied at its lowest point.

(a) Define the moment of a force.

(b) Write down the number of the bucket that provides the largest moment about the axle of the wheel.

(c) Write down the numbers of those buckets containing water that cause a moment about the axle.

(d) Calculate, for the wheel in the position shown in Fig 5.38, the total resultant moment about the centre of the wheel of the water in the buckets.

FORCES

Forces in Equilibrium

require

Condition 1:
The resultant force must be zero.
1) $\Sigma F = 0$, $\Sigma F_x = 0$ and $\Sigma F_y = 0$

2) The vector addition of the forces must yield a CLOSED polygon.

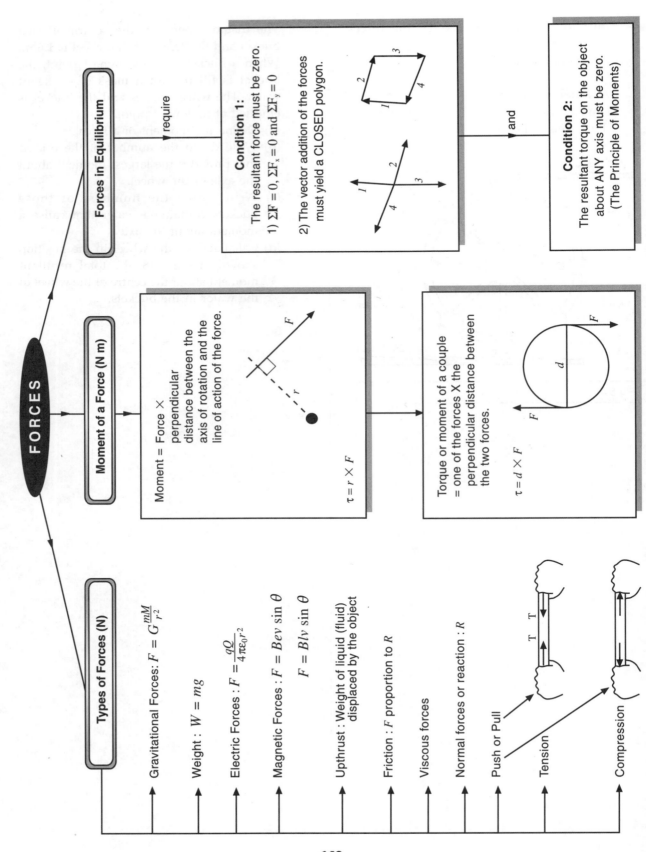

and

Condition 2:
The resultant torque on the object about ANY axis must be zero.
(The Principle of Moments)

Moment of a Force (N m)

Moment = Force $\times$ perpendicular distance between the axis of rotation and the line of action of the force.

$$\tau = r \times F$$

Torque or moment of a couple = one of the forces $\times$ the perpendicular distance between the two forces.

$$\tau = d \times F$$

Types of Forces (N)

Gravitational Forces: $F = G\frac{mM}{r^2}$

Weight : $W = mg$

Electric Forces : $F = \frac{qQ}{4\pi\varepsilon_0 r^2}$

Magnetic Forces : $F = Bev\sin\theta$

$F = Blv\sin\theta$

Upthrust : Weight of liquid (fluid) displaced by the object

Friction : F proportion to R

Viscous forces

Normal forces or reaction : R

Push or Pull

Tension

Compression

140

6

Work, Energy and Power

ENERGY CONVERSION AND CONSERVATION

WORK

POTENTIAL ENERGY, KINETIC ENERGY AND INTERNAL ENERGY

POWER

Syllabus Objectives

In this chapter you should be able to:

- give examples of energy in different forms, its conversion and conservation, and apply the principle of energy conservation to simple examples.
- show an understanding of the concept of work in terms of the product of a force and displacement in the direction of the force.
- calculate the work done in a number of situations, including the work done by a gas which is expanding against a constant external pressure: $W = p\Delta V$.
- derive, from the equations of motion, the formula $E_k = \frac{1}{2}mv^2$.
- recall and apply the formula $E_k = \frac{1}{2}mv^2$.
- distinguish between gravitational potential energy, electric potential energy and elastic potential energy.
- show an understanding of, and use the relationship between, force and potential energy in a uniform field to solve problems.
- derive, from the defining equation $W = Fs$, the formula $E_p = mgh$ for potential energy changes near the Earth's surface.
- recall and use the formula $E_p = mgh$ for potential energy changes near the Earth's surface.
- show an understanding of the concept of internal energy.
- show an appreciation for the implications of energy losses in practical devices and use the concept of efficiency to solve problems.
- define power as work done per unit time and derive power as the product of force and velocity.

ENERGY CONVERSION AND CONSERVATION

- Energy is the capacity to do work. In this chapter, the concept of work is defined and its applications elaborated.

- Energy appears in different forms. Table 6.1 summarises some common types of energy.

Forms of Energy	Description
Chemical	Energy released when chemical bonds between atoms and molecules are broken. Fossil fuels such as petroleum, natural gas and coal are rich sources
Electrical	Energy that is associated with the flow of electrical charges. These charges could be electrons, protons, positive and negative ions.
Heat	Energy that flows from one place to another as a result of a temperature difference. Heat is conducted by intermolecular vibrations of atoms or molecules or the movement of free electrons within metals.
Internal	Sum total of kinetic and potential energy of atoms or molecules within a body. All objects above absolute zero possess internal energy.
Nuclear	Energy released by the splitting of heavy nuclei such as uranium-235 or the fusion of light nuclei such as hydrogen.
Mass	Energy released when there is a loss of small amount of mass in a nuclear process. The amount of energy can be calculated from Einstein's mass-energy equation, $E = mc^2$.
Radiant Heat	Energy associated with infra-red radiation
Light	Electromagnetic energy that are visible to the human eye
Sound	Energy transmitted through the propagation of a series of compression and rarefaction in solid, liquid or gas.
Mechanical (a) Kinetic (b) Potential (gravitational) (c) Potential (elastic)	Energy associated with the motion of a body Energy associated with the position of a body in a gravitational field Energy stored in a compressed or stretched spring

Table 6.1 Forms of energy

142

- Energy can be changed from one form to another. The conversion of several forms of energy are summarised in Table 6.2.

Examples	Energy converted	
	From	To
Charging a battery	Electrical	Chemical
Dynamo	Mechanical	Electrical
Photosynthesis	Light	Chemical
Loud speaker	Electrical	Sound
Microphone	Sound	Electrical
Bullet striking a block and coming to rest	Kinetic	Internal
Ball thrown up	Kinetic	Potential
Ball dropped from rest	Potential	Kinetic
Thermocouple	Heat	Electrical

Table 6.2 Conversion of energy

- In many situations, energy conversions are more complicated and involve the conversion of several kinds of energy at different stages. The following are examples:

(a) Lighting a match

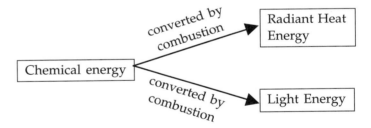

(b) Cutting a piece of wood with an axe

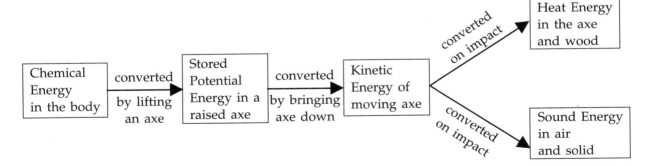

143

(c) A car accelerates from rest, but is brought to a halt a few seconds later.

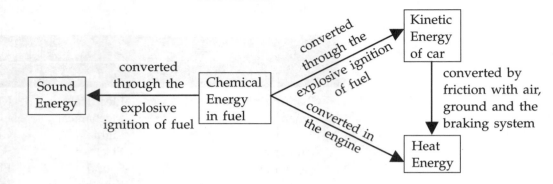

(d) Hydroelectric power station

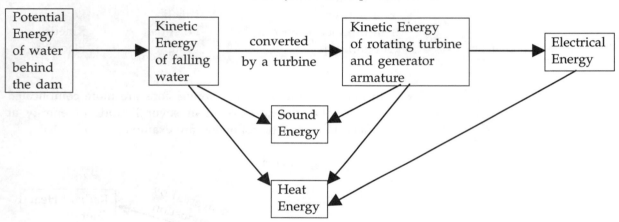

(e) Nuclear power station

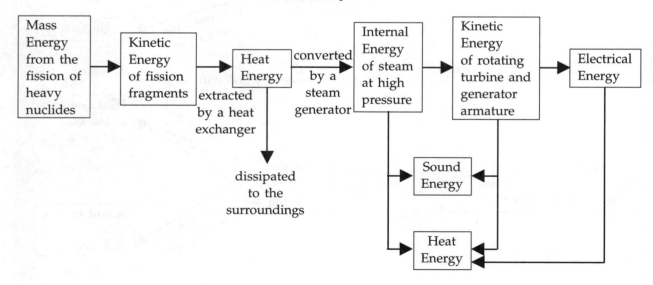

The Principle of Conservation of Energy

- The total energy in a given system is always constant. It can be transformed from one form to another but cannot be created or destroyed.

WORK | Work done by a constant force

- Work done on a particle by a constant force is the product of the magnitude of the force and the displacement of the particle in the direction of the force.

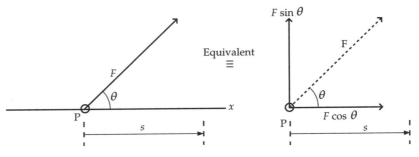

Fig 6.1 Work done on a particle by a constant force

- In Fig 6.1, the work done in moving a particle P through a displacement s is given by:

  Work Done = Force × Displacement

  $$W = (F \cos \theta)s$$
  $$= Fs \cos \theta$$

- Work done on an object is zero when $F = 0$ or $s = 0$ or $\theta = 90°$ (i.e. force exerted is perpendicular to the displacement). These three examples are illustrated in Fig 6.2.

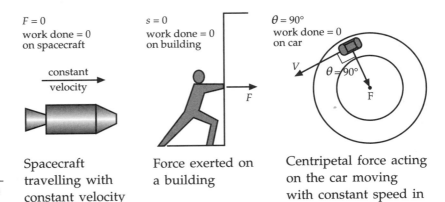

Fig 6.2 Examples of situations where work done is zero

Spacecraft travelling with constant velocity

Force exerted on a building

Centripetal force acting on the car moving with constant speed in a circle

- Work done is a scalar quantity.
- The S.I. unit for work done is the joule (J). The joule is defined as the work done by a force of $1\,N$ which results in a displacement of 1 m in the direction of the force.

  $$1\,J = 1\,N\,m$$
  $$= 1 \text{ kg m}^2 \text{ s}^{-2}$$

145

- The following are examples of work done by a constant force.
  (a) Work done by the man on a box (Fig 6.3).

  $$W = Fs \cos \theta$$
  $$= (10)(10) \cos 30°$$
  $$= 86.6 \text{ J}$$
  $$= 87 \text{ J}$$

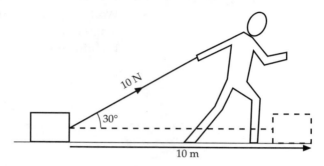

Fig 6.3   Positive work done

(b) Work done by the man in opposing the sliding box (Fig 6.4).

$$W = Fs \cos \theta$$
$$= (10)(10) \cos 120°$$
$$= -50 \text{ J}$$

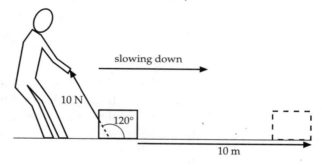

Fig 6.4   Negative work done

(c) Work done by the frictional force in opposing the sliding box (Fig 6.5).

$$W = Fs \cos \theta$$
$$= (2)(10) \cos 180°$$
$$= -20 \text{ J}$$

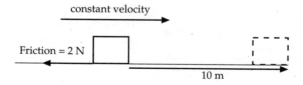

Fig 6.5   Work done by friction

(d) Work done by gravity on sliding box (Fig 6.6).

$$W = Fs \cos \theta$$
$$= (20 \sin 30°)(10) \cos 0°$$
$$= 100 \text{ J}$$

146

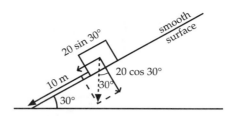

Fig 6.6 Work done by friction

Positive work done involves the transfer of energy to an object and displacing it in the direction of the applied force. Negative work done is the transfer of energy out of that object.

(e) Expansion of a gas

Consider the expansion of a gas in a frictionless piston of cross-sectional area A (Fig 6.7a). Two forces act on the piston. They are:

F_1 – the force exerted on the piston by the gas

F_2 – the force exerted on the gas by the piston

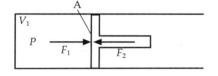

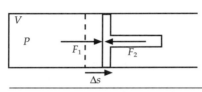

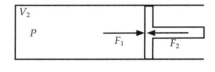

Fig 6.7a Frictionless piston

Fig 6.7b Gas pushes against the piston

The gas expands by pushing the piston through a distance of Δs. This distance is so small that the pressure P can be considered to be a constant (Fig 6.7b).

Work done by the gas

$$\Delta W = F_1\, \Delta s$$
$$= PA\, \Delta s$$
$$= P\, \Delta V$$

Work done by the gas in expanding from V_1 to V_2

$$W = \int_{V_1}^{V_2} P\, dV$$
$$= P(V_2 - V_1)$$

Work done by the piston on the gas is given by

$$\Delta W' = (F_2 \cos 180°)\Delta s$$
$$= -F_2\, \Delta s$$

Work done by the piston on the gas as it expands from V_1 to V_2.

$$W' = -P \int_{V_1}^{V_2} P\, dV$$
$$= -P(V_2 - V_1)$$

147

POTENTIAL ENERGY

- An object can have energy by virtue of its position or configuration (Shape). This is called potential energy.
- There are three kinds of potential energy (P.E.). They are summarised in Table 6.3.

Strain Energy (Elastic PE)	Gravitational PE	Electric PE
Interaction between charges on atoms and molecules	Interaction between masses	Interaction between charges
Involves attractive and repulsive forces	Involves only attractive forces	Involves attractive and repulsive forces
Energy is given by $W = \frac{1}{2}kx^2$ where k is force constant and x is extension	Energy is given by $U = mgh$ (applicable near the surface of the Earth where g is constant)	Energy is given by $U = \frac{q_1 q_2}{4\pi\varepsilon_0 r}$ where q_1 is charge on body, q_2 is charge on body, r is distance between charges and ε_0 is the permittivity for a vacuum.

Table 6.3 Types of potential energy

- Strain energy (Elastic Potential Energy)

  This is the work done by a variable force. Consider a spiral spring which can be stretched or compressed horizontally as shown in Fig 6.8.

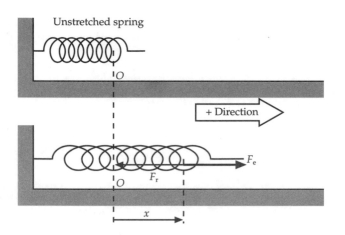

Fig 6.8 Elastic potential energy

Two variable forces act on the spring. They are:
(a) Force of extension (F_e)
(b) Restoring force (F_r)

148

The force of extension obeys Hooke's law, i.e.

$$F_e = kx \text{ where } k \text{ is a spring constant.}$$

Take O on the unstretched spring as the origin and the direction to the right as positive.
The work done by F_e in stretching the spring by Δx is

$$\Delta W = F_e \Delta x$$
$$= kx \Delta x$$

The work done by F_e in stretching the spring from O to x is

$$W = \int_0^x kx \, dx$$

Hence $W = \dfrac{1}{2}kx^2$

This is stored as elastic potential energy or sometimes called the strain energy in the spring.
The work done by F_r in stretching the spring from O to x is

$$W = -\frac{1}{2}kx^2.$$

If a force-extension graph is plotted (Fig 6.9), the area under the line represents the work done by F_e.

Area under the $(F\text{-}x)$ graph $=$ base $\times$ height

$$= \frac{1}{2}(x)(F_e)$$

$$= \frac{1}{2}(x)(kx)$$

$$= \text{work done in stretching the spring from 0 to } x$$

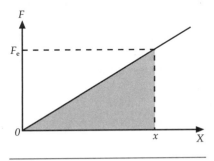

Fig 6.9   Area under the (F − x) graph

Gravitational Potential Energy

- Gravitational potential energy of an object is the energy it possesses by virtue of its position in a gravitational field.
- Consider a mass m being lifted from h_1 to h_2 on the surface of the Earth. This is done in small steps Δl without changing its kinetic energy. A force that is equal and opposite to mg must be applied to the mass (Fig 6.10).

$$\text{Work done} = \text{Force} \times \text{Displacement}$$
$$\Delta W = F \Delta l \cos \theta$$
$$= mg \Delta h$$

Total work done in moving the mass from h_1 to h_2 is given by

$$W = \int_{h_1}^{h_2} mg \, dh$$
$$= mgh_2 - mgh_1$$

$$\boxed{W = \Delta U = mgh_2 - mgh_1}$$

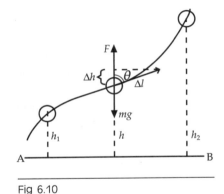

Fig 6.10

The reference line AB, in Fig 6.10 is arbitrary and chosen for convenience. Setting $h_1 = 0$ and $h_2 = h$, we have

$$W = mgh$$
$$= \text{Gravitational potential energy}$$

The above formula gives the work done on a mass when it is moved from the Earth's surface to any point in the gravitational field near the surface. This is known as the gravitational potential energy.

• The following points should be noted:

(a) Gravitational potential energy is a relative and not an absolute quantity. It is always taken in relation to a reference line which can be chosen arbitrarily. What is more important is the change in the gravitational P.E. with reference to this line (Fig 6.11). Consider the change in potential energy (ΔU) of a 10 kg mass along path 1 and 2.

Choosing AB as the reference line,
$$\Delta U = (10)(10)(10) - (10)(10)(0)$$
$$= 1000 \text{ J}$$
Choosing CD as the reference line,
$$\Delta U = (10)(10)(20) - (10)(10)(10)$$
$$= 1000 \text{ J}$$

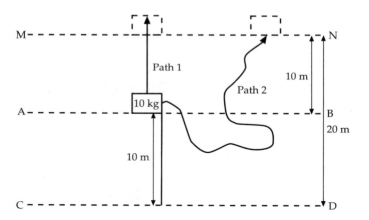

Fig 6.11 Change in ΔU near the surface of the curve

(b) The work done on the mass in moving it between two positions is dependent only on the initial and final positions and independent of the path taken by the mass. ΔU remains the same for path 1 and 2 in Fig 6.11.

(c) The above formula assumes that gravitational acceleration is constant. Hence, this is applicable only near the surface of the Earth.

KINETIC ENERGY | Kinetic Energy and the Work-Energy Theorem

- Figure 6.12 shows a constant force F acting in the direction of a moving body of mass m. The body accelerates uniformly from an initial velocity u to a final velocity v. The displacement of the body is s.

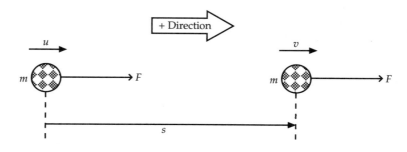

Fig 6.12   Constant force acting on mass

- Take the direction to the right as positive.
  The final velocity is given by
  $v^2 = u^2 + 2as$ where a is constant acceleration.
  Multiply both sides of the equation by m:
  $$mv^2 = mu^2 + 2mas$$
  $$\text{or} \quad mas = \frac{1}{2}mv^2 - \frac{1}{2}mu^2$$
  But work done $W = F \times s$
  $$= mas$$
  $$W = \frac{1}{2}mv^2 - \frac{1}{2}mu^2$$

- The term $\frac{1}{2}mv^2$ is known as the kinetic energy (KE) for a body moving with velocity v. It is the work done in moving the body from rest to v. Similarly, $\frac{1}{2}mu^2$ is the kinetic energy of a body moving with velocity u.

- The equation also shows that the net work done on an object is equal to the change in kinetic energy. This is known as the Work–Energy theorem.
  $$W = K_2 - K_1$$
  $$= \Delta \text{KE}$$

151

A block of mass 2.0 kg placed on a smooth table is pressed against a spring as shown in Fig 6.13. The spring is compressed by a distance of 10.0 cm from its unstretched length. The block is released and it accelerates until it leaves the spring at O. The spring has a spring constant of 500 N/m. Calculate
(a) the work done in compressing the spring,
(b) the speed of the block when it leaves O.

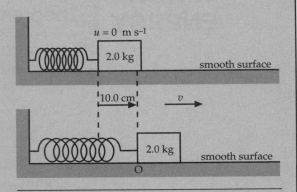

Fig 6.13

(a) Work done in compressing the spring $W = \dfrac{1}{2}kx^2$

$$= \frac{1}{2}(500)(0.100)^2$$

$$= 2.5\,\text{J}$$

(c) The stored potential energy is converted entirely to kinetic energy of the block.

Hence $\dfrac{1}{2}mv^2 - \dfrac{1}{2}mu^2 = 2.5\,\text{J}$

where the initial speed of the block $u = 0\ \text{m s}^{-1}$,
v is the speed of the block when it leaves O,
m is the mass of the block.

$$\therefore v = \sqrt{\frac{2 \times 2.5}{2}} = 1.6\,\text{m s}^{-1}$$

A raindrop of mass m is falling vertically through the air with a steady speed v. It experiences a retarding force kv due to the air, where k is a constant. The acceleration of free fall is g. What is the kinetic energy of the raindrop?

Cambridge

When the raindrop falls with steady speed, the retarding force is equal in magnitude but opposite in direction to the weight of the raindrop. This is illustrated in Fig 6.14.

$$kv = mg$$

$$v = \frac{mg}{k}$$

$$\therefore KE = \frac{1}{2}mv^2$$

$$= \frac{1}{2}m\left(\frac{mg}{k}\right)^2 = \frac{m^3g^2}{2k^2}$$

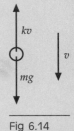

Fig 6.14

Mechanical Energy and its conservation

- The law of conservation of mechanical energy states that the sum of the total kinetic energy and the potential energy in an isolated system is constant.

- Consider the motion of a 1 kg mass when it was projected vertically upwards with an initial speed of 4.43 m s^{-1} on the surface of the Earth. The kinetic energy K of the mass is converted to gravitational potential energy U as it rises from O to A. As it falls back to O, potential energy is converted into kinetic energy.

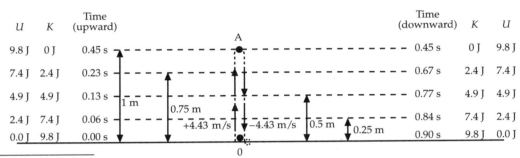

Fig 6.15 Conservation of mechanical energy

- A graph of energy against time is illustrated in Fig 6.16.

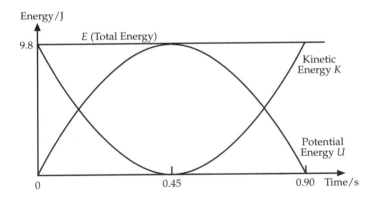

Fig 6.16 Graph of energy against time

If E is the total energy for the isolated system,

$$E = K + U$$
$$= \text{constant}$$

If K_1 and U_1 are the kinetic and potential energies of the system at one time and K_2 and U_2 are their respective values at a later time, then the constancy of E implies

$$K_1 + U_1 = K_2 + U_2$$
$$\text{or} \quad U_1 - U_2 = (K_2 - K_1)$$

$$\Delta U = -\Delta K$$

This is known as the conservation of mechanical energy.

153

Figure 6.17a shows two bodies X and Y connected by a light cord passing over a light, free running pulley, X starts from rest and moves on a smooth plane inclined at 30° to the horizontal.
What will be the total kinetic energy of the system when X has travelled 2.00 m along the plane?
($g = 9.81$ m s^{-2})

Cambridge

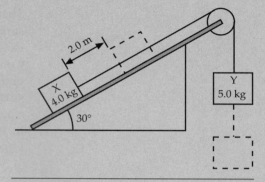

Fig 6.17a

Forces acting on X and Y are shown in Fig 6.17b. The two masses start from rest with constant acceleration a. The pulleys are frictionless; hence the tensions T on either side are equal.
Consider the forces acting on each of the masses.
For 5.0 kg mass:

$$5.0(9.81) - T = (5.0)a$$
$$\therefore T = 49.05 - 5.0a \text{ ———— Equation (1)}$$

For 4.0 kg mass:

$$T - 4.0(9.81) \sin 30° = (4.0)a \text{ —— Equation (2)}$$

Substituting equation (1) into (2)

$$49.05 - 5.0a - 19.62 = 4.0a$$
$$9.0a = 29.43$$
$$\therefore a = 3.27 \text{ m s}^{-2}$$

Fig 6.17b

The velocity v when each of the masses has moved 2.00 m is given by

$$v^2 = u^2 + 2as$$

where $u = 0$ m s^{-1}, $a = 3.27$ m s^{-2} and $s = 2.00$ m.

$$v = \sqrt{2(3.27)(2.00)}$$
$$= 3.62 \text{ m s}^{-1}$$

Total kinetic energy of the system
= Sum of the kinetic energies of the two masses

$$= \frac{1}{2}(4.0)(3.62)^2 + \frac{1}{2}(5.0)(3.62)^2$$
$$= 58.97 \text{ J}$$
$$= 59 \text{ J}$$

Alternatively; the above problem can be solved by apply the principle of conservation of mechanical energy.
Gain in kinetic energy of X and Y + Gain in potential energy of X = loss in potential energy of Y
Kinetic energy of X and Y + (4.0)(9.81) (2.00 Sin 30°) = (5.0)(9.81)(2.00)

$$\therefore \text{ Kinetic energy of X and Y} = 98.1 - 39.24$$
$$= 58.86$$
$$= 59 \text{ J}$$

A frictionless metal track is curved in a shape as shown in Fig. 6.18. A toy car of mass 1.0 kg is released from rest at A and slides down the slope.

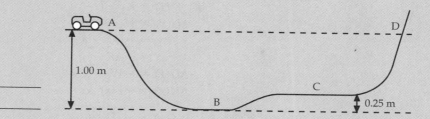

Fig 6.18

(a) Assuming that the air resistance is negligible, state where the toy car would come to rest momentarily.
(b) Calculate the speed of the car at C.
(c) After some time, the metal track turned rusty and frictional forces acting along ABC causes the car to stop at C. Calculate the energy lost due to friction.

(a) It will stop momentarily at D.
(b) Applying the conservation of mechanical energy

$$KE_C + PE_C = KE_A + PE_A$$

$$\frac{1}{2}mv^2 + mg(0.25) = 0 + mg(1.00)$$

$$v = \sqrt{2(9.81)(0.75)} = 3.8 \text{ ms}^{-1}$$

(c) Energy lost due to friction
= loss in PE
= (1.0)(9.81)(0.75)
= 7.4 J

An object of mass m passes a point X with a velocity v and slides up a frictionless incline to stop at point Y which is at a height h above X.

A second object of mass $\frac{1}{2}m$ passes X with a velocity of $\frac{1}{2}v$.
To what height will it rise?

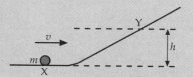

Cambridge

Choose the horizontal line through X as the reference line.
Conservation of Mechanical Energy for mass m at X and Y implies that

$$K_X + U_X = K_Y + U_Y$$

$$\frac{1}{2}mv^2 + 0 = 0 + mgh$$

$$\therefore v^2 = 2gh \quad \text{———— Equation (1)}$$

If mass $\frac{1}{2}m$ rises to height h'

$$\frac{1}{2}\left(\frac{1}{2}m\right)\left(\frac{1}{2}v\right)^2 = \left(\frac{1}{2}m\right)gh'$$

$$\frac{1}{8}v^2 = gh' \quad \text{———— Equation (2)}$$

Dividing equation (2) by (1)

$$\frac{gh'}{2gh} = \frac{\frac{1}{8}v^2}{v^2}$$

$$\therefore h' = \frac{1}{4}h$$

155

Force and Potential Energy

- Consider a one-dimensional situation where the force $F(x)$ is dependent on the potential energy $U(x)$. From the Work-Energy theorem,

$$K_2 + U_2 = K_1 + U_1$$
$$\Delta U(x) = U_2 - U_1$$
$$= -(K_2 - K_1)$$
$$= -\Delta K$$
$$\Delta U(x) = -W$$
$$\Delta U(x) = -F(x)\,\Delta x$$
$$F(x) = -\frac{\Delta U(x)}{\Delta x}$$

In the limit as $\Delta x \to 0$,

$$F(x) = -\lim_{\Delta x \to 0} \frac{\Delta U(x)}{\Delta x}$$

$$F(x) = -\frac{dU(x)}{dx}$$

Q A particle moves so that its potential energy U varies with the square of its displacement r from the origin (Fig 6.19). Plot a graph of F against r.

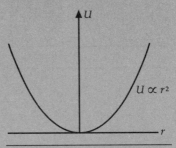

Fig 6.19

A
$$U \propto r^2$$
$$U = kr^2 \text{ where } k \text{ is a constant}$$
$$\frac{dU}{dr} = 2kr$$

But $F = -\dfrac{dU}{dr}$

$\therefore F = -2kr$

The graph of F against r is shown in Fig 6.20.

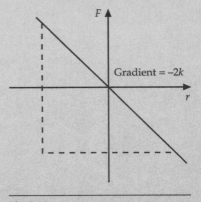

Fig 6.20

156

INTERNAL ENERGY

- Internal energy is the sum total of the kinetic and potential energies associated with the random motion of molecules and atoms within an object.

- The internal energy of an object can increase by the transfer of heat energy from the environment to the object. The heat absorbed is positive. For example, when a beaker of water is heated over fire, the internal energy of the water increases as heat flows from the fire to the water.

- The internal energy of an object can decrease by the transfer of heat energy from the object to the environment. The heat lost is negative. For example, when electric current flows through the resistance of an electric heater, the internal energy increases. Part of this energy is lost as heat flows away from the resistance into the surroundings.

- Internal energy can increase or decrease by doing work on the object or by the object.

- The First Law of Thermodynamics describes the relationship between internal energy, work done and heat. This is discussed in Chapter 11.

Electric Energy

- Electric energy can be transformed into many types of useful energy. For example, it can be converted into mechanical energy in motors, heat energy in an electric heater and light energy in a filament lamp.

- Electrons make numerous collisions with atoms when it flows through a wire. Part of the kinetic energy of the electrons is converted into kinetic energy of the vibrations of the atoms. There will be an increase in the internal energy (thermal energy) of the material. This could be lost to the surroundings through conduction, convection and radiation of energy.

Power

- Power is defined as the rate at which work is done. If work is done on an object at a steady rate, power can be written as

$$\text{Power} = \frac{\text{work done}}{\text{time taken}}$$

$$= \frac{\text{energy change}}{\text{time taken}}$$

$$P = \frac{W}{t}$$

157

The SI unit for power is joules per second or watt (W)

$$\text{i.e.} \quad 1\,W = \frac{1\,J}{1\,s}$$

- If the work done on an object is not steady, the average power is used. It is defined as:

$$\text{Average power } <P> = \frac{\text{total work done}}{\text{total time taken}}$$

$$= \frac{W}{t}$$

- The power at a particular instant, also known as the instantaneous power of a body is given by

$$P = \frac{dW}{dt}$$

- Suppose work is done on an object by a constant force F and it moves a distance s in the direction of the force in time t. The power is given by

$$P = \frac{W}{t}$$

$$= \frac{Fs}{t}$$

$$= F\left(\frac{s}{t}\right)$$

$$= Fv$$

Efficiency

- The conservation of energy states that the total energy in any system is constant. This means that the total energy input is equal to the total energy output. However, not all the energy output is useful because part of it is usually lost as friction or heat loss to the surroundings.

  In general,

  energy input = useful energy output + useless energy output

- The efficiency of a machine is defined as follows:

$$\text{Efficiency} = \frac{\text{useful energy output}}{\text{energy input}} \times 100\%$$

Alternatively,

$$\text{Efficiency} = \frac{\text{useful power output}}{\text{power input}} \times 100\%$$

 Figure 6.21 shows an arrangement used to find the output power of an electric motor. The wheel attached to the motor's axle has a circumference of 0.5 m and the belt which passes over it is stationary when the weights have the values shown.
If the wheel makes 20 revolutions per second, what is the output power?

Cambridge

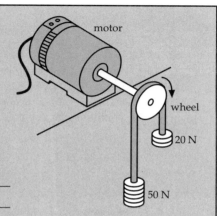

Fig 6.21

Since the belt is stationary, the friction F acting on the belt is given by
$$F + 20 = 50$$
$$F = 30 \text{ N}$$
When the wheel makes 20 revolutions, a point on the circumference of the wheel would have moved a distance d of (0.5×20) m.

$$\therefore \text{ Power} = \frac{\text{work done}}{\text{time}}$$
$$= \frac{Fd}{t}$$
$$= \frac{30 \times (0.5 \times 20)}{1}$$
$$= 300 \text{ W}$$

 An electric motor is required to haul a cage of mass 400 kg up a mine shaft through a vertical height of 1200 m in 2.0 minutes. What will be the electrical power required if the overall efficiency is 80%?
[Take g as 10 m s^{-2}]

Cambridge

 The useful power P_u required to raise the cage through a vertical height of 1200 m in 2.0 minutes is given by

$$P_u = \frac{\text{work done}}{\text{time}}$$
$$= \frac{mgh}{t}$$
$$= \frac{(400)(10)(1200)}{(2.0 \times 60)}$$
$$= 40\,000 \text{ W}$$

If the electrical power required is P, the overall efficiency is given by,

$$E = \frac{P_u}{P} \times 100\%$$
$$\text{i.e. } 80\% = \frac{40\,000}{P} \times 100\%$$
$$P = 50\,000 \text{ W}$$
$$= 50 \text{ kW}$$

159

Q

(a) In what way is the momentum of a body affected by the resultant force acting on it?

(b) A conveyor belt travelling at a speed of 3.0 m s⁻¹ and at an angle of 20° to the horizontal has 18 kg of sugar dropped on to it each second as shown in Fig 6.22.

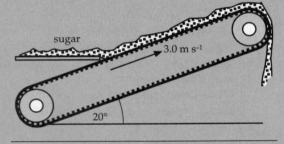

Fig 6.22

Assuming that the sugar has negligible speed before reaching the belt, calculate
(i) the momentum gained in each second by the sugar,
(ii) the force which the belt must exert on the sugar to accelerate it to the speed of the belt,
(iii) the work done per second by the belt on the sugar in exerting this force,
(iv) the potential energy gained in each second by all the 36 kg of the sugar which is on the belt.

(c) From your answers to (b), find the extra power required by the driving motor when the belt is loaded rather than unloaded.

Cambridge

A

(a) Since the resultant force is the rate of change of momentum, it can increase or decrease the magnitude of the momentum or alter its direction.

(b) (i) Momentum gained in each second

$$= \frac{mv - mu}{t}$$

$$= \frac{(18)(3.0) - (18)(0)}{1}$$

$$= 54 \text{ kg m s}^{-2}$$

(ii) Force = Momentum gained in each second
$$= 54 \text{ N}$$

(iii) Power required to move 18 kg of sugar
= Work done per second by the belt on the sugar
$$= Fv$$
$$= 54 \times 3.0$$
$$= 162 \text{ W}$$

(iv) Power required to raise 36 kg of sugar
= Potential energy gained in each second by 36 kg of sugar

$$= \frac{mgh}{t}$$

$$= \frac{(36)(9.81)(3.0 \sin 20°)}{1}$$

$$= 362.4 \text{ W}$$
$$= 360 \text{ W}$$

(c) The extra power required by the driving motor $= 162 + 362.4$
$$= 524.4 \text{ W}$$
$$= 524 \text{ W}$$

A car is travelling along a horizontal road with steady speed v, measured in metres per second. The power P, measured in watts, required to overcome external forces opposing the motion is given by the expression $P = cv + kv^3$ where c and k are constants.

(a) Use base units to obtain an SI unit for the constant k.

(b) For one particular car, the numerical values, in SI units, of c and of k are 240 and 0.98 respectively. Calculate the power required to enable the car to travel along a horizontal road at 31 m s^{-1}.

(c) The car has mass 720 kg. Using your answer to (b) where appropriate, calculate, for the car travelling at 31 m s^{-1},
 (i) its kinetic energy,
 (ii) the magnitude of the external force opposing the motion of the car,
 (iii) the work done in overcoming the force in (ii) during a time of 5.0 minutes.

(d) By reference to your answers in (c), suggest with a reason, whether it would be worthwhile to develop a system whereby, when the car slows down, its kinetic energy would be stored for re-use when the car speeds up again.

 (a) (Units of k) $(\text{m s}^{-1})^3 = \text{J s}^{-1}$

$$\text{Units of } k = \frac{(\text{kg m}^2 \text{ s}^{-2})(\text{s}^{-1})}{\text{m}^3 \text{ s}^{-3}}$$
$$= \text{kg m}^{-1}$$

(b) When $c = 240 \text{ kg m s}^{-2}$, $k = 0.98 \text{ kg m}^{-1}$ and $v = 31 \text{ m s}^{-1}$,
$$P = cv + kv^3$$
$$= (240)(31) + (0.98)(31)^3$$
$$= 36\,635.2 \text{ W}$$
$$= 3.7 \times 10^4 \text{ W}$$

(c) (i) $\text{KE} = \dfrac{1}{2}mv^2$

$$= \frac{1}{2}(720)(31)^2$$
$$= 345\,960 \text{ J}$$
$$= 3.5 \times 10^5 \text{ J}$$

(ii) If F is the external force opposing the motion of the car,
$$P = Fv$$
$$F = \frac{P}{v}$$
$$= \frac{36\,635.2}{31}$$
$$= 1181.8$$
$$= 1.2 \times 10^3 \text{ N}$$

(iii) Work done = Power × time
$$= (36\,635.2)(5.0 \times 60)$$
$$= 1.1 \times 10^7 \text{ J}$$

(d) Not all kinetic energy can be stored as some of it will be lost as heat and work done against the large external force opposing the motion of the car. There is not enough energy to accelerate the car to its original speed unless energy is constantly supplied to the system. Hence it is not worthwhile to develop the system that relies solely on the conversion and storage of kinetic energy.

Q A water wheel has eight buckets equally spaced around its circumference, as illustrated in Fig 6.23.

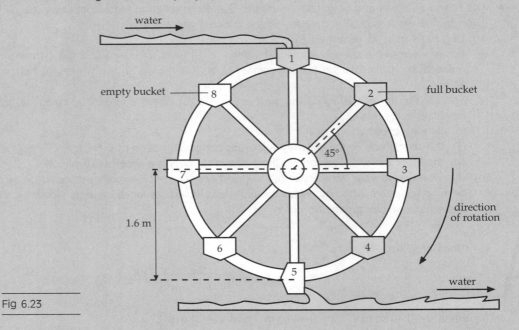

Fig 6.23

The distance between the centre of each bucket and the centre of the wheel is 1.6 m.

When a bucket is at its highest point, the bucket is filled with a mass of 40 kg of water. The wheel rotates and the bucket is emptied at its lowest point. The wheel makes six revolutions per minute. Calculate

(a) (i) the total change in potential energy of the water in the buckets in one revolution of the wheel

(ii) the average input power to the wheel.

(b) Suggest why a larger number of small buckets is preferred to a smaller number of large buckets containing the same total mass of water.

Cambridge

A (a) (i) Total change in the potential energy of the water in one revolution
$$= \Delta PE$$
$$= 8[(40)(9.81)(3.2)]$$
$$= 10\,045.4$$
$$\approx 10\,000 \text{ J}$$

(ii) Average input power $= \dfrac{\Delta PE}{t}$

$$= \frac{10\,045.4}{60/6}$$
$$= 1004.5 \text{ W}$$
$$\approx 1 \text{ kW}$$

(b) Positioning smaller buckets at positions with larger moment arm will increase the total torque on the wheel.

Exercise 6

Multiple-Choice Questions

1   A mass m moves on a rough plane inclined at an angle θ to the horizontal and, when moving, experiences a constant frictional force F. Mass M is attached to it by means of a light inelastic cord running over a smooth pulley. Mass M is allowed to fall a vertical distance x, causing m to move up the plane as shown in the diagram below.

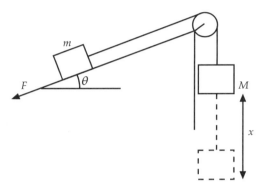

How much heat is generated by friction in this process?

A Fx
B mgx
C $Mgx \sin \theta$
D $Mgx \sin \theta - Fx$

2   What is the power required to give a body of mass m a forward acceleration a when it is moving with velocity v up a frictionless track inclined at an angle θ to the horizontal?

A $mav \sin \theta$
B $mav \sin \theta + mgv$
C $mav + mgv \sin \theta$
D $(mav + mgv) \sin \theta$

3   A constant force is applied to a body which is initially stationary but free to move in the direction of the force. Assuming that the effects of friction are negligible, which of the following graphs best represents the variation of P, the power supplied, with time t?

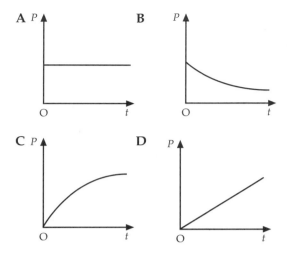

4   A crate is pushed 10 m along a horizontal surface by a force of 80 N. The frictional force opposing the motion is 60 N. How much of the work done is converted into thermal energy and how much into kinetic energy of the crate?

	thermal energy/J	kinetic energy/J
A	200	600
B	200	800
C	600	200
D	600	800

5   A mass m, attached to the end of an unstretched spring, is initially supported by a platform as shown in Fig 6.24. This platform is then removed and the mass falls, eventually coming to rest at the position shown in Fig 6.25.

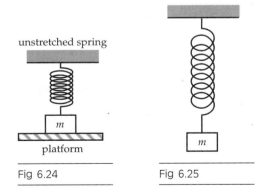

Fig 6.24   Fig 6.25

Which of the following correctly relates the changes in potential energy and heat dissipation which may occur during this process?

163

A decrease of gravitational potential energy = increase of strain energy

B decrease of gravitational potential energy = increase of strain energy + energy dissipated as heat

C decrease of gravitational potential energy = decrease of strain energy + energy dissipated as heat

D decrease of gravitational potential energy + energy dissipated as heat = increase in strain energy

6 A body of mass m moves at constant speed v for a distance s against a constant force F. What is the power required to sustain this motion?

A mv **B** $\frac{1}{2}mv^2$

C $\frac{1}{2}Fs$ **D** Fv

7 A small metal sphere of mass m is moving through a viscous liquid.
When it reaches a constant downward velocity v, which of the following describes the changes with time in the kinetic energy and gravitational potential energy of the sphere?

	kinetic energy	gravitational potential energy
A	constant and equal to $\frac{1}{2}mv^2$	decreases at a rate of mgv
B	constant and equal to $\frac{1}{2}mv^2$	decreases at a rate of $\left(mgv + \frac{1}{2}mv^2\right)$
C	constant and equal to $\frac{1}{2}mv^2$	decreases at a rate of $\left(\frac{1}{2}mv^2 - mgv\right)$
D	increases at a rate of mgv	decreases at a rate of mgv

8 A force of 1000 N is needed to lift the hook of a crane at a steady velocity. The crane is then used to lift a load of mass 1000 kg at a velocity of 0.5 m s^{-1}. How much of the power developed by the motor of the crane is used in lifting the hook and the load? [Take $g = 10 \text{ m s}^{-2}$]

A 5.0 kW **B** 5.5 kW
C 20 kW **D** 22 kW

9 A boat moving at constant speed v through still water experiences a total frictional drag F. What is the power developed by the boat?

A $\frac{1}{2}Fv$ **B** Fv

C $\frac{1}{2}Fv^2$ **D** Fv^2

10 A pail of mass 100 g is moved in a vertical plane from position A to position B on a circular track of radius 10 m.
[Take $g = 10 \text{ m s}^{-2}$]

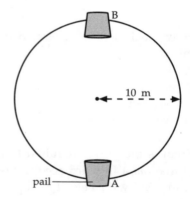

What is the change in energy?
A 10 J **B** 20 J
C 40 J **D** 60 J

11 A body moves in a circle at constant speed. The work done by the centripetal force on this body is zero, because

164

A the centripetal force acting on the body is always perpendicular to the direction of its motion.

B the speed and acceleration of the body are constant.

C the net displacement of the body after each revolution is zero.

D the average force on the body over each revolution is zero.

Structured Questions

1 Values of mass and velocity for a truck and a car are given in the table below.

   (a) Use these values to calculate values for the momentum and kinetic energy of the truck and of the car.

   (b) Both vehicles are now subjected to a constant braking force of 2.0×10^4 N. From your values of momentum and kinetic energy, make calculations to determine

   (i) the time taken for each vehicle to stop.

   (ii) the distance taken for each vehicle to stop.

	truck	car
mass	3000 kg	1000 kg
velocity	20 m s^{-1}	40 m s^{-1}
momentum		
kinetic energy		
stopping time		
stopping distance		

2 (a) What is meant by the *centre of gravity* of a body?

   (b) In a children's game, small balls are thrown at wood blocks to turn them over. One such block, of mass 150 g with each side of length 10 cm is shown in Fig 6.26(a).

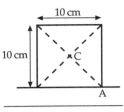

Fig 6.26(a)

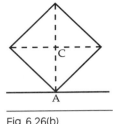

Fig 6.26(b)

In order to turn the block over, the centre of gravity C of the block must be raised so that C is vertically above the corner A, as shown in Fig 6.26(b).

(i) For the block as shown in Fig 6.26(b),

   1. calculate the vertical height through which the centre of gravity has been raised,

   2. show that the gain in potential energy of the block is approximately 0.031 J.

(ii) The block is struck by a ball of mass 11 g traveling horizontally towards C, as shown in Fig 6.27.

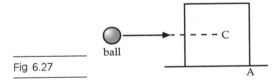

Fig 6.27

The collision is perfectly elastic and, without sliding, the block turns about the corner A.

The block is able to reach the position in Fig 6.26(b). 25% of the kinetic energy of the ball is transferred to the block. Calculate

   1. the kinetic energy of the ball just before it strikes the block,

   2. the speed with which the ball strikes the block,

   3. the speed with which the ball rebounds from the block.

165

(iii) For the collision in (ii) of the ball with the block, calculate
1. the change in momentum of the ball,
2. the average force on the block, assuming the ball and the block are in contact for 0.15 s.

(c) A student comments that, by loading the block with an extra mass as shown in Fig 6.28, the centre of gravity would be lowered, and consequently, less energy would be required to turn the block.

Fig 6.28

Comment on the validity of this statement.

3 *(a)* Starting with the definition of work, deduce the change in the gravitational potential energy of a mass m, when moved a distance h upwards against a gravitational field of field strength g.

(b) By using the equations of motion, show that the kinetic energy E_k of an object of mass m traveling with speed v is given by

$$E_k = \frac{1}{2}mv^2.$$

(c) A cyclist, together with his bicycle, has a total mass of 90 kg and is traveling with a constant speed of $15\,\mathrm{m\,s^{-1}}$ on a flat road at A, as illustrated in Fig 6.29. He then goes down a small slope to B so descending 4.0 m.

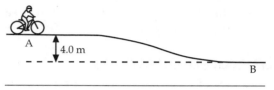

Fig 6.29

Calculate
(i) the kinetic energy at A,
(ii) the loss of potential energy between A and B.
(iii) the speed at B, assuming that all the lost potential energy is transformed into kinetic energy of the cyclist and bicycle.

(d) (i) A cyclist traveling at a constant speed of $15\,\mathrm{m\,s^{-1}}$ on a level road provides a power of 240 W. Calculate the total resistive force.

(ii) The cyclist now travels at a higher constant speed. Explain why the cyclist needs to provide a greater power.

(e) It is often stated that many forms of transport transform chemical energy into kinetic energy. Explain why a cyclist traveling at constant speed is not making this transformation. Explain what transformations of energy are taking place.

166

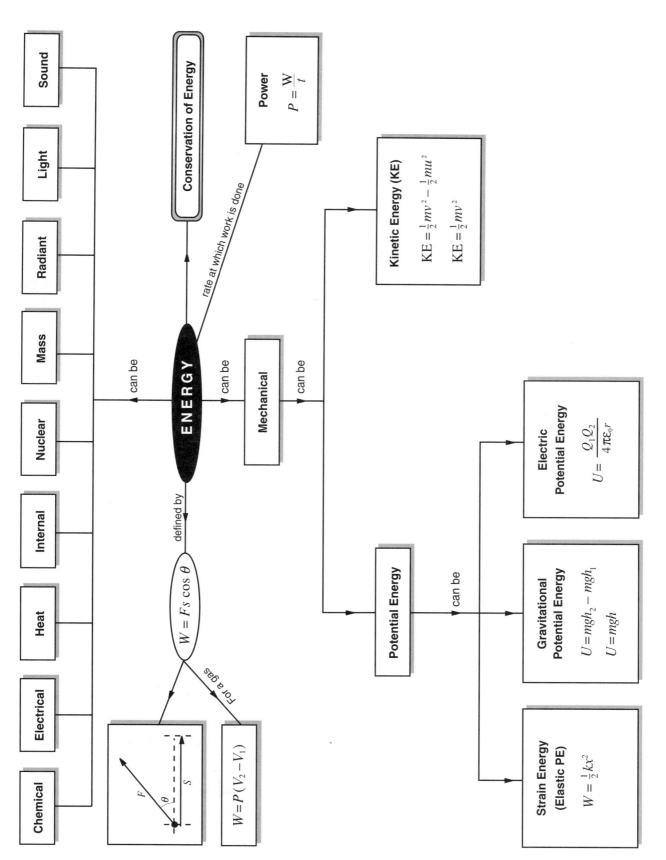

Chemical — Electrical — Heat — Internal — Nuclear — Mass — Radiant — Light — Sound

ENERGY

can be

defined by

$W = Fs \cos \theta$

For a gas

$W = P(V_2 - V_1)$

Conservation of Energy

rate at which work is done

Power

$P = \dfrac{W}{t}$

can be

Mechanical

can be

Kinetic Energy (KE)

$KE = \dfrac{1}{2}mv^2 - \dfrac{1}{2}mu^2$

$KE = \dfrac{1}{2}mv^2$

Potential Energy

can be

Strain Energy (Elastic PE)

$W = \dfrac{1}{2}kx^2$

Gravitational Potential Energy

$U = mgh_2 - mgh_1$

$U = mgh$

Electric Potential Energy

$U = \dfrac{Q_1 Q_2}{4\pi\varepsilon_0 r}$

167

7

Gravitational Field

FORCE BETWEEN
POINT MASSES

GRAVITATIONAL FIELD
OF A POINT MASS

FIELD NEAR TO THE
SURFACE OF THE
EARTH

GRAVITATIONAL
POTENTIAL

Syllabus Objectives

In this chapter you should be able to:

- show an understanding of the concept of a gravitational field as an example of field of force and define gravitational field strength as force per unit mass.

- recall and use Newton's law of gravitation in the form $F = \dfrac{Gm_1m_2}{r^2}$.

- derive, from Newton's law of gravitation and the definition of gravitational field strength, the equation $g = \dfrac{Gm}{r^2}$ for the gravitational field strength of a point mass.

- recall and solve problems by using the equation $g = \dfrac{Gm}{r^2}$ for the gravitational field strength of a point mass.

- show an appreciation that on the surface of the Earth g is approximately constant and is called the acceleration of free fall.

- describe an experiment to determine the acceleration of free fall, using a falling body.

- define potential at a point as the work done in bringing unit mass from infinity to the point.

- solve problems by using the equation $\phi = -\dfrac{Gm}{r}$ for the potential in the field of a point mass.

- recognise the analogy between certain qualitative and quantitative aspects of gravitational and electric fields.

- analyse circular orbits in inverse square law fields by relating the gravitational force to the centripetal acceleration it causes.

- Show an understanding of geostationary orbits and their application.

FORCE BETWEEN POINT MASSES

Newton's Law of Gravitation

- Newton's law of universal gravitation is stated as follows:
A point mass will attract another point mass in any part of the universe with a force that is directly proportional to the product of masses and inversely proportional to the square of the distance between them.

Mathematically, $F \propto \dfrac{m_1 m_2}{r^2}$ or $F = G\dfrac{m_1 m_2}{r^2}$ where

F = Gravitational Force,
m_1 = mass of particle 1
m_2 = mass of particle 2
r = distance between particle 1 and 2
G = Gravitational Constant

- This law is applicable only between point masses and particles. Every spherical object with constant density can be reduced to a point mass at the centre of the sphere. Non-spherical objects with varying density cannot be treated so simply. The use of the calculus is required to determine the gravitational force.

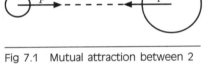

- The gravitational forces between two masses are equal and opposite and constitute an action and reaction pair of forces (Fig. 7.1). They are always attractive in nature and the forces always act along the line joining the two point masses.

Fig 7.1 Mutual attraction between 2 masses

- The gravitational forces between two bodies cannot be shielded or modified by an intervening medium.

- G is known as the universal gravitational constant and has a value of $6.67 \times 10^{-11}\,\text{N m}^2\,\text{kg}^{-2}$. It is not affected by the type of substances considered or the nature of the intervening materials. Temperature has no effect on its value. It is therefore a constant throughout the universe. Since G is very small, gravitational forces become significant only when we are dealing with massive bodies. Gravitational forces between atoms and molecules are insignificant.

- **Sign conventions**
  (a) The positive direction is taken as the direction of increasing distance from a fixed point (Fig 7.2). In the case of the Earth, any displacement away from the Earth's centre is positive.
  (b) The gravitational force acting on the moon due to the Earth is directed towards the Earth's centre. This force is attractive in nature and can be written as:

$$F = -G\frac{m_1 m_2}{r^2}$$

The negative sign is normally ignored when only the magnitude of the force is required.

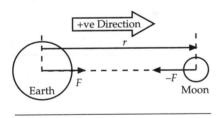

Fig 7.2

169

Q (a) (i) The first definition of the metre was one ten-millionth of the distance between the North Pole and the equator of the Earth. Use this information to estimate the radius of the Earth. State one assumption which you have made in your estimation.

(ii) Use your answer to (i) and the Newton's law of gravitation to deduce the gravitation force acting on a 1.0 kg mass at the Earth's surface. The Earth may be considered to be a sphere of mass 6.0×10^{24} kg.

(b) What gravitational force does the Earth exert on a 1.0 kg mass which is at a distance of 3.8×10^8 m from the centre of the Earth?

Cambridge

A (a) (i) In the figure,

s = distance between the north pole and the equator,
r = radius of the Earth
$s = r\theta$

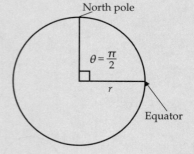

Since $1 \text{ m} = \dfrac{1}{10\,000\,000}\, s$

$s = 10\,000\,000$ m

and $\theta = \dfrac{\pi}{2}$

$\therefore r\left(\dfrac{\pi}{2}\right) = 10\,000\,000$

$r = 6\,366\,198$
$= 6.4 \times 10^6$ m

Assumption: The Earth is a sphere of radius r.

(ii) $m = 1.0$ kg $M = 6.0 \times 10^{24}$ kg

$F = \dfrac{GmM}{r^2}$

$= \dfrac{(6.67 \times 10^{-11})(1.0)\,(6.0 \times 10^{24})}{(6\,366\,198)^2}$

$= 9.9$ N

(b) If $r = 3.8 \times 10^8$ m

$F = \dfrac{GmM}{r^2}$

$= \dfrac{(6.67 \times 10^{-11})(1.0)\,(6.0 \times 10^{24})}{(3.8 \times 10^8)^2}$

$= 2.8 \times 10^{-3}$ N

170

Q Two stationary particles of masses M_1 and M_2 are a distance d apart. A third particle, lying on the line joining the particles, experiences no resultant gravitational force. What is the distance of this particle from M_1?

Cambridge

A

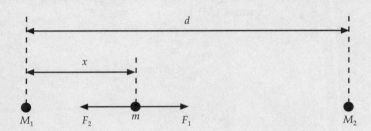

Let the third particle m be at a distance x from M_1. At this position, the gravitational forces due to M_1 and M_2 are equal and opposite
i.e. $F_1 = F_2$

$$\frac{GmM_2}{(d-x)^2} = \frac{GmM_1}{x^2}$$

Take the square root of both sides of the equation

$$\frac{\sqrt{M_2}}{d-x} = \frac{\sqrt{M_1}}{x}$$

$$\sqrt{M_2}\, x = d\sqrt{M_1} - \sqrt{M_1}\, x$$

$$\left(\sqrt{M_1} + \sqrt{M_2}\right) x = d\sqrt{M_1}$$

$$\therefore x = d\left(\frac{\sqrt{M_1}}{\sqrt{M_1} + \sqrt{M_2}}\right)$$

GRAVITATIONAL FIELD OF A POINT MASS

- A gravitational field is said to exist at a point if a gravitational force (F) is exerted on a test mass (m) placed at that point in the gravitational field.

- The gravitational field strength (g) at a point is defined as:

$$g = \frac{\text{force}}{\text{mass}}$$

$$= \frac{F}{m}$$

This is a vector quantity. Gravitational field strength is also known as gravitational acceleration or the free-fall acceleration. Its S. I. units are N kg^{-1} or m s^{-2}.

- Another formula for the gravitational field strength at a point can be obtained by considering the mass (m) placed at a distance (r) from another point mass (M). The gravitational force acting on m is $F = \dfrac{GMm}{r^2}$.

  The gravitational field strength at a point, distance r to mass (M) is

  $$g = \frac{F}{m}$$

  $$= \frac{GMm}{r^2} \times \frac{1}{m}$$

  $$\therefore g = \frac{GM}{r^2}$$

FIELD NEAR TO THE SURFACE OF THE EARTH

- The free-fall acceleration (g) measured at different parts of the Earth's surface differs slightly about a typical value of 9.81 m s^{-2}. The gravitational field strength on the surface of the Earth is only approximately constant. This is because:

  (a) The Earth's surface is not uniform. The density of the Earth increases with depth. It also varies from region to region on the Earth's surface.

  (b) The Earth is not a sphere. It is flattened at the poles and bulges at the equator. The gravitational acceleration is greater at the poles as it is nearer to the dense core of the Earth.

  (c) The Earth is rotating. A more in-depth description of the effects of rotation on g can be found in chapter 8.

- The variation of g with distance above the Earth's surface is illustrated in Fig 7.3. It obeys the inverse square law.

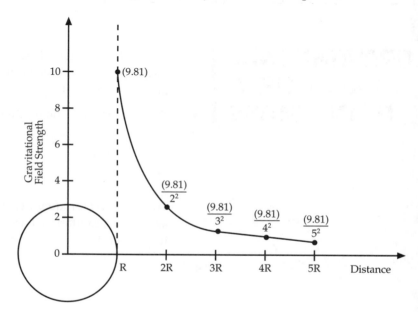

Fig 7.3 The variation of g with distance from the Earth's surface

172

- Experimental determination of the acceleration of free-fall
  (a) Fig 7.4 shows apparatus which can be used to determine the acceleration of free-fall.

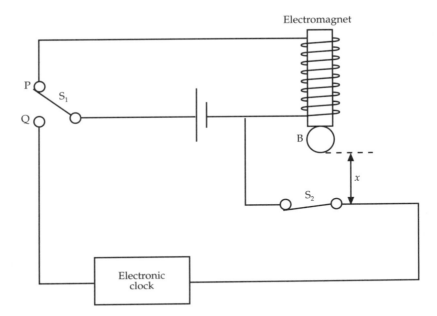

Fig 7.4 Determination of free-fall acceleration

(b) A small soft iron ball B is held by an electromagnet. When the switch S_1 is flicked quickly from contact P to contact Q, the ball is released and the electronic clock is started. After falling a distance x, the ball strikes the switch S_2. This breaks the timing circuit and stops the electronic clock. The vertical distance, x, is measured with a metre-rule and the time of fall, t_1, is noted. This is repeated and an average time for the free-fall is calculated.

(c) A total of six sets of values for x should be obtained and recorded in Table 7.1.

$\dfrac{x}{m}$	Time of free-fall				$\dfrac{t^2}{s^2}$
	$\dfrac{t_1}{s}$	$\dfrac{t_2}{s}$	$\dfrac{t_3}{s}$	Average time $\dfrac{t}{s}$	

Table 7.1

173

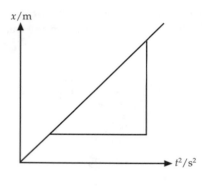

x/m

t²/s²

Fig 7.5 Graph of x against t^2

(d) Using the formula $s = ut + \frac{1}{2}at^2$

Since $s = x$, $u = 0$ m s^{-1} and
$a = g$ (acceleration of free-fall)

we have, $x = \frac{1}{2}gt^2$

The graph of x against t^2 is a straight line passing through the origin. This is illustrated in Fig 7.5.
From the graph,

$$\text{gradient} = \frac{1}{2}g$$

$$\therefore g = 2 \times \text{gradient}$$

Q The acceleration of free fall on the surface of the Earth is about six times its value on the surface of the Moon. The mean density of the Earth is about $\frac{5}{3}$ times the mean density of the Moon.
Using the data, find the value of the ratio of the radius of the Earth to the radius of the Moon.

Cambridge

A If g and g_M are the accelerations of free fall on the Earth and the Moon respectively, ρ and ρ_M are the densities of the Earth and the Moon respectively, M and m are the masses of the Earth and the Moon respectively and r_E and r_M are the radii of the Earth and the Moon respectively, then

$$g = 6g_M, \quad \rho = \frac{5}{3}\rho_M$$

$$\text{and } g = \frac{GM}{r_E^2}$$

$$= \frac{G\left[\rho\left(\frac{4}{3}\pi r_E^3\right)\right]}{r_E^2}$$

$$g = \frac{4}{3}G\rho\pi r_E \underline{\hspace{2cm}} \text{Equation (1)}$$

$$\text{Similarly } g_m = \frac{4}{3}G\rho_M\pi r_M \underline{\hspace{2cm}} \text{Equation (2)}$$

Dividing Equation (1) by Equation (2)

$$\frac{\frac{4}{3}G\rho\pi r_E}{\frac{4}{3}G\rho_M\pi r_M} = \frac{g}{g_M}$$

$$\therefore \frac{r_E}{r_M} = \frac{g}{g_M} \times \frac{\rho_M}{\rho}$$

$$= \frac{6g_M}{g_M} \times \frac{\rho_M}{\frac{5}{3}\rho_M}$$

$$= \frac{6 \times 3}{5}$$

$$= 3.6$$

174

Two small masses m_1 and m_2 are placed at X and Y respectively and are separated by a distance r as shown in Fig 7.6.

Fig 7.6

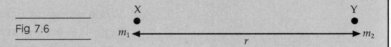

(a) Draw on Fig 7.6 the direction of the gravitational field which m_1 causes at Y.
(b) What is the value of the gravitational field strength which m_1 causes at Y?
(c) What is the force which m_1 causes on m_2?

Cambridge

(a)

Gravitational field which m_1 causes at Y

(b) Gravitational field strength which m_1 causes at Y $= g = \dfrac{Gm_1}{r^2}$

(c) Force which m_1 causes on $m_2 = \dfrac{Gm_1 m_2}{r^2}$

GRAVITATIONAL POTENTIAL

- When a mass m moves in a gravitational field, the work done on the mass can be positive, negative or zero.

- In Fig 7.7, gravitational forces F_A, F_B, F_C act on the mass m at A, B and C. B and C lie on the arc of a circle CB of radius r_B and centre O. From the diagram $r_B = r_C$ while A is further away (i.e. $r_A > r_B$).

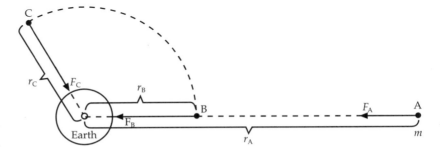

Fig 7.7

175

(a) When m moves from B to A or C to A, work done on m is positive and gravitational potential energy U increases. The change in potential energy as mass m moves from B to A is given by:

$$\Delta U_{BA} = U_A - U_B$$

(b) When m moves from A to B or A to C, work done on m is negative and gravitational potential energy decreases. The potential energy that is lost is transformed into kinetic energy if m moves freely.

(c) When m moves along CB, no work is done as the gravitational force acting on m is always perpendicular to the direction of motion.

- The gravitational potential energy U of a mass m at a point is the work done by an external force in bringing that mass from infinity to the point.

- The gravitational potential ϕ at a point is the work done by an external force in bringing unit mass from infinity to the point.

- The gravitational potential ϕ at a point may also be defined as the gravitational potential energy U of unit mass placed at that point.

- Mathematically, ϕ is written as: $\phi = \dfrac{W}{m} = \dfrac{U}{m}$

  i.e. $W = U = m\phi$

  where ϕ = the gravitational potential at a point

  and W = the work done in bringing a mass m from infinity to that point.

  The SI unit for potential is $J\ kg^{-1}$.

- If an external force F move a mass m, placed at r from a fixed mass M, by a small displacement Δr, the work done ΔW is

$$\Delta W = \frac{GMm}{r^2} \Delta r$$

Total work done is

$$W = \int_r^{\infty} \frac{GMm}{r^2}\ dr$$

$$W = \frac{GMm}{r}$$

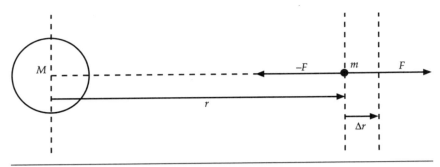

Fig 7.8

Gravitational potential energy increases to its maximum value $\dfrac{GMm}{r}$ at infinity. Conversely, if a mass m is moved by the external force F from infinity to r, the potential energy is

$$U = \int_{\infty}^{r} \frac{GMm}{r^2} \, dr$$

$$U = -\frac{GMm}{r}$$

This means that the potential energy at infinity is zero and has a negative value at any other positions.

- The gravitational force F acting on a mass m in the presence of another mass M is the negative of the potential energy gradient (refer to page 156). Similarly, the gravitational field strength g is the negative of the gravitational potential gradient.

$$F = -\frac{dU}{dr} \quad \text{and} \quad g = -\frac{d\phi}{dr}$$

- The variation of ϕ with distance r from the Earth's surface is illustrated in Fig 7.9.

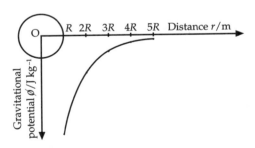

Fig 7.9 Graph of ϕ against r

177

A satellite of mass m is lifted to an orbit of radius r from the surface of the Earth (Fig 7.10). If the radius of the Earth is R and its mass is M, show that the change in gravitational potential is

$$\Delta U = GMm\left(\frac{1}{R} - \frac{1}{r}\right)$$

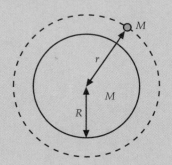

Fig 7.10

At a distance R from the centre of the Earth, the satellite has a gravitational potential energy of

$$U_{surface} = -\frac{GMm}{R}.$$

When the satellite is in orbit, the gravitational potential energy is

$$U_{orbit} = -\frac{GMm}{r}.$$

The change in gravitational potential energy is

$$\Delta U = U_{orbit} - U_{surface}$$

$$= -\frac{GMm}{r} - \left(-\frac{GMm}{R}\right)$$

$$= GMm\left(\frac{1}{R} - \frac{1}{r}\right)$$

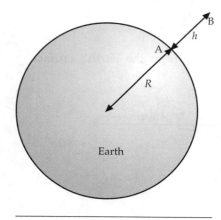

Fig 7.11

- The change in gravitational potential close to the Earth's surface can be obtained by considering a 1 kg mass placed at B, which is at a height h close to the Earth's surface (Fig 7.11).

The change in gravitational potential from A to B is given by:

$$\Delta\phi_{AB} = \phi_B - \phi_A$$

$$= -\frac{GM}{(R + h)} - \left(-\frac{GM}{R}\right)$$

$$= \frac{GM}{R} - \frac{GM}{(R + h)}$$

$$= \frac{GMh}{R(R + h)}$$

$$= \frac{GMh}{R^2\left(1 + \dfrac{h}{R}\right)}$$

If $h << R$; $R^2\left(1 + \dfrac{h}{R}\right) = R^2$

i.e. $\Delta\phi_{AB} = \dfrac{GMh}{R^2} = gh$

$\therefore \phi_B - \phi_A = gh$

178

- The change in gravitational potential energy close to the Earth's surface is:

$$U_B - U_A = mgh$$

Note that the above formula applies to objects near the Earth's surface where gravitational acceleration g is approximately constant.

A mass of 2 kg is at a point P, a height 3 m above the surface of the Earth. Taking the gravitational potential at the surface of the Earth to be zero, state
(a) the gravitational field strength at P,
(b) the gravitational potential at P,
(c) the gravitational force acting on the mass,
(d) the gravitational potential energy of the mass, given that $G = 6.67 \times 10^{-11}$ N m^2 kg^{-2}, $M_E = 6.0 \times 10^{24}$ kg and $R_E = 6.4 \times 10^6$ m.

Cambridge

(a) The gravitational field strength at P is given by,

$$g = \frac{GM_E}{(R_E + 3)^2}$$

$$= \frac{6.67 \times 10^{-11} \times 6.0 \times 10^{24}}{(6.4 \times 10^6 + 3)^2}$$

$$= 9.8 \text{ N kg}^{-1}$$

(b) The gravitational potential at P is given by,

$$\phi_P - \phi_S = gh$$

where ϕ_P is the gravitational potential at P and
ϕ_S is the gravitational potential at S, on the surface of the Earth.

Since $\phi_S = 0$, $\phi_P = gh$

$$= 9.8 \times 3$$
$$= 29.4 \text{ J kg}^{-1}$$

(c) The gravitational force acting on the mass is given by

$$F = \frac{GM_E m}{R_E{}^2}$$

$$= mg$$
$$= 2 \times 9.8$$
$$= 19.6 \text{ N}$$
$$= 20 \text{ N}$$

(d) The gravitational potential energy of the mass is given by

$$U_P = m\phi_P$$
$$= 2 \times 29.4$$
$$= 58.8 \text{ J}$$
$$= 59 \text{ J}$$

- The theoretical zero of the gravitational potential is defined as a point at infinity. This means that potential has its highest value at this point and potential is negative at other locations. As an object moves away from infinity, the potential decreases (i.e. becomes more negative). Sometimes the zero of the potential is assigned to the surface of the Earth to simplify calculations. This is perfectly permissible as the exact position of the theoretical zero is unimportant. This is because any change in potential between two points with respect to any arbitrarily assigned zero remains the same. This is illustrated in Fig 7.12.

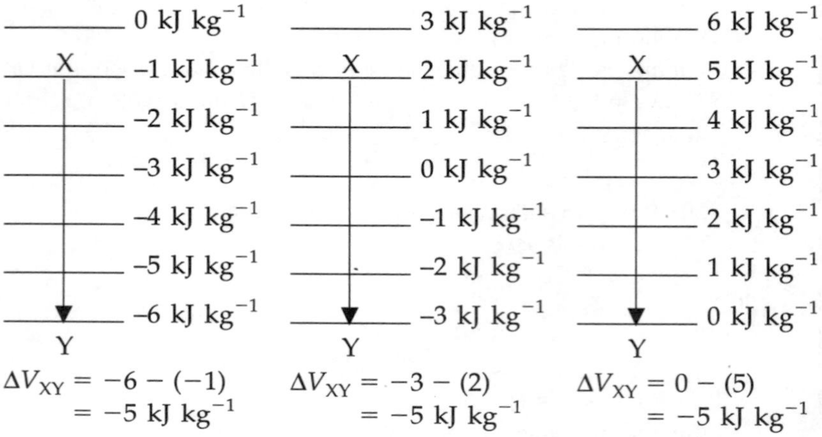

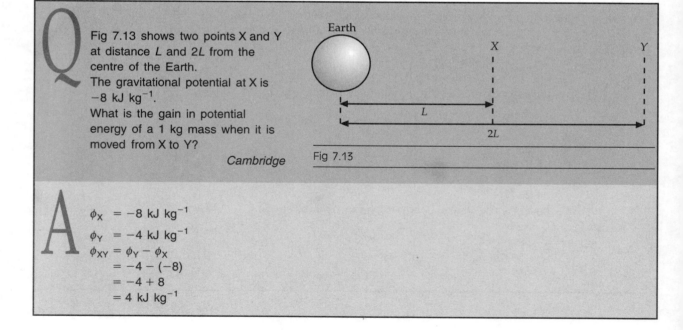

Fig 7.12

$\Delta V_{XY} = -6 - (-1)$
$= -5 \text{ kJ kg}^{-1}$

$\Delta V_{XY} = -3 - (2)$
$= -5 \text{ kJ kg}^{-1}$

$\Delta V_{XY} = 0 - (5)$
$= -5 \text{ kJ kg}^{-1}$

Q Fig 7.13 shows two points X and Y at distance L and $2L$ from the centre of the Earth.
The gravitational potential at X is -8 kJ kg^{-1}.
What is the gain in potential energy of a 1 kg mass when it is moved from X to Y?

Cambridge

Fig 7.13

A
$\phi_X = -8 \text{ kJ kg}^{-1}$
$\phi_Y = -4 \text{ kJ kg}^{-1}$
$\phi_{XY} = \phi_Y - \phi_X$
$= -4 - (-8)$
$= -4 + 8$
$= 4 \text{ kJ kg}^{-1}$

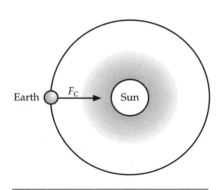

Fig 7.14

The Period of the Earth

- The force F_c which provides the centripetal acceleration $R\omega^2$ that keeps the Earth in circular motion round the Sun (Fig 7.14) is given by

$$F_c = m_E R\omega^2$$

where m_E is the mass of the Earth,
R is the radius of circular motion and
ω is the angular velocity.

- The centripetal force is due to the gravitational force of attraction exerted on the Earth by the Sun. It is given by Newtons Law of Universal Gravitation.

$$F_g = G\frac{m_E m_S}{R^2}$$

where G is the Universal constant and
m_S is the mass of the Sun

As $F_g = F_c$

$$G\frac{m_E m_S}{R^2} = m_E R\omega^2$$

As $\omega = \dfrac{2\pi}{T}$, where T is the period of revolution of the Earth, we have

$$G\frac{m_E m_S}{R^2} = m_E R\left(\frac{2\pi}{T}\right)^2$$

$$\therefore T^2 = \left(\frac{4\pi^2}{Gm_S}\right)R^3$$

or $T^2 \propto R^3$

- This is known better as Kepler's third law which states that the squares of the periods of revolution of the planets are directly proportional to the cubes of their mean distances from the Sun. From the above equation, it should be noted that the period is independent of the mass that is orbiting round the Sun.

Orbits Round the Earth

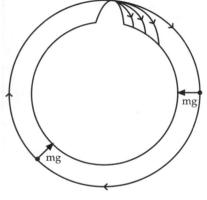

Fig 7.15

- An object projected horizontally near the Earth's surface follows a parabolic trajectory (Fig 7.15). As the velocity of projection increases, there will be an occasion in which the trajectory follows the curvature of the Earth's surface. If air resistance is negligible, the object will orbit round the Earth and will never meet the Earth's surface.

- The force near the surface is the weight mg.

Hence $\dfrac{mv^2}{r} = mg$

where v is the velocity required for the object to go into orbit.

$\therefore v = \sqrt{rg}$

Taking $r = 6.4 \times 10^6$ m and $g = 9.81$ m s^{-2},

$$v = \sqrt{6.4 \times 10^6 \times 9.81}$$
$$= 7\,923.6 \text{ m s}^{-1}$$
$$\approx 8.0 \times 10^3 \text{ m s}^{-1}$$

Geostationary Orbit

- If the rotational speed of a satellite in its orbit is the same as the rotational speed of the Earth as it turns about its axis, the satellite is said to be in geostationary orbit and will exhibit the following characteristics:
  (a) It will revolve in the same direction as the Earth.
  (b) It will rotate with the same period of rotation as that of the Earth.
  (c) It will move directly above the Earth's equator.
  (d) The centre of a geostationary orbit is at the centre of the Earth.

Q A satellite orbits the Earth with uniform circular motion of period 24 h, so that it is always directly above the same point on the Earth.
(a) Explain why the orbit of the satellite must lie in the plane that includes the centre of the Earth. (Assume that the Earth is a uniform sphere.)
(b) Find the radius of the orbit.
  [$g = 9.81$ m s^{-2}; 24 h $= 8.64 \times 10^4$ s; radius of Earth $= 6.4 \times 10^6$ m]

Cambridge

A (a) The centripetal force is due to the gravitational force exerted by the Earth on the satellite. This force is directed towards the centre of the Earth if the Earth is a uniform sphere. The geostationary orbit must therefore lie in a plane that includes the centre of the Earth.
(b) As gravitational force = centripetal force

$$\frac{GMm}{r^2} = mr\omega^2$$

where M is the mass of the Earth,
  m is the mass of the satellite,
  r is the radius of the orbit and
  ω is the angular velocity of the satellite.

Rearranging,

$$\frac{GMm}{r^3} = m\omega^2 \text{———————— Equation (1)}$$

On the Earths surface,

$$\frac{GMm}{r_E^2} = mg \text{———————— Equation (2)}$$

Divide Equation (2) by Equation (1)

$$\frac{\frac{GMm}{r_E^2}}{\frac{GMm}{r^3}} = \frac{mg}{m\omega^2}$$

i.e. $\dfrac{r^3}{r_E^2} = \dfrac{g}{\omega^2}$

or $r = \sqrt[3]{\dfrac{gr_E^2}{\omega^2}}$

Since $g = 9.81$ m s^{-2}; $r_E = 6.4 \times 10^6$ m and $\omega = \dfrac{2\pi}{8.64 \times 10^4} = 7.27 \times 10^{-5}$ rad s^{-1}

$$\therefore r = \sqrt[3]{\frac{9.81 \times (6.4 \times 10^6)^2}{(7.27 \times 10^{-5})^2}}$$

$$= 4.236 \times 10^7 \text{ m}$$
$$\approx 4.2 \times 10^7 \text{ m}$$
$$= 4.2 \times 10^4 \text{ km}$$

Kinetic Energy of a Satellite

- Consider a satellite of mass m orbiting the Earth of mass M with a radius r and speed v.

  The kinetic energy of the satellite is

  $$K E = \frac{1}{2}mv^2 \text{_____ (1)}$$

  as $\dfrac{mv^2}{r} = \dfrac{GMm}{r^2}$ (centripetal force = gravitational force)

  $$v^2 = \frac{GM}{r}$$

  Substituting for v^2 in equation (1), the kinetic energy of the orbiting satellite is given by

  $$K E = \frac{1}{2}\frac{GMm}{r}$$

183

Total Energy of a Satellite

- The total energy of the above satellite (T) is the sum of the kinetic energy and potential energies of the satellite.

  Hence $T = K E + P E$

  $$= \frac{1}{2}\frac{GMm}{r} - \frac{GMm}{r}$$

  $$T = -\frac{GMm}{2r}$$

- The escape velocity (v_{min}) from a point in the gravitational field is the minimum velocity required to project a mass m to infinity in outer space.

  For m to reach infinity,

  K E of m at infinity ≥ 0 and P E of m at infinity $= 0$

  i.e. Total energy $E = K E + P E \geq 0$

  $$\therefore \frac{1}{2}mv^2 - \frac{GMm}{r} \geq 0$$

  where v is the velocity of projection and

  r is the distance from the Earth's centre to mass m.

  Hence $v_{min} = \sqrt{\dfrac{2GM}{r}}$

  or $v_{min} = \sqrt{2gr}$

Certain meteorites (tektites) found on Earth have an composition identical with that of lunar granite. It is thought that they may be debris from a volcanic eruption on the Moon. Fig 7.16 which is not to scale, shows how the gravitational potential between the surface of the Moon and the surface of the Earth varies along the line of centres. At the point P the gravitational potential is a maximum.

(a) By considering the separate contributions of Earth and Moon to the gravitational potential, explain qualitatively why the graph has a maximum and why the curve is asymmetrical.

(b) State how the resultant gravitational force on the tektite at any point between the Moon and the Earth could be deduced from Fig 7.16.

(c) When a tektite is at P the gravitational forces on it due to Moon and Earth are F_M and F_E respectively. State the relation which applies between F_M and F_E. Hence find the value of $\dfrac{x}{y}$, where x and y are the distances of P from the centre of the Moon and the centre of the Earth respectively.

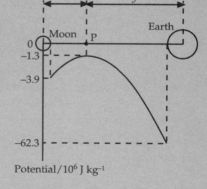

Fig 7.16

(d) If a tektite is to reach the Earth, it must be projected from the volcano on the Moon with a certain minimum speed v_0. Making use of appropriate values from Fig 7.16, find this speed. Explain your reasoning.

(e) Discuss very briefly whether a tektite will reach the Earth's surface with a speed less than, equal to or greater than the speed of projection. (Neglect atmospheric resistance)

(Mass of Moon $= 7.4 \times 10^{22}$ kg; mass of Earth $= 6.0 \times 10^{24}$ kg).

Cambridge

A (a)

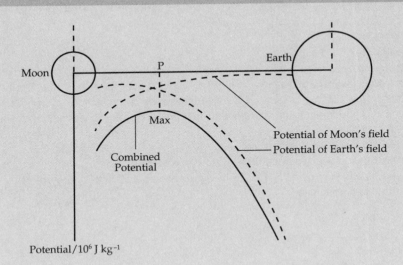

The separate potentials of the Earth's and the Moon's field are illustrated above.

The combined potential is the algebraic sum of the separate potentials. This gives a maximum potential at P. Since the separate curves are asymmetrical due to the different masses of the two bodies, the combined potential curve is also asymmetrical.

(b) Since $F = -\dfrac{dU}{dr}$

$$= -\frac{d(m\phi)}{dr}$$

$$= -m\frac{d\phi}{dr}$$

The resultant gravitational force on the tektite can be obtained by the product of the mass of the tektite and the gradient of the graph at a point.

185

(c) As $g = 0$ at P, the resultant gravitational force $= 0$
i.e. $F_M = F_E$

$$\frac{GM_M m}{x^2} = \frac{GM_E m}{y^2}$$

$$\therefore \frac{x}{y} = \sqrt{\frac{M_M}{M_E}}$$

$$= \sqrt{\frac{7.4 \times 10^{22}}{6.0 \times 10^{24}}}$$

$$= 0.11$$

(d) For a tektite to reach the Earth, the speed of projection from the volcano must be high enough for it to move past P. Once across this point, gravitational force from the Earth will accelerate the tektite to the Earth's surface. The minimum speed of projection, v_o, will cause the tektite to just reach P. The kinetic energy is zero at this point. By the conservation of energy,
$KE_V + PE_V = KE_P + PE_P$
KE_V is the kinetic energy at the volcano.
PE_V is the gravitational potential energy at the volcano.
KE_P is the kinetic energy at P. PE_P is the gravitational potential energy at P.
If m is the mass of tektite,

$$\frac{1}{2} m v_o^2 - 3.9 \times 10^6 m = 0 - 1.3 \times 10^6 m$$

$$\therefore v_o = \sqrt{2(3.9 - 1.3) \times 10^6}$$
$$= 2.28 \times 10^3 \text{ m s}^{-1}$$
$$\approx 2.3 \times 10^3 \text{ m s}^{-1}$$

(e) By the principle of conservation of energy

$$\frac{1}{2} m v_E^2 - 62.3m = \frac{1}{2} m v_o^2 - 3.9m$$

where v_E is the speed of tektite at the Earth's surface

$$\therefore \frac{1}{2} m v_E^2 = \frac{1}{2} m v_o^2 + 58.4m$$

i.e. $v_E > v_o$
The speed of tektite reaching the Earth's surface is greater than the speed of projection from the volcano.

Q

(a) Fig 7.17 shows part of the orbit of a satellite round the Earth.

The mass M of the Earth is 6.0×10^{24} kg. It may be assumed that the gravitational field of the Earth is the same as that of a point mass M situated at the centre of the Earth.

(i) On Fig 7.17 show, by means of an arrow, the direction of the gravitational force on the satellite.

(ii) Explain why the satellite does not move in the direction of the gravitational force.

(iii) Show that v, the linear speed of the satellite in its orbit of radius R, is given by the expression

$$v = \sqrt{\frac{GM}{R}},$$

where G is the gravitational constant.

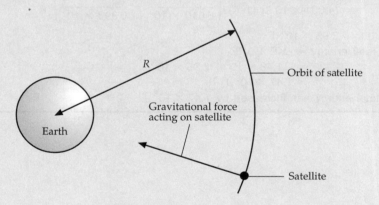

Fig 7.17

(b) The satellite is orbiting the Earth with a radius R of 6610 km at a speed v of 7 780 m s^{-1}. The satellite is boosted into higher orbit of radius 6 890 km. Show that the speed of the satellite in the new orbit is 7 620 m s^{-1}.

(c) (i) In (b), the satellite, of mass 120 kg, moves from one orbit to another. Using the data in (b), calculate, for this satellite, the change in
    1. kinetic energy,
    2. gravitational potential energy,
    3. total energy.

(ii) State whether this change in total energy is an increase or a decrease.

Cambridge

A

(a) (i)

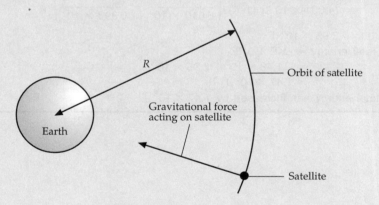

(ii) The satellite has a momentum that is perpendicular to the direction of the gravitational force.

(iii) $\dfrac{mv^2}{R} = \dfrac{GMm}{R^2}$

$\therefore v = \sqrt{\dfrac{GM}{R}}$

187

(b) $v = \sqrt{\dfrac{GM}{R}}$

$7\,780 = \sqrt{\dfrac{GM}{6\,610 \times 10^3}}$

$GM = 4.001 \times 10^{14}$

Speed of satellite in new orbit $v = \sqrt{\dfrac{4.001 \times 10^{14}}{6\,890 \times 10^3}}$

$= 7\,620.3$

$\approx 7\,620 \text{ m s}^{-1}$

(c) (i) 1.) Change in Kinetic Energy, $\Delta KE = \dfrac{1}{2} mv_2^2 - \dfrac{1}{2} mv_1^2$

where v_2 is the speed at the higher orbit and
v_1 is the speed at the lower orbit

$\Delta KE = \dfrac{1}{2} m (v_2^2 - v_1^2)$

$= \dfrac{1}{2}(120)(7\,620^2 - 7\,780^2)$

$= -1.48 \times 10^8 \text{ J}$

2.) Change in potential energy, $\Delta PE = -\dfrac{GMm}{R_H} - \left(-\dfrac{GMm}{R_L}\right)$

where R_H is the radius of the higher orbit and
R_L is the radius of the lower orbit.

$\Delta PE = GMm \left(\dfrac{1}{R_L} - \dfrac{1}{R_H}\right)$

$= (4.001 \times 10^{14})(120)\left(\dfrac{1}{6\,610 \times 10^3} - \dfrac{1}{6\,890 \times 10^3}\right)$

$= 2.95 \times 10^8 \text{ J}$

3.) Total energy $= \Delta KE + \Delta PE$

$= -1.48 \times 10^8 + 2.95 \times 10^8$

$= 1.47 \times 10^8 \text{ J}$

(ii) The total energy has increased by 1.47×10^8 J.

E x e r c i s e 7

Multiple Choice Questions

1   The gravitational constant G has the SI unit
   A $m\,s^{-2}$ **B** $N\,m^{-2}\,kg^{-2}$
   C $m^3\,kg^{-1}\,s^{-2}$ **D** $m^2\,kg^{-2}$

2   Assuming that the Earth is spherical and of radius r, its mean density is

   A $\dfrac{4\pi rG}{3g}$ **B** $\dfrac{3rG}{4\pi G}$

   C $\dfrac{4\pi rg}{3G}$ **D** $\dfrac{3g}{4\pi rG}$

3   The Earth may be considered to be a uniform sphere of mass M and radius R. Which one of the following equations correctly relates the universal gravitational constant G to the acceleration of free fall g at the surface of the Earth?

   A $G = \dfrac{gM}{R^2}$ **B** $G = \dfrac{R^2}{gM}$

   C $G = \dfrac{gR^2}{M}$ **D** $G = \dfrac{M}{gR^2}$

4   A satellite of mass m is in circular orbit of radius r about the Earth, mass M, and remains at a vertical height h above the Earth's surface. Taking the zero of the gravitational potential to be at an infinite distance from the Earth, what is the gravitational potential energy of the satellite?

   A mgh **B** $-mgh$
   C $\dfrac{-GMm}{r}$ **D** $\dfrac{-GMm}{2r}$

5   Which one of the following diagrams shows the variation of gravitational force F on a point mass and gravitational potential energy U of the mass at a distance r from another point mass?

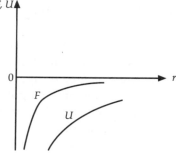

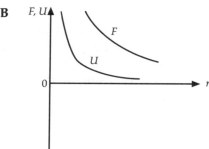

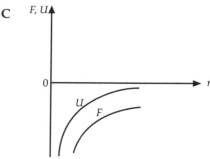

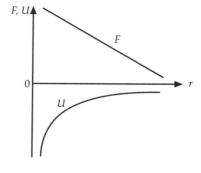

189

6   On the ground the gravitational force on a satellite is W. What is the gravitational force on the satellite when at a height $\frac{R}{50}$, where R is the radius of the Earth?
    A   1.04W B   1.02W
    C   1.00W D   0.96W

7   X and Y are two points at respective distances R and $2R$ from the centre of the Earth, where R is greater than the radius of the Earth. The gravitational potential at X is -800 kJ kg^{-1}. When a 1 kg mass is taken from X to Y, the work done on the mass is
    A -400 kJ   B -200 kJ
    C $+200$ kJ   D $+400$ kJ

8   A 20 kg mass is situated 4 m above the Earth's surface. Taking g as 10 m s^{-2}, what are the gravitational field strength and gravitational force acting on the mass?

	gravitational field strength/N kg^{-1}	gravitational force/N
A	0.5	10
B	10	10
C	10	200
D	40	200

9   An experimental satellite is found to have a weight W when assembled before launching from a rocket site. It is placed in a circular orbit at a height $h = 6R$ above the surface of the Earth (of radius R).
    What is the gravitational force acting on the satellite whilst in orbit?
    A $\dfrac{W}{6}$ B $\dfrac{W}{7}$
    C $\dfrac{W}{36}$ D $\dfrac{W}{49}$

10 The gravitational field strength at a point P on the Earth's surface is numerically equal to
    A   the acceleration of free fall at P.
    B   the change in potential energy per unit distance from P.
    C   the force acting on any body placed at P.
    D   the work done in bringing unit mass from infinity to P.

11 The Earth may be taken to be a uniform sphere of radius r and density ρ.
    How is the gravitational field strength g at its surface related to these quantities and to the gravitational constant G?

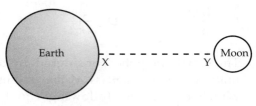

    A $g = \dfrac{G\rho}{r^2}$ B $g = \dfrac{3G}{4\pi r \rho}$

    C $g = \dfrac{4\pi r \rho G}{3}$ D $g = \dfrac{4\pi r^2 \rho G}{3}$

12 The diagram (not to scale) represents the relative positions of the Earth and the Moon.

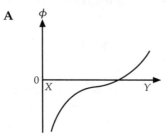

    The line XY joins the surface of the Earth to the surface of the Moon.
    Which graph represents the variation of gravitational potential ϕ along the line XY?

A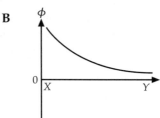

B

C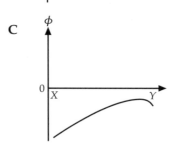

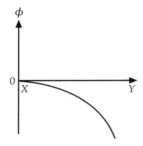

13 Which statement about geostationary orbits is false?

A A geostationary orbit must be directly above the equator.

B All satellites in geostationary orbits must have the same mass.

C The period of a geostationary orbit must be 24 hours.

D There is only one possible radius for a geostationary orbit.

14 Outside of a uniform sphere of mass M, the gravitational field strength is the same as that of a point mass M at the centre of the sphere. The Earth may be taken to be a uniform sphere of radius r. The gravitational field strength at its surface is g.

What is the gravitational field strength at a height h above the ground?

A $\dfrac{gr^2}{(r + h)^2}$ B $\dfrac{gr}{(r + h)}$

C $\dfrac{g(r + h)}{r}$ D $\dfrac{g(r + h)^2}{r^2}$

15 A satellite of mass 50 kg moves from a point where the gravitational potential due to the Earth is -20 MJ kg^{-1}, to another point where the gravitational potential is -60 MJ kg^{-1}.

In which direction does the satellite move and what is its change in potential energy?

A closer to the Earth and a loss of 2000 MJ of potential energy

B closer to the Earth and a loss of 40 MJ of potential energy

C further from the Earth and a gain of 2000 MJ of potential energy

D further from the Earth and a gain of 40 MJ of potential energy

Structured Questions

1 Values for the gravitational potential due to the Earth are given in the table below.

Distance from the Earth's surface/m	Gravitational potential/MJ kg^{-1}
0	-62.72
390 000	-59.12
400 000	-59.03
410 000	-58.94
Infinity	0

(i) If a satellite of mass 700 kg falls from a height of 400 000 m to the Earth's surface, how much potential energy does it lose?

(ii) Deduce a value for the Earth's gravitational field at a height of 400 000 m.

2 (a) Give an expression for *Newton's law of Gravitation*, explaining the symbols you use.

(b) Show that g, the gravitational field strength at height h above the surface of a uniform planet of mass M and radius R, is given by

$$g = \frac{GM}{(R + h)^2}$$

(c) Information related to the Earth and the Moon is given below.

$$\frac{\text{Radius of Earth}}{\text{Radius of Moon}} = 3.7$$

$$\frac{\text{Mass of Earth}}{\text{Mass of Moon}} = 81$$

Distance of Moon from Earth $= 3.84 \times 10^8$ m

Gravitational field strength due to the Earth at its surface $= 9.8$ N kg^{-1}

(i) Using these data, calculate the gravitational field strength due to the Moon at its surface.

(ii) There is a point on the line between the Earth and the Moon at which their combined gravitational field strength is zero. Calculate the distance between this point and the centre of the Earth.

191

3 (a) Explain how an object travelling in a circle with constant speed has an acceleration. In which direction is this acceleration?

(b) A satellite P of mass 2400 kg is placed in a geostationary orbit at a distance 4.23×10^7 m from the centre of the Earth.

(i) Explain what is meant by the term *geostationary orbit*.

(ii) Calculate
1. the angular velocity of the satellite,
2. the speed of the satellite,
3. the acceleration of the satellite,
4. the force of attraction between the Earth and the satellite,
5. the mass of the Earth.

(c) Explain why a geostationary satellite
(i) must be place vertically above the equator,
(ii) must move from west to east.

(d) Why is a satellite in a geostationary orbit often used for telecommunications?

4 (a) (i) Define *gravitational field strength*.
(ii) State a unit for gravitational field strength.
(iii) The gravitational field strength near the surface of the Earth is also known as the acceleration of free fall. Use base units to check that the unit of gravitational field strength is the same as that of acceleration.

(b) (i) State an equation to represent Newton's law of gravitation, and explain the symbols used.
(ii) Use Newton's law of gravitation and the definition of gravitational field strength to derive an expression for the gravitational field strength g at a distance r from a point mass M.

(iii) At any point above the surface of the Earth, the Earth may be assumed to be a point mass situated at its centre. Explain why the acceleration of free fall is approximately constant between the Earth's surface and a point 1000 m above it.

(c) The graph below shows the variation with time t of the distance d fallen from rest by an object in a vacuum near the Earth's surface.

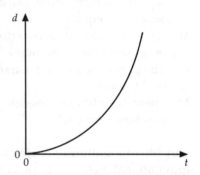

(i) Explain how it is possible to deduce from the graph that the object is undergoing accelerated motion.
(ii) Copy the graph and draw a line on it to represent the variation with time t of distance d when the object is falling from rest *through air* at the same location on the Earth's surface. Label the line A.

(d) The potential in the gravitational field of point mass decreases with decreasing distance from the mass. In the electric field of a point charge, electric potential may increase or decrease with decreasing distance from the charge. Explain this difference.

192

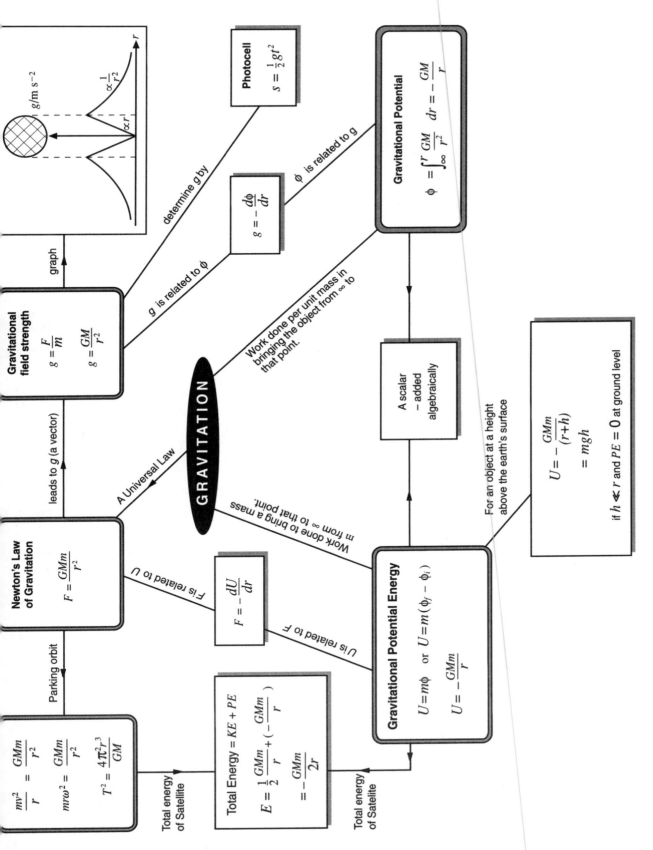

GRAVITATION

Gravitational field strength

$g = \dfrac{F}{m}$

$g = \dfrac{GM}{r^2}$

graph — $g/\text{m s}^{-2}$, $\propto r^1$, $\propto \dfrac{1}{r^2}$, r

determine g by

Photocell

$s = \tfrac{1}{2}gt^2$

g is related to ϕ

$g = -\dfrac{d\phi}{dr}$

ϕ is related to g

Gravitational Potential

$\phi = \displaystyle\int_{\infty}^{r} \dfrac{GM}{r^2}\, dr = -\dfrac{GM}{r}$

Work done per unit mass in bringing the object from ∞ to that point.

A scalar – added algebraically

A Universal Law

Work done to bring a mass m from ∞ to that point.

Newton's Law of Gravitation

$F = \dfrac{GMm}{r^2}$

leads to g (a vector)

F is related to U

$F = -\dfrac{dU}{dr}$

U is related to F

Gravitational Potential Energy

$U = m\phi \quad$ or $\quad U = m(\phi_f - \phi_i)$

$U = -\dfrac{GMm}{r}$

For an object at a height above the earth's surface

$U = -\dfrac{GMm}{(r+h)}$

$= mgh$

if $h \ll r$ and $PE = 0$ at ground level

Parking orbit

$\dfrac{mv^2}{r} = \dfrac{GMm}{r^2}$

$mr\omega^2 = \dfrac{GMm}{r^2}$

$T^2 = \dfrac{4\pi^2 r^3}{GM}$

Total energy of Satellite

Total Energy = KE + PE

$E = \tfrac{1}{2}\dfrac{GMm}{r} + \left(-\dfrac{GMm}{r}\right)$

$= -\dfrac{GMm}{2r}$

Total energy of Satelite

193

8 Motion in a Circle

KINEMATICS OF UNIFORM CIRCULAR MOTION

CENTRIPETAL ACCELERATION

CENTRIPETAL FORCE

Syllabus Objectives

In this chapter you should be able to:
- express angular displacement in radians.
- understand and use the concept of angular velocity to solve problems.
- recall and use $v = r\omega$ to solve problems.
- describe qualitatively motion in a curved path due to a perpendicular force, and understand the centripetal acceleration in the case of uniform motion in a circle.
- recall and use centripetal acceleration $a = r\omega^2$, $a = \dfrac{v^2}{r}$.
- recall and use centripetal force $F = mr\omega^2$, $F = \dfrac{mv^2}{r}$.

KINEMATICS OF UNIFORM CIRCULAR MOTION

- Uniform circular motion of a particle about the axis of rotation can be described by the angular position (θ) of a reference line with respect to the x-axis (Fig 8.1).

$$\theta = \frac{s}{r} \text{ (radian measure)}$$

s is the length of arc.
r is the radius of the circular motion.

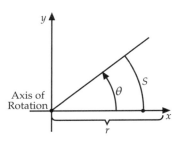

Fig 8.1 Angular position

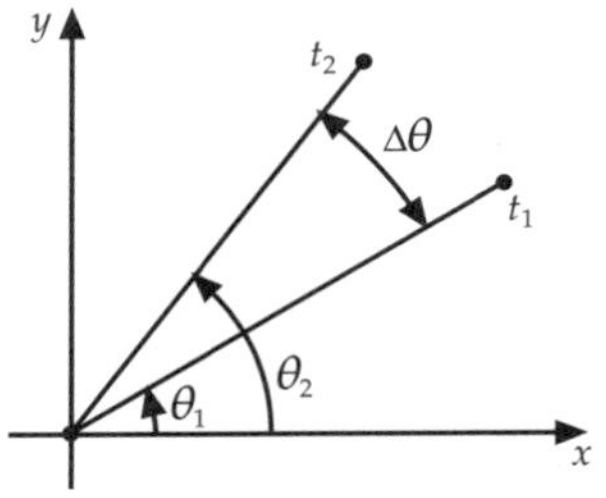

Fig 8.2 Angular displacement

- If the particle changes its angular position of the reference line from θ_1 to θ_2 (Fig 8.2), the angular displacement $\Delta\theta$ is given by
$$\Delta\theta = \theta_2 - \theta_1$$
$\Delta\theta$ is positive if the motion is anticlockwise.
$\Delta\theta$ is negative if the motion is clockwise.

- Average angular velocity is the total displacement over the time taken for the change in angular displacement.

$$<\omega> = \frac{\theta_2 - \theta_1}{t_2 - t_1}$$

$$= \frac{\Delta\theta}{\Delta t}$$

- Instantaneous angular velocity is the rate of change of angular displacement at a particular instant.

$$\omega = \lim_{t\to 0}\left(\frac{\Delta\theta}{\Delta t}\right)$$

$$= \frac{d\theta}{dt}$$

- The angular velocity at any point on a rigid body will be a constant. Consider a rigid body pivoted at O and rotating in an anticlockwise direction. Two points A and B on the body has angular positions θ_A and θ_B respectively (Fig 8.3).
θ_A is given by
$$\theta_A = \theta_B + \alpha \quad \text{where } \alpha \text{ is a constant.}$$
Differentiating with respect to t, we have

$$\frac{d\theta_A}{dt} = \frac{d\theta_B}{dt} + \frac{d\alpha}{dt}$$

$$\omega_A = \omega_B$$

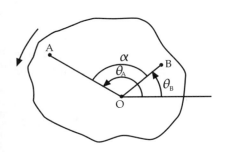

Fig 8.3 Rotation of a rigid body

195

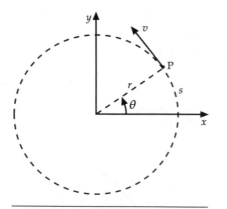

Fig 8.4 Particle P moves along the arc of a circle

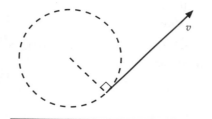

Fig 8.5 Tangential velocity

Hence the angular velocities of all the particles in a rotating rigid body are the same.

- When a rigid body rotates about an axis, every particle in the body moves in a circle. We can describe that particle with linear variables such as displacement (s), velocity (v) or angular variables such as angular position (θ) or angular velocity (w). Consider a particle P moving through a distance s along the arc of a circle when it rotates through an angle θ (Fig 8.4).

$$s = r\theta$$

Differentiating with respect to t

$$\frac{ds}{dt} = r\,\frac{d\theta}{dt}$$

$$v = r\omega$$

where v is the tangential velocity and
ω is the instantaneous angular velocity.

- The advantage of using the angular description for rotational motion is that angular variables are the same for all particles in a rotating rigid body. Hence each particle will have the same period T and the same angular velocity ω given by $\omega = \dfrac{2\pi}{T}$.

- Describing uniform circular motion
  The following terms are commonly used to describe uniform circular motion.
  (a) Tangential velocity (v) refers to the linear velocity of a point moving in a circle. It is directed tangentially to the circular path (Fig 8.5).

  $$v = r\omega$$

  $$\text{Also } v = \frac{2\pi r}{T}$$

  (b) Angular velocity (ω) is the rate of change of angular displacement.

  $$\omega = \frac{2\pi}{T}$$

  (c) One revolution of an object corresponds to the angular displacement of 2π radians
  (d) The period (T) of an object in circular motion is the time taken for one complete revolution.
  (e) Frequency (f) is the number of revolutions or rotations completed in one second. Common units used are hertz (Hz) or revolution per second or revolutions per minute (rpm).

  $$1 \text{ Hz} = 1 \text{ rev/s}$$

  The word 'revolution' is not a unit. Hence the SI unit for frequency is written as s^{-1}

Also $f = \dfrac{1}{T}$ or $T = \dfrac{1}{f}$

and $f = \dfrac{\omega}{2\pi}$ or $w = 2\pi f$

- Some examples of conversion are illustrated below.

(a) Convert 1800° to radians.

$$1800° = (1800 \ \cancel{\text{deg}})\left(\frac{\pi \ \text{rad}}{180 \ \cancel{\text{deg}}}\right)$$

$$= 31.4 \ \text{rad}$$
$$\approx 31 \ \text{rad}$$

(b) Convert 1.2 radians to degrees.

$$1.2 \ \text{radians} = (1.2 \ \cancel{\text{rad}})\left(\frac{180 \ \text{deg}}{\pi \ \cancel{\text{rad}}}\right)$$

$$= 68.8°$$
$$\approx 69°$$

(c) Convert 900 rpm to rad/s.

$$900 \ \text{rpm} = \left(900 \ \frac{\cancel{\text{rev}}}{\cancel{\text{min}}}\right)\left(\frac{1 \ \cancel{\text{min}}}{60 \ \text{s}}\right)\left(\frac{2\pi \ \text{rad}}{1 \ \cancel{\text{rev}}}\right)$$

$$= 94.2 \ \text{rad/s}$$
$$\approx 94 \ \text{rad/s}$$

(d) Convert 20 rad/s to rev/min.

$$20 \ \text{rad/s} = \left(20 \ \frac{\cancel{\text{rad}}}{\cancel{\text{s}}}\right)\left(\frac{60 \ \cancel{\text{s}}}{1 \ \text{min}}\right)\left(\frac{1 \ \text{rev}}{2\pi \ \cancel{\text{rad}}}\right)$$

$$= 191 \ \text{rev/min}$$

A simple pendulum of length 40.0 cm swings through an arc of 10.0 cm as shown in Fig 8.6. Find the angle θ in radians and in degrees.

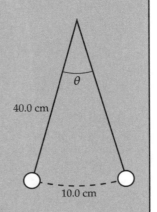

Fig 8.6

197

A Since $s = r\theta$

$$\theta = \frac{s}{r}$$

$$= \frac{10.0}{40.0}$$

$$= 0.250 \text{ rad}$$

$$\theta \text{ in degrees} = (0.250 \text{ rad})\left(\frac{360°}{2\pi \text{ rad}}\right)$$

$$= 14.3°$$

Q The minute hand of a large clock is 3.0 m long.
What is its mean angular speed?

A The period of the minute hand T is (60×60) s.

$$\therefore \omega = \frac{2\pi}{T}$$

$$= \frac{2\pi}{60 \times 60}$$

$$= 1.7 \times 10^{-3} \text{ rad s}^{-1}$$

Q The radius of the circular orbit of an electron in a hydrogen atom is 5.0×10^{-11} m. If the period of motion is 1.5×10^{-16} s, calculate
(a) the frequency of rotation,
(b) the angular velocity,
(c) the linear speed.

A
(a) $f = \frac{1}{T}$

$$= \frac{1}{1.5 \times 10^{-16}}$$

$$= 6.67 \times 10^{15} \text{ Hz}$$

$$= 6.7 \times 10^{15} \text{ Hz}$$

(b) $\omega = 2\pi f$

$$= 2\pi (6.67 \times 10^{15})$$

$$= 4.19 \times 10^{16} \text{ rad s}^{-1}$$

$$= 4.2 \times 10^{16} \text{ rad s}^{-1}$$

(c) $v = r\omega$

$$= (5.0 \times 10^{-11})(4.19 \times 10^{16})$$

$$= 2.1 \times 10^{6} \text{ m s}^{-1}$$

CENTRIPETAL ACCELERATION

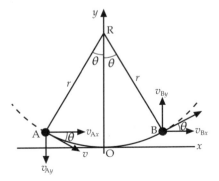

Fig 8.7 Motion of a particle along the arc of a circle

- Consider a particle moving with constant speed v in uniform circular motion of radius r. Fig 8.7 shows the particle at A moving to B along the arc AOB in a time interval of Δt.

The x and y components of v at A and B are as follows.

$$v_{Ax} = v \cos \theta; \quad v_{Bx} = v \cos \theta$$
$$v_{Ay} = -v \sin \theta; \quad v_{By} = v \sin \theta$$

The change in speed along the x-axis is given by

$$\Delta v_x = v_{Bx} - v_{Ax}$$
$$= v \cos \theta - v \cos \theta$$
$$= 0$$

Hence the x-component of the average acceleration is

$$a_x = \frac{\Delta v_x}{\Delta t}$$
$$= 0$$

The change in speed along the y-axis is given by

$$\Delta v_y = v_{By} - v_{Ay}$$
$$= v \sin \theta - (-v \sin \theta)$$
$$= 2v \sin \theta$$

Hence the y-component of the average acceleration is

$$a_y = \frac{\Delta v_y}{\Delta t}$$
$$= \frac{2v \sin \theta}{\Delta t} \qquad\qquad (1)$$

The time Δt for the particle to move from A to B is given by Δt, where

$$\Delta t = \frac{\text{arc length AOB}}{v}$$
$$= \frac{2\theta r}{v}$$

Substituting Δt into equation (1), we have

$$<a_y> = \frac{2v \sin \theta}{2\theta r / v}$$
$$= \frac{v^2}{r} \left(\frac{\sin \theta}{\theta} \right)$$

As θ approaches zero, $\frac{\sin \theta}{\theta}$ has a limiting value of 1.

The average acceleration approaches the instantaneous acceleration at O as θ approaches zero. This acceleration is also called the centripetal acceleration. It is a vector. Its magnitude is given by

$$a = \frac{v^2}{r}$$
$$= r\omega^2 \text{ (centripetal acceleration)}$$

It is always directed towards R, the centre of circular motion.

Q A man stands on the Earth's equator. Find
(a) his angular velocity,
(b) his linear speed,
(c) his acceleration,
due to the rotation of the Earth about its axis.
[1 day = 8.6×10^4 s; radius of the Earth = 6.4×10^6 m]

Cambridge

A (a) Angular velocity $\omega = \dfrac{2\pi}{T}$

$$= \frac{2\pi}{8.6 \times 10^4}$$
$$= 7.306 \times 10^{-5}\ \text{rad s}^{-1}$$
$$= 7.3 \times 10^{-5}\ \text{rad s}^{-1}$$

(b) Linear speed $v = r\omega$
$$= (6.4 \times 10^6)\,(7.306 \times 10^{-5})$$
$$= 467.59\ \text{m s}^{-1}$$
$$= 470\ \text{m s}^{-1}$$

(c) Acceleration $a = \dfrac{v^2}{r}$

$$= \frac{(467.59)^2}{6.4 \times 10^6}$$
$$= 3.4 \times 10^{-2}\ \text{m s}^{-2}$$

Q When the hour hand rotates from 12 pm (noon) to 1 pm, the minute hand will be inclined to the hour hand at an angle of $\dfrac{1}{2}\pi$ radians on two occasions. Find these times.

A Figure 8.8 shows 2 positions in which the hour and minute hand are inclined at $\dfrac{1}{2}\pi$ radians to each other.

θ_1 and θ_2 are the angular displacements as indicated in the diagrams. ω_h and ω_m are the angular velocities of the hour hand and minute hand respectively.
In Fig 8.8(a), t_1 is the time taken for the hour hand and minute hand to rotate from the vertical to the positions indicated. Hence

$$\theta_1 = \omega_h t_1 \quad\text{———— equation (1)}$$

and $\quad \theta_1 + \dfrac{\pi}{2} = \omega_m t_1 \quad\text{———— equation (2)}$

Substituting θ_1 into equation (2) and solving for t_1,

$$t_1 = \frac{\dfrac{\pi}{2}}{\omega_m - \omega_h}$$

$$= \frac{\dfrac{\pi}{2}}{\dfrac{2\pi}{60} - \dfrac{2\pi}{12 \times 60}}$$

$$= 16.36\ \text{min}$$
$$= 16\ \text{min}$$

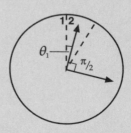

Fig 8.8a

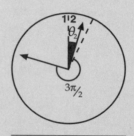

Fig 8.8b

200

Hence, the hour and minute hand will be inclined at $\frac{1}{2}\pi$ radian to each other at 12.16 pm.

In Fig 8.8b, t_2 is the time taken for the hour and minute hand to rotate from the vertical to the positions indicated. Hence

$$\theta_2 = \omega_h t_2 \quad\text{————————— equation (3)}$$

$$\text{and}\quad \theta_2 + \frac{3\pi}{2} = w_m t_2 \quad\text{————————— equation (4)}$$

Substituting θ_2 into equation (4) and solving for t_2,

$$t_2 = \frac{\dfrac{3\pi}{2}}{\omega_m - \omega_h}$$

$$= \frac{\dfrac{3\pi}{2}}{\dfrac{2\pi}{60} - \dfrac{2\pi}{12 \times 60}}$$

$$= 49.09 \text{ min}$$

$$= 49 \text{ min}$$

Hence the hour and minute hand will be inclined at $\frac{1}{2}\pi$ radians again at 12.49 pm.

CENTRIPETAL FORCE

- Any object moving with uniform circular motion has a centripetal acceleration directed towards the centre of the circular motion.

- From Newton's Second Law of motion, a force must be associated with the centripetal acceleration. This force is known as the centripetal force and is given by

$$F = ma_c$$
$$F = \frac{mv^2}{r}$$
$$= mr\omega^2$$

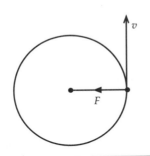

Fig 8.9 Centripetal force

- The centripetal force is perpendicular to the instantaneous velocity and directed towards the centre of the circular motion (Fig 8.9). Sudden removal of the force would allow the object to move along the tangent to the circular motion.

- The centripetal force may be due to a single force or a combination of several forces. In the latter case, the resultant is known as the **centripetal** force. **For circular motion, this resultant force must always be constant in magnitude.**

- The centripetal force does no work done on an object as it moves around a circle. This is because the force is perpendicular to the displacement of the object throughout the circular motion.

201

Q An object of mass 2.00 kg rotates at constant speed in a horizontal circle of radius 5.00 m. The time for one complete revolution is 3.00 s.
What is the magnitude of the resultant force acting on the object?

A Magnitude of the resultant force $= mr\omega^2$

$$= mr\left(\frac{2\pi}{T}\right)^2$$

$$= (2.00)(5.00)\left(\frac{2\pi}{3.00}\right)^2$$

$$= 43.9 \text{ N}$$

Conical Pendulum

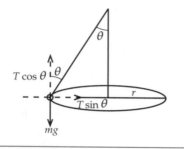

Fig 8.10   Conical Pendulum

- The weight of a conical pendulum is supported by the vertical component of the tension (Fig 8.10).
  Hence $T \cos \theta = mg$
  The centripetal force is contributed by the horizontal component of the tension.

  Hence $T \sin \theta = \dfrac{mv^2}{r}$

  For a conical pendulum, θ cannot be equal to 90° (i.e. string cannot be horizontal). This is because the vertical component of the tension T is required to balance the weight.

Q An aircraft flies with its wings tilted as shown in Fig 8.11 in order to fly in a horizontal circle of radius r. The aircraft has mass 4.00×10^4 kg and has a constant speed of 250 m s^{-1}.

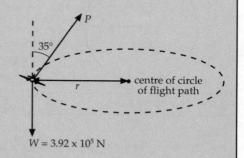

Fig 8.11

$W = 3.92 \times 10^5$ N

With the aircraft flying in this way, two forces acting on the aircraft in the vertical plane are the force P acting at an angle of 35° to the vertical and the weight W.

(a) State the vertical component of P for horizontal flight.
(b) Calculate P.
(c) Calculate the horizontal component of P.
(d) Use Newton's second law to determine the acceleration of the aircraft towards the centre of the circle.
(e) Calculate the radius r of the path of the aircraft's flight.

A

(a) Vertical component of $P = (4.00 \times 10^4)(9.81)$
$$= 3.92 \times 10^5 \text{ N}$$

(b) $P \cos 35° = 3.92 \times 10^5 \text{ N}$
$$P = \frac{3.92 \times 10^5}{\cos 35°}$$
$$= 4.785 \times 10^5 \text{ N}$$
$$\approx 4.79 \times 10^5 \text{ N}$$

(c) Horizontal component of $P = P \sin 35°$
$$= (4.785 \times 10^5) \sin 35°$$
$$= 2.744 \times 10^5 \text{ N}$$
$$\approx 2.74 \times 10^5 \text{ N}$$

(d) Using Newton's 2nd law,
$$ma = 2.744 \times 10^5$$
where a is the acceleration of the aircraft and m is the mass of the aircraft.
$$a = \frac{2.744 \times 10^5}{4.00 \times 10^4}$$
$$= 6.86 \text{ m s}^{-2}$$

(e) Given the constant speed $v = 250 \text{ m s}^{-1}$; r = radius
$$\frac{v^2}{r} = a$$
$$r = \frac{v^2}{a}$$
$$= \frac{(250)^2}{6.86}$$
$$= 9.11 \times 10^3 \text{ m}$$

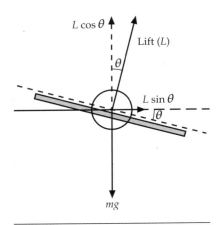

Fig 8.12 Forces acting on a plane in flight

Circular Motion of an Aeroplane

- The centripetal force required to turn an aeroplane is contributed by the horizontal component of the lift force L (Fig 8.12), i.e.

$$L \sin \theta = \frac{mv^2}{r} \quad\text{---------- equation (1)}$$

The weight is supported by the vertical component of the lift force (L), i.e.

$$L \cos \theta = mg \quad\text{---------- equation (2)}$$

Dividing equation (1) by (2)

$$\tan \theta = \frac{v^2}{rg}$$

203

A model airplane of mass 0.50 kg is attached to one end of a light inextensible cord of length 40 m and the other end firmly fixed to the ground. When the plane is airborne, the cord is taut and makes an angle of 70° to the vertical. The plane flies with constant speed of 30 m s^{-1} in a horizontal circle without tilting (Fig 8.13).

Fig 8.13

(a) Draw a free body diagram of all forces acting on the plane.
(b) Find (i) the angular velocity of the plane,
         (ii) the tension in the cord,
         (iii) the lift on the plane.

(a)

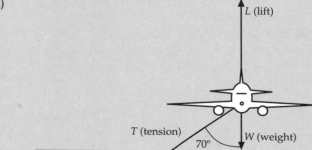

Fig 8.14a

(b) (i)

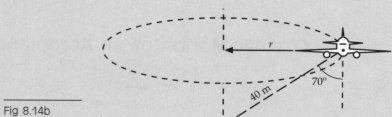

Fig 8.14b

Radius of circular motion $r = 40 \sin 70°$

Angular velocity $= \dfrac{v}{r}$

$$= \dfrac{30}{40 \sin 70°}$$

$$= 0.798$$

$$\approx 0.80 \text{ rad s}^{-1}$$

204

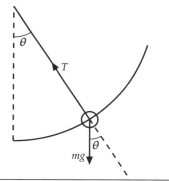

Fig 8.15 Motion along the arc of a vertical cricle

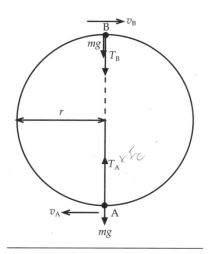

Fig 8.16 Motion in a vertical circle

Motion in a Vertical Circle

- An object of mass m tied to an inelastic string is moving in a vertical circle of radius r. Figure 8.15 shows the mass and the taut string inclined at an angle θ to the vertical. The forces acting on the mass m are the tension T and its weight mg.

- Resolving forces along the string
Resultant force = Centripetal force

$$T - mg \cos \theta = \frac{mv^2}{r} \quad \text{where } v \text{ is the tangential speed}$$

$$T = mg \cos \theta + \frac{mv^2}{r} \quad\text{————————— (1)}$$

(a) When $\theta = 0°$ at A (Fig 8.16)
$$T = T_A \quad \text{and} \quad v = v_A$$
From equation (1), we have

$$T_A = mg + \frac{mv_A^2}{r}$$

(b) When $\theta = 180°$ at B (Fig 8.16)
$$T = T_B \quad \text{and} \quad v = v_B$$
From equation (1), we have

$$T_B = mg \cos 180° + \frac{mv_B^2}{r}$$

$$T_B = \frac{mv_B^2}{r} - mg$$

T_A is always positive and greater than mg.
Tension is greatest at A and smallest at B.
The velocity of the mass changes as it moves around the circular path.

205

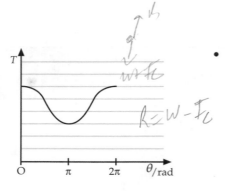

Fig 8.17 Graph of T against θ

- If the mass m is fixed to one end of a light rod, it would be possible to rotate the mass in a vertical circle at constant speed. The tension in the rod is given by

$$T = mg \cos \theta + \frac{mv^2}{r}$$

where mg and $\frac{mv^2}{r}$ are constants.

Fig 8.17 shows how the tension in the rod varies with the angle of inclination θ.

Going over a Hump

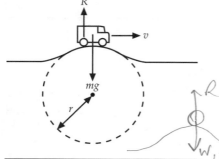

Fig 8.18 Motion of a car over a hump

- Figure 8.18 shows a car of mass m driving over a hump shaped in the arc of a circle of radius r. R is the normal reaction of the road on the car.

When the car reaches the highest point on the hump, the net vertical force is the centripetal force. Therefore

$$mg - R = \frac{mv^2}{r}$$

$$R = mg - \frac{mv^2}{r}$$

When $R > 0$, the car is always in contact with the ground, i.e. $v^2 < rg$.

When $R = 0$, the car is losing contact with the ground, i.e. $v^2 = rg$.

When $R < 0$, the car has lost contact with the ground. It is moving off the hump tangentially, i.e. $v^2 > rg$.

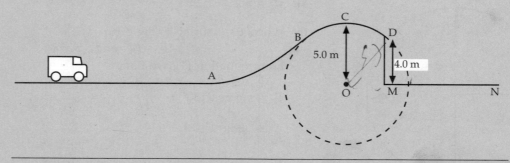

A car of mass 2.0×10^5 N drives along a ramp ABCD. The stretch from B to D is shaped in the arc of a circle of radius 5.0 m and centre at O (Fig 8.19).

Fig 8.19

(a) What minimum speed should the car attain if it is to become airborne at the highest point C on the ramp?

(b) How far horizontally from DM would the car land if it left C with this minimum speed?

A

(a) Along BD, $mg - R = \dfrac{mv^2}{r}$

where m is the mass of the car,
R is the reaction force and
v is the tangential speed.
When car is airborne at C, $R = 0$.

Hence $v = \sqrt{rg}$
$= \sqrt{(5.0)(9.81)}$
$= 7.00 \text{ m s}^{-1}$
$= 7.0 \text{ m s}^{-1}$

(b) Use $Y = u_y t + \frac{1}{2} a_y t^2$ and take the downward direction as positive
$Y = 5.0 \text{ m}$, $u_y = 0 \text{ m s}^{-1}$ and $a_y = g = 9.81 \text{ m s}^{-2}$

$5.0 = \frac{1}{2}(9.81) t^2$
$\therefore t = 1.01 \text{ s}$
$\approx 1.0 \text{ s}$

If X is the horizontal distance from O to the point of impact,
$$X = u_x t$$
where $u_x = v = 7.00 \text{ m s}^{-1}$

$X = (7.00)(1.01)$
$= 7.07$
$= 7.1 \text{ m}$

$OM = \sqrt{OD^2 - DM^2}$
$= \sqrt{5.0^2 - 4.0^2}$
$= 3.0 \text{ m}$

Horizontal distance from DM to point of impact $= 7.1 - 3.0$
$= 4.1 \text{ m}$

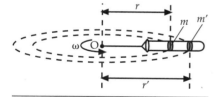

Fig 8.20   Centrifuge

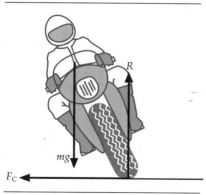

Fig 8.21   Cyclist moving in a
horizontal circle

Theory of the Centrifuge

- Masses of different densities suspended in a liquid can be separated by a centrifuge. The contents and the test tube are rotated with constant angular velocity ω. Masses of the same density would congregate together (Fig 8.20).

The centripetal force necessary to keep mass m at r from O is given by

$$F = mr\omega^2$$

If mass $m' >$ mass m, the above centripetal force would be insufficient to keep m' at the same position. It will move further away from O.

Cyclist Moving in a Horizontal circle

- Figure 8.21 shows a motor cyclist of mass m moving round a horizontal circle of radius r. The centripetal force is provided by the friction between the wheel and the ground.

Vertically: $R = mg$

For circular motion:
Centripetal force $F_C \leqslant$ Maximum frictional force
$$F_C \leqslant F$$

If the motor cyclist moves round with speed v without skidding

$$\frac{mv^2}{r} \leqslant F \text{ where } F \text{ is friction}$$

$$v^2 \leqslant \frac{rF}{m}$$

If $v < \sqrt{\dfrac{rF}{m}}$, the motor cyclist moves safely round the circle.

If $v = \sqrt{\dfrac{rF}{m}}$, the cyclist could skid off the track at any time.

If $v > \sqrt{\dfrac{rF}{m}}$, the cyclist cannot maintain circular motion.

- Taking moments about the centre of gravity (Fig 8.22)
$$Rh \sin \theta = F_C h \cos \theta$$
$$\tan \theta = \frac{F_C}{R}$$
$$= \frac{\dfrac{mv^2}{r}}{mg} = \frac{v^2}{rg}$$

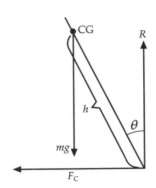

Fig 8.22

A cyclist must lean at an angle of θ from the vertical when moving in a circle. This angle is dependent on the speed of the cyclist, the radius of circular motion and the gravitational acceleration.

(a) A body moves at constant angular velocity ω in a circle of radius r. State its acceleration.

(b) In a ride at an entertainment park, two people, each of mass 80 kg, sit in cages which travel at constant speed in a vertical circle of radius 8.0 m as shown in Fig 8.23. Each revolution takes 4.2 s. When a cage is at the top of the circle (position A) the person in it is upside down.
For the person in cage A, calculate the magnitudes of
(i) the angular velocity,
(ii) the linear speed,
(iii) the centripetal acceleration. Fig 8.23

(c) (i) Draw a vector diagram to show the directions of the following forces acting on the person in cage at A in Fig 8.23:
the weight W of the person,
the force F exerted by the cage on the person.
(ii) Draw the corresponding diagram for the person at the bottom of the circle (position B).
(iii) What must be the value of the resultant of these two forces at both A and B?
(iv) Explain why the person remains on the floor of the cage at the top of the circle.
(v) State the position of the cage at which the force it exerts on the person has its maximum value. Calculate the magnitude of this force.

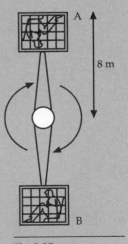

Fig 8.23

208

(d) Draw a vector diagram showing W, F and their resultant when the line joining the cages is horizontal. Numerical values are not required for this part of the question, but the force vectors should be drawn so that they have approximately correct relative sizes.

Cambridge

(a) Acceleration $= r\omega^2$

(b) (i) Angular velocity $\omega = \dfrac{2\pi}{T}$

$= \dfrac{2\pi}{4.2}$

$= 1.5 \text{ rad s}^{-1}$

(ii) Linear speed $v = r\omega$

$= (8.0)(1.5)$

$= 12 \text{ m s}^{-1}$

(iii) Centripetal acceleration $= r\omega^2$

$= (8.0)(1.5)^2$

$= 18 \text{ m s}^{-2}$

(c) (i) At A

W = weight of the person
F_A = Force exerted by the cage on the person at A

(ii) At B

F_B = Force exerted by the cage on the person at B

(iii) Resultant force at A
= Resultant force at B
= Centripetal force
= $mr\omega^2$
= $(80)(8.0)(1.5)^2$
= 1440 N
= 1.4×10^3 N

(iv) To move in a circle, the centripetal force of 1440 N must be exerted on the man at A. Part of this is contributed by the weight of the man while the rest has to come from the force exerted by the cage floor on the man. He therefore remains in contact with the floor as long as he maintains circular motion.

(v) The cage is at position B when the force acting on the person is at its maximum. If this force is F_B, then
$F_B - W = mr\omega^2$
$F_B = 1440 + (80)(9.81)$
$= 2224.8$ N
$= 2.2 \times 10^3$ N

(d) The vector diagram showing W, F_H and their resultant force is illustrated in Fig 8.24.

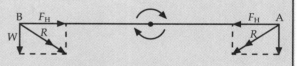

Fig 8.24

209

Apparent Weight on the Earth's Surface

- If the weight of an object is measured by a spring balance at the North Pole and at the equator, one can detect a small difference in the weight measured.

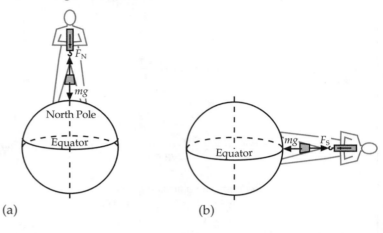

(a)   (b)

Fig 8.25

- Figure 8.25 shows a man weighing a mass m at the North Pole. Since the mass is on the axis of rotation, the Earth's circular motion has no effect on him and the mass. Hence,

  $F_N = mg$ where F_N is the reading on the spring balance at the North Pole.

At the equator (Fig 8.25), the effect of the centripetal force is at its maximum. Two unequal forces act on mass m. They are the weight mg and the apparent weight F_S indicated by the spring balance at the equator. The magnitude of the net force on the mass provides the centripetal force. Hence,

$$mg - F_S = mR\omega^2$$

where R is the radius of the Earth.

As $\omega = \dfrac{2\pi}{T}$ where T is the period of the Earth's rotation,

$$mg - F_S = mR\left(\frac{2\pi}{T}\right)^2$$

$$= \frac{4\pi^2 mR}{T^2}$$

i.e.
$$F_S = mg\left[1 - \frac{4\pi^2 R}{gT^2}\right]$$

As $R = 6.37 \times 10^6$ m and $T = 24$ h $= 8.64 \times 10^4$ s

$$F_S = mg\left[1 - \frac{4\pi^2(6.37 \times 10^6)}{(9.81)(8.64 \times 10^4)^2}\right]$$

$$F_S = 0.9965mg$$

The effect of the Earth's rotation on the apparent weight of an object is small, even at the equator where the effect is at its maximum.

210

Exercise 8

Multiple Choice Questions

1 A passenger is sitting in a railway facing in the direction in which the train is travelling. A pendulum hangs down in front of him from the carriage roof. The train travels along a circular arc bending to the right. Which one of the following diagrams shows the positions of the pendulum as seen by the passenger and the directions of the forces acting on it?

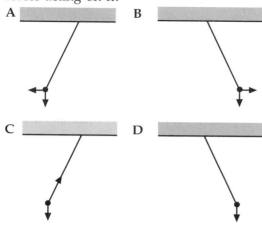

2 A particle travels in uniform circular motion. Which of the following correctly describes the linear velocity, angular velocity and linear acceleration of the particle?

	linear velocity	*angular velocity*	*linear acceleration*
A	constant	constant	varying
B	constant	constant	zero
C	constant	varying	constant
D	varying	constant	varying

3 A record on a turntable is rotating at a constant number of revolutions per second. Which graph best represents the relation between the speed v of a point on the record and its distance r from the centre of rotation?

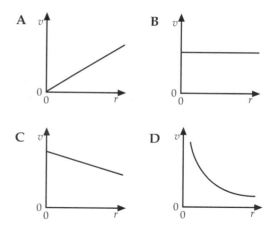

4 When the aircraft Concorde is moving in a horizontal plane at a constant speed of 650 m s^{-1}. Its turning circle has a radius of 80 km. What is the ratio of the centripetal force to the weight of the aircraft?

  A 8.3×10^{-4} **B** 0.54
  C 1.9   **D** 52

5 The diagram represents a cyclist making a left turn on a rough road surface at a constant speed v, as viewed from behind. The total mass of the bicycle and the rider is m and their combined centre of gravity is at G.

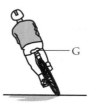

If R is the resultant force of the normal reaction and the frictional force, which vector diagram represents the directions of the forces acting on the bicycle and its rider?

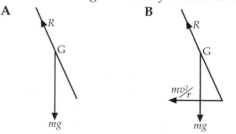

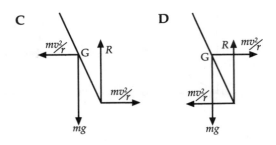

C, D diagrams with labels mv^2/r, G, R, mg

6 An artificial satellite travels in a circular orbit about the Earth. Its rocket engine is then fired and produces a force on the satellite exactly equal and opposite to that exerted by the Earth's gravitational field. The satellite would start to move

   A along a spiral path towards the Earth's surface.
   B along the line joining it to the centre of the Earth (i.e. radially).
   C along a tangent to the orbit.
   D in a circular orbit with a longer period.

7 A ball of mass 0.10 kg is attached to a string and swung in a vertical circle of radius 0.50 m, as shown. Its speed at the top of the circle is 6.0 m s^{-1}. [Take g as 10 m s^{-2}.]

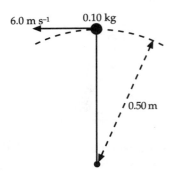

What is the tension in the string at this moment?

   A 1.0 N   B 6.2 N
   C 7.2 N   D 8.2 N

8 The maximum safe speed of a car rounding an unbanked corner is 20 m s^{-1} when the road is dry. The maximum frictional force between the road surface and the wheels of the car is halved when the road is wet.

What is the maximum safe speed for the car to round the corner when the road is wet?

   A $\dfrac{20}{4}$ m s^{-1} B $\dfrac{20}{2\sqrt{2}}$ m s^{-1}

   C $\dfrac{20}{2}$ m s^{-1} D $\dfrac{20}{\sqrt{2}}$ m s^{-1}

9 A satellite moves at constant speed in a circular orbit about the Earth. Which statement about the momentum and kinetic energy of the satellite is correct?

	momentum	kinetic energy
A	constant	changing
B	constant	constant
C	changing	changing
D	changing	constant

10 A disc is rotating about an axis through its centre and perpendicular to its plane. A point P on the disc is twice as far from the axis as a point Q.
At a given instant what is the value of $\dfrac{\text{the linear velocity of P}}{\text{the linear velocity of Q}}$?

   A 4   B 2

   C $\dfrac{1}{2}$ D $\dfrac{1}{4}$

11 A point mass moves through a circular arc of length l and radius r in time t.
What is its angular velocity about the centre of the circle?

   A $\dfrac{l}{rt}$ B $\dfrac{r}{lt}$

   C $\dfrac{2\pi}{lt}$ D $\dfrac{2\pi r}{t}$

12 An object of mass 2 kg rotates at constant speed in a horizontal circle of radius 5 m. The time for one complete revolution is 3 s. What is the magnitude of the resultant force acting on the object?

   A $\dfrac{4\pi^2}{9}$ N   B $\dfrac{40\pi^2}{9}$ N

   C $\dfrac{100\pi^2}{9}$ N   D $\dfrac{400\pi^2}{9}$ N

Structured Questions

1 Explain the circumstances under which a particle moving with uniform speed can experience an acceleration.

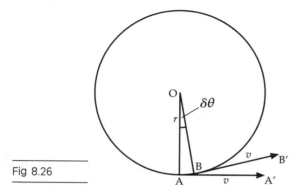

Fig 8.26

A particle moves in a circle of radius r with uniform angular speed. At one instant the particle is at A, and its instantaneous velocity is v in the direction AA'; a time δt later the particle has moved to B, a distance $r\delta\theta$ along the arc (where $\delta\theta$ is a small angle), where its velocity is v in the direction BB'.

(a) Draw a vector diagram to show δv, the change of velocity that occurs during this time.

(b) Show that the magnitude of δv is approximately equal to $\dfrac{v^2\delta t}{r}$.

(c) Hence find the magnitude and direction of the acceleration of the particle.

2 An aircraft is travelling at a constant speed of 180 m s^{-1} in a horizontal circle of radius 20 km. A plumbline, attached to the roof of the cabin, settles at an angle ϕ to the true vertical while the aircraft is turning.

(i) Find the centripetal acceleration of the aircraft.

(ii) Name the forces which act on the bob of the plumbline, and draw a labelled diagram to show the directions of these forces, and of their resultant. (Indicate the centre of the circle on your sketch.)

(iii) Find the angle ϕ.

(iv) Show by means of a simple sketch of the cross-section of the aircraft and its cabin how the plumbline is oriented with respect to the aircraft.

3 Each blade on a turbine wheel is attached separately to a small section of the rim of the wheel as shown in Fig 8.27. The blades are small and each behaves like a point mass of 0.72 kg at a distance of 0.65 m from the axis of rotation.

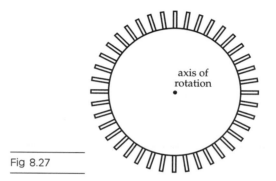

Fig 8.27

The wheel is tested by spinning it at high speed. The plane of the wheel is kept horizontal with the axis of rotation vertical. It is found that blades break off at angular velocities greater than 540 rad s^{-1}.

(a) Outline an experimental method for measuring the angular velocity of the wheel.

(b) Calculate the linear speed of the blades when the angular velocity is 540 rad s^{-1}. What is the corresponding centripetal acceleration?

(c) Use Newton's laws to explain why a blade might break off at high angular velocities.

(d) Calculate the minimum radial force required to pull a blade off the wheel.

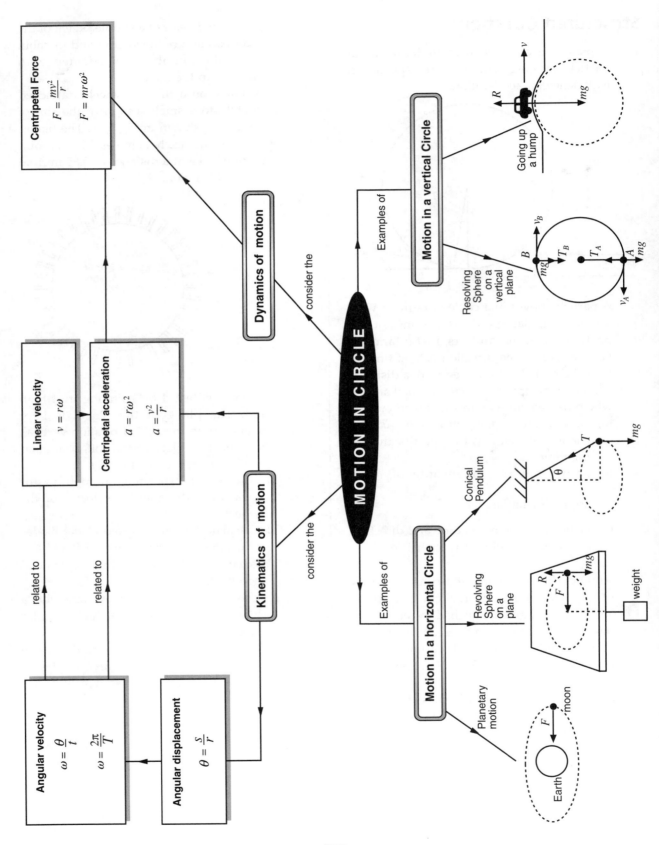

MOTION IN CIRCLE

Centripetal Force

$F = \dfrac{mv^2}{r}$

$F = mr\omega^2$

Linear velocity

$v = r\omega$

Centripetal acceleration

$a = r\omega^2$

$a = \dfrac{v^2}{r}$

Angular velocity

$\omega = \dfrac{\theta}{t}$

$\omega = \dfrac{2\pi}{T}$

Angular displacement

$\theta = \dfrac{s}{r}$

Dynamics of motion

Kinematics of motion

related to

consider the

Motion in a vertical Circle

Going up a hump

Resolving Sphere on a vertical plane

Examples of

Motion in a horizontal Circle

Conical Pendulum

Revolving Sphere on a plane

weight

Planetary motion

Earth

moon

Examples of

Ideal Gases

BROWNIAN MOTION

EQUATION OF STATE

KINETIC THEORY OF GASES

PRESSURE EXERTED BY AN IDEAL GAS

KINETIC ENERGY OF A MOLECULE

Syllabus Objectives

In this chapter you should be able to:

- infer from Brownian Motion experiment the evidence for the movement of molecules.

- recall and solve problems by using the equation of state for an ideal gas expressed as $pV = nRT$. (n = number of moles.)

- state the basic assumptions of the kinetic theory of gases.

- explain how molecular movement causes the pressure exerted by a gas and hence deduce the relationship, $p = \frac{1}{3}\frac{Nm}{V} <c^2>$. ($N$ = number of molecules.) [A rigorous derivation is not required.]

- compare $pV = \frac{1}{3}Nm <c^2>$ with $pV = NkT$ and hence deduce that the average translational kinetic energy of a molecule is proportional to T.

BROWNIAN MOTION

- Brownian motion provides indirect evidence that atoms or molecules in gases and liquids are in random and continuous motion.

- Figure 9.1 shows the experimental set up for observing Brownian motion.

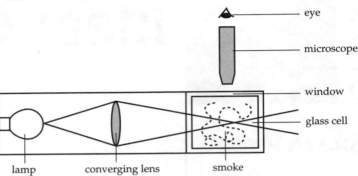

Fig 9.1 Experimental set up for observing Brownian motion

- The smoke-filled glass is illuminated by light. A microscope is used to observe the smoke particles in the cell.

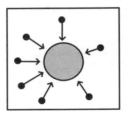 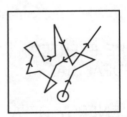

Smoke particle is bombarded by invisible air molecules.

Erratic random motion of smoke particles.

Fig 9.2 Erratic motion of smoke particles caused by the random bombardment of air molecules

- The observations of the smoke particles and its explanation are tabulated in Table 9.1.

Observations	Explanations
Bright sparks of light can be seen through the microscope	These are the reflected light from the tiny smoke particles suspended in the glass cell.
The smoke particles move randomly and haphazardly.	The smoke particles are bombarded unevenly on all sides by unseen air molecules. These random, continuous bombardments cause the irregular, jerky motion of the smoke particles. This is also known as Brownian motion. It is indirect evidence that atoms or molecules in gases and liquid are in continuous random motion.
The smoke particles appear and disappear from the field of view.	The smoke particles are out of focus when they move randomly up and down.

216

The smaller particles move faster while the larger particles are less agitated.	Larger particles have greater inertia. Small changes in the resultant forces impart small changes in their speeds and momentum. Large particles are less agitated than small particles.
Smoke particles move faster when temperature increases.	An increase in temperature will cause an increase in the kinetic energies of invisible air molecules. The resultant force acting on the smoke particle increases and it will move faster.

Table 9.1   Characteristics of Brownian motion

EQUATION OF STATE

Boyle's Law

- Boyle's Law states that the pressure of a fixed mass of gas at constant temperature is inversely proportional to its volume.

$$p \propto \frac{1}{V} (T = \text{constant})$$

or $pV = \text{constant}$

or $p_1 V_1 = p_2 V_2$

- Boyle's Law can be represented graphically as shown in Fig 9.3.

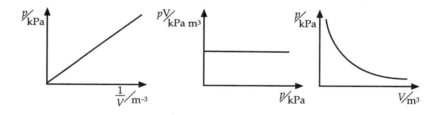

Fig 9.3   Boyle's Law

Q A large tank contains water at a uniform temperature to a depth of 20 m. The tank is open to the atmosphere and atmospheric pressure is equivalent to that of 10 m of water. An air bubble is released from the bottom of the tank and rises to the surface. Assuming surface tension effects to be negligible, show that the volume of the air bubble doubles before it reaches the surface.

A Using $p_1 V_1 = p_2 V_2$

where p_1 = pressure of the air bubble at the surface,
p_2 = pressure of the air bubble at a depth of 20 m,
V_1 = volume of the air bubble at the surface,
V_2 = volume of the air bubble at a depth of 20 m.

Also $p_1 \equiv 10$ m of water;
$p_2 \equiv (10 + 20) \equiv 30$ m of water

Using $p_1 V_1 = p_2 V_2$
$10\ V_1 = 30\ V_2$
$V_1 = 3\ V_2$

The volume of the air bubble at the surface is three times the volume of the bubble at a depth of 20 m. Hence the volume of the air bubble doubles before it reaches the surface.

Charles' Law

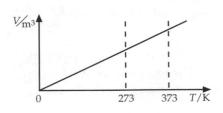

- Charles' Law states that the volume of a fixed mass of gas at constant pressure is directly proportional to its absolute temperature.

$$V \propto T \text{ (pressure = constant)}$$

or $\dfrac{V}{T} = \text{constant}$

or $\dfrac{V_1}{T_1} = \dfrac{V_2}{T_2}$

Fig 9.4 Graph of volume against temperature for a fixed mass of gas at constant pressure

- Charles' Law can be represented graphically as shown in Fig 9.4.

An ideal gas is defined as one for which, at constant pressure, the volume of the gas is proportional to the absolute temperature. Calculate the absolute temperature T when an ideal gas has volume 0.00783 m^3, assuming that the same mass of the ideal gas has volume 0.00308 m^3 when at the same pressure and at temperature 273 K.

Using $\dfrac{V_1}{T_1} = \dfrac{V_2}{T_2}$ when $V_1 = 0.00783$ m^3, $T_1 =$ unknown temperature, $V_2 = 0.00308$ m^3, $T_2 = 273$ K

$$T_1 = \frac{(0.00783)(273)}{0.00308}$$

$$= 694 \text{ K}$$

The Pressure Law

- The pressure law states that the pressure of a fixed mass of gas at constant volume is directly proportional to its absolute temperature.

$$p \propto T \text{ (volume = constant)}$$

or $\dfrac{p}{T} = \text{constant}$

or $\dfrac{p_1}{T_1} = \dfrac{p_2}{T_2}$

- The pressure law can be represented graphically as shown in Fig 9.5.

Fig 9.5 Graph of pressure against temperature for a fixed mass of gas at constant volume

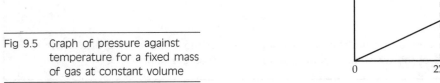

The Equation of State for an Ideal Gas

- An ideal gas is a perfect gas which obeys the three gas laws described above exactly. There is no ideal gas in nature as no gas obeys the gas laws completely. Nevertheless, the concept of an ideal gas is useful as real gases behave like an ideal gas when their pressures are low and temperatures are way above the point where gases liquefy.

- The three gas laws can be combined into a general law or the equation of state. Consider how an ideal gas in a container changes its pressure (p_1), volume (V_1) and temperature (T_1) to p_2, V_2 and T_2 (Fig 9.6)

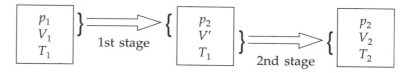

Fig 9.6 Change in state of an ideal gas in a container

In the first stage, temperature is kept at T_1 while p_1 and V_1 changes to p_2 and V'.

Using Boyle's Law:

$$p_2 V' = p_1 V_1$$

$$\therefore V' = \frac{p_1 V_1}{p_2} \qquad \text{——— (1)}$$

In the second stage, pressure is kept constant at p_2 and V' and T_1 changes to V_2 and T_2 respectively.

Using Charles' Law:

$$\frac{V'}{T_1} = \frac{V_2}{T_2}$$

$$\therefore V' = \frac{V_2 T_1}{T_2} \qquad \text{——— (2)}$$

Equating equation (1) with equation (2)

$$\frac{p_1 V_1}{p_2} = \frac{V_2 T_1}{T_2}$$

Rearranging,

$$\frac{p_1 V_1}{T_1} = \frac{p_2 V_2}{T_2}$$

or $\quad \dfrac{pV}{T} = \text{constant} \qquad \text{——— (3)}$

- Consider 1 mole of gas at standard temperature and pressure, $T = 273$ K, $P = 101.3$ kPa, $V_m = 0.0224$ m^3

From equation (3),

$$\frac{pV_m}{T} = \frac{101.3 \times 10^3 \times 0.0224}{273}$$

$$= 8.31 \text{ J K}^{-1} \text{ mol}^{-1}$$

219

We call 8.31 J K^{-1} mol^{-1} the molar gas constant and is represented by the symbol R. This value is the same for all gases. This is illustrated when we plot a graph of $\frac{pV}{T}$ against p for several gases (Fig 9.7). As the pressure approaches zero, all extrapolated curves converge to 8.31 J K^{-1} mol^{-1}.

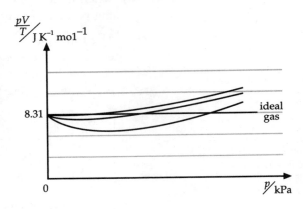

Fig 9.7　Graph of $\frac{pV}{T}$ against p

If 1 mole occupies a volume of V_m at a pressure p and absolute temperature T, we write

$$pV_m = R\,T$$

In general, if n moles occupy a volume of $n\,V_m$ (or V) at a pressure p and absolute temperature T, the equation of state is written as

$$pV = nRT$$

- The equation of state can be written in other forms.

(a) As $n = \dfrac{m'}{M}$ where m' is the mass of the gas and M is the molecular mass in kg.

The equation of state is $pV = \left(\dfrac{m'}{M}\right)RT$.

(b) If we denote the gas constant per unit molecular mass by r $\left(i.e.\ r = \dfrac{R}{M}\right)$, the equation of state becomes

$$pV = m'rT$$

(c) For N molecules, the number of moles n is given by

$$n = \frac{N}{N_A} \text{ where } N_A \text{ is the Avogadro's constant.}$$

The equation of state becomes $pV = \left(\dfrac{N}{N_A}\right)RT$.

(d) If the Boltzmann constant is defined as

$$k = \frac{R}{N_A} = 1.38 \times 10^{-23} \text{ J K}^{-1},$$

the equation of state becomes $pV = NkT$.

220

Q What is the approximate number of atoms in a cubic metre of an ideal monatomic gas at a temperature of 27°C and a pressure of 1×10^5 Pa?

Cambridge

A Make use of $pV = \left(\dfrac{N}{N_A}\right)RT$ where N = Number of atoms in cubic metre,

N_A = Avogadro constant,
R = Molar gas constant,
T = Temperature of the gas in kelvins,
V = Volume of the gas,
p = Pressure of the gas.

We have $N = \dfrac{pVN_A}{RT}$

$$= \frac{(1 \times 10^5 \text{ Pa})(1 \text{ m}^3)(6.02 \times 10^{23} \text{ mol}^{-1})}{(8.31 \text{ JK}^{-1} \text{ mol}^{-1})(300 \text{ K})}$$

$$= 2.4 \times 10^{25}$$

Q Two vessels X and Y of volumes 10×10^{-4} m^3 and 5×10^{-4} m^3 connected by a tube of negligible volume and kept at temperatures 400 K and 200 K respectively, contain the same ideal gas. What is the value of the ratio $\dfrac{\text{number of molecules of X}}{\text{number of molecules of Y}}$?

A Pressure in X, p_X = Pressure in Y, p_Y
$= p$

$$pV_X = \frac{N_X}{N_A}RT_X \quad \text{——— (1)}$$

where N_X = number of molecules of X

and $pV_Y = \dfrac{N_Y}{N_A}RT_Y \quad \text{——— (2)}$

where N_Y = number of molecules of Y and N_A = Avogadro constant
Dividing (1) by (2)

$$\frac{V_X}{V_Y} = \left(\frac{N_X}{N_Y}\right)\frac{T_X}{T_Y}$$

$$\frac{N_X}{N_Y} = \frac{V_X}{V_Y}\frac{T_Y}{T_X}$$

$$= \left(\frac{10 \times 10^{-4}}{5 \times 10^{-4}}\right)\left(\frac{200}{400}\right)$$

$$= 1$$

Q A gas cylinder is fitted with a safety valve which releases gas when the pressure inside the cylinder reaches 2.0×10^6 Pa. Given that the maximum mass of this gas the cylinder can hold at 10°C is 15 kg, what would be the maximum mass at 30°C?

A Since pressure and volume remain constant

$$pV = \left(\frac{m_1}{M}\right)RT_1 = \left(\frac{m_2}{M}\right)RT_2$$

where m_1 is the mass of the gas at temperature 283 K = 15 kg,
m_2 is the mass of the gas at temperature 303 K
$m_1 T_1 = m_2 T_2$
303 m_2 = (15) (283)
$\therefore m_2 = 14$ kg

Q (a) Some cars are fitted with bags packed into the steering column. In an accident, gas is forced under pressure into the bag and the bag of gas quickly acts as a cushion between the driver and the steering wheel. In one such system, the volume of gas used in the bag is 0.037 m^3 when pressure is 1.8×10^5 Pa and the temperature of the gas is 6°C. Calculate
(i) the temperature of the gas in kelvin,
(ii) the amount of gas used, in mol,
(iii) the pressure in the bag when the temperature rises to 18°C assuming the volume to remain constant while the temperature rises.
(b) Explain why the use of the bag described in (a) can reduce injuries.

A (a) (i) Temperature of the gas in kelvin = 273 + 6
= 279 K
(ii) Given $V = 0.037$ m^3, $p = 1.8 \times 10^5$ Pa and $T = 279$ K,
Make use of $pV = nRT$

$$n = \frac{pV}{RT}$$

$$= \frac{(1.8 \times 10^5)(0.037)}{(8.31)(279)}$$

= 2.87 mol
= 2.9 mol

(iii) Since V is constant, $\dfrac{p}{T} = \dfrac{p'}{T'}$ where $T' = 291$ K and p' is the pressure in the bag when temperature is 291 K.

$$\frac{p'}{291} = \frac{1.8 \times 10^5}{279}$$

$\therefore p' = 1.877 \times 10^5$ Pa
$\approx 1.9 \times 10^5$ Pa

(b) The retarding force acting on the driver is spread over a larger area. Hence the reduced pressure on the driver reduces injuries.

The diagram below shows a cylinder filled with air. Use the kinetic theory of matter to answer the following:
(a) How does air exert a pressure on the walls of the cylinder?
(b) Why is the pressure the same at every point in the cylinder?
(c) The piston is pushed forward slowly, reducing the volume of the air at constant temperature. If no air escapes from the cylinder, explain why the pressure increases.
(d) Explain why the pressure increases when the cylinder is heated to a higher temperature.

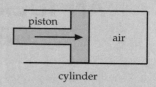

(a) When an air molecule collides with a molecule from the wall, action and reaction forces are exerted on each other momentarily. Within the cylinder, air

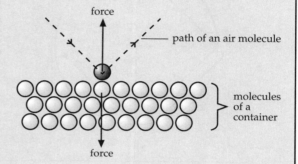

molecules are constantly bombarding the walls at any instant. The sum total of all forces acting on the wall per unit area gives rise to the pressure on the walls of the cylinder.

(b) The random motion of molecules causes an even distribution of molecules throughout the cylinder. Approxmately equal number of molecules strike every unit area of the cylinder with the same average force. Hence pressure is the same at every point in the cylinder.

(c) When the volume decreases, the area of the cylinder also decreases. This would mean that there will be an increase in the number of collisions per unit area every second. The force per unit area increases and hence pressure increases.

(d) Higher temperature causes air molecules to move faster with greater kinetic energies. Molecular forces exerted on the container increase, leading to an increase in pressure.

KINETIC THEORY OF GASES

- The main assumptions of the kinetic theory of gases are:
  (a) All gases are made up of atoms or molecules.
  (b) All atoms or molecules move randomly and haphazardly.
  (c) The volume of the atoms or molecules is negligible when compared with the volume occupied by the gas.
  (d) The intermolecular forces are negligible except during collisions
  (e) Inter-atomic or molecular collisions are elastic.
  (f) The duration of a collision is negligible compared with the time spent travelling between collisions.
  (g) Atoms and molecules move with constant velocity between collisions. Gravity has no effect on molecular motion.

  The assumptions above describe an ideal gas.

223

PRESSURE EXERTED BY AN IDEAL GAS

Derivation of $p = \frac{1}{3}\rho<c^2>$

- Consider one molecule of mass m moving with speed v in a spherical container of radius r (Fig 9.8a). On each elastic collision with the wall of the spherical container, the angle of incidence (θ) is the same as the angle of reflection.

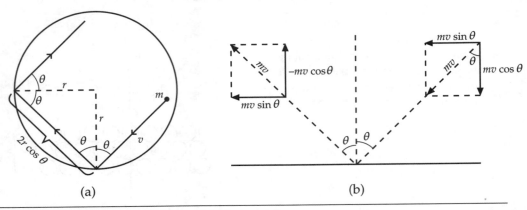

Fig 9.8   Collisions of one molecule in a spherical container

- Consider momentum horizontally and vertically (Fig 9.8b),

Change in the horizontal component of the momentum
$= mv \sin \theta - mv \sin \theta = 0$

Change in the vertical component of the momentum
$= mv \cos \theta - (-mv \cos \theta)$
$= 2\, mv \cos \theta$

Therefore the change in momentum $\Delta p = 2mv \cos \theta$

The molecule has to travel a distance $2r \cos \theta$ before it next collides with the wall of the container. The time for the trip is Δt where $\Delta t = \dfrac{2r \cos \theta}{v}$

Force exerted on the molecule by the wall is given by:

$$F = \frac{\Delta p}{\Delta t}$$

$$= \frac{2mv \cos \theta}{\dfrac{2r \cos \theta}{v}}$$

$$= \frac{mv^2}{r}$$

By Newton's third law, the molecule exerts an equal but oppositely directed force on the wall, hence

Force on wall $= \dfrac{mv^2}{r}$

224

As the force is distributed over the whole spherical surface of the container, the average pressure due to one molecule is given by:

$$\text{Average pressure} = \frac{\text{Force}}{\text{Area}}$$

$$= \frac{\frac{mv^2}{r}}{4\pi r^2}$$

$$= \frac{mv^2}{4\pi r^3}$$

$$= \frac{mv^2}{3V}$$

$$\left[\text{since volume of sphere } V = \frac{4}{3}\pi r^3\right]$$

If there are N molecules in the container, the speeds of the molecules are $v_1, v_2, \ldots v_N$

Therefore, pressure exerted by the gas is given by

$$\text{Pressure } p = \frac{mv_1^2}{3V} + \frac{mv_2^2}{3V} + \frac{mv_3^2}{3V} + \ldots + \frac{mv_N^2}{3V}$$

$$= \frac{m}{3V}[v_1^2 + v_2^2 + v_3^2 + \ldots + v_N^2] \quad\text{———} \quad (4)$$

The average value of $[v_1^2 + v_2^2 + v_3^2 + \ldots]$ can be represented by the mean square speed $<c^2>$ where,

$$<c^2> = \frac{v_1^2 + v_2^2 + v_3^2 + \ldots + v_N^2}{N}$$

$$[v_1^2 + v_2^2 + v_3^2 + \ldots + v_N^2] = N<c^2>$$

Hence, substituting $N<c^2>$ into equation (4), the pressure p exerted on the wall of the container is given by

$$p = \frac{m}{3V}[N<c^2>] \quad \text{or} \quad p = \frac{1}{3}\frac{Nm}{V}<c^2>$$

Since the density of the gas $\rho = \frac{Nm}{V}$, we have $p = \frac{1}{3}\rho<c^2>$

Root-Mean-Square Speed

The root-mean-square speed is the square root of the mean-square speed.

$$\text{i.e.} \quad c_{rms} = \sqrt{<c^2>} = \sqrt{\frac{c_1^2 + c_2^2 + c_3^2 + \ldots + c_N^2}{N}}$$

In kinetic theory, the root-mean-square speed of the gas molecules is more commonly used.

The speeds of nine particles are distributed as follows:

Speed/m s^{-1}	1.0	2.0	3.0	4.0	5.0	6.0
No. of particles	1	1	4	1	1	1

Find the root mean square speed

Cambridge

$$C_{r.m.s.} = \sqrt{\frac{(1)(1.0)^2 + (1)(2.0)^2 + (4)(3.0)^2 + (1)(4.0)^2 + (1)(5.0)^2 + (1)(6.0)^2}{(1 + 1 + 4 + 1 + 1 + 1)}}$$

$$= 3.6 \ ms^{-1}$$

 Five molecules are moving with the speeds and directions shown in the diagram.

$$\overset{\longleftarrow}{\underset{300 \text{ m s}^{-1}}{\bigcirc}} \quad \overset{\longleftarrow}{\underset{100 \text{ m s}^{-1}}{\bigcirc}} \quad \overset{\longrightarrow}{\underset{100 \text{ m s}^{-1}}{\bigcirc}} \quad \overset{\longrightarrow}{\underset{300 \text{ m s}^{-1}}{\bigcirc}} \quad \overset{\longrightarrow}{\underset{500 \text{ m s}^{-1}}{\bigcirc}}$$

What is the root mean square (r.m.s.) velocity of these molecules?

$$C_{r.m.s.} = \sqrt{\frac{(-300)^2 + (-100)^2 + (100)^2 + (300)^2 + (500)^2}{5}}$$

$$= 300 \ m \ s^{-1}$$

(a) Consider a cubical box of side *l* which contains *N* molecules, each of mass *m*, all moving horizontally with speed *u* at right angles to wall A.
When a molecule hits a wall, it bounces off with no loss of speed and travels in the opposite direction.
Deduce
(i) the momentum of a molecule just before a collision with the wall,
(ii) the change in momentum of a molecule when it collides with the wall,
(iii) the time taken by one molecule between collisions with wall A,
(iv) the total number of collisions per unit time made with wall A by all the molecules,
(v) the rate of change of momentum for all the molecules colliding with wall A.

(b) Use your answer to (a) to show that the pressure *P* on wall A is given by

$$P = \frac{Mu^2}{V}$$

where *M* is the total mass of all the molecules and *V* is the internal volume of the box.

(c) The conditions considered in (a) are highly improbable. Explain briefly how the conditions may be altered to provide a better model of an ideal gas. State, how the equation in (b) might be modified.

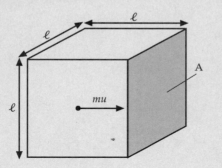
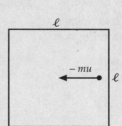

(a) (i) Take direction to the right as positive.
Before elastic collision with the wall,
momentum of a molecule $= p_i$
$$= mu$$

(ii) After elastic collision with the wall,
momentum of a molecule $= p_f$
$$= -mu$$

Change in momentum of the molecule $= p_f - p_i$
$$= -mu - (mu)$$
$$= -2mu$$

(iii) To collide again with the same wall A, the molecule has to travel a distance of $2l$. Since the speed of the molecule is u,

the time taken by one molecule between collisions with wall A $= \dfrac{\text{distance}}{\text{speed}} = \dfrac{2l}{u}$

(iv) The total number of collisions per unit time made with wall A by all the molecules

$$= \frac{\text{Total number of collision}}{\text{time taken}}$$

$$= \frac{N}{\frac{2l}{u}}$$

$$= \frac{Nu}{2l}$$

(v) The rate of change of momentum for all the molecule colliding with wall A

$$= \left(\frac{\text{Total number of collision}}{\text{time taken}}\right)(\text{change in momentum of one molecule})$$

$$= \left(\frac{Nu}{2l}\right)(-2mu)$$

$$= -\frac{Nmu^2}{l}$$

227

(b) The total force exerted by wall on all the molecules $= -\dfrac{Nmu^2}{l}$

By Newton's third law of motion, the total force exerted by all the molecules on the

wall $= \dfrac{Nmu^2}{l}$

Pressure (P) on wall A is given by

$$P = \frac{\text{total force}}{\text{area of A}}$$

$$= \frac{Nmu^2}{l} \div l^2$$

$$P = \frac{Nmu^2}{l^3}$$

$$\therefore P = \frac{Mu^2}{V}$$

where $M = Nm =$ Total mass of all the molecules

and $V =$ Internal volume of the box.

(c) The conditions considered in (a) are highly improbable for 2 reasons:

(i) Molecules do not travel in the x-direction only. They could move in any direction. The speed c of a molecule moving in 3-dimensional space can be resolved along the x, y and z axis. (See Appendix)

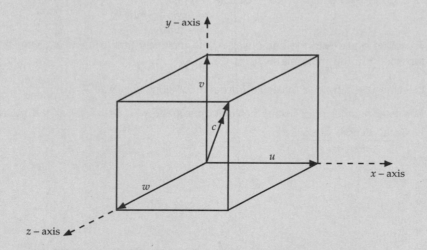

Using Pythagoras' theorem.

$$c^2 = u^2 + v^2 + w^2$$

(ii) Molecules do not have same speed. For N molecuels, their speeds are:

$$c_1^2 = u_1^2 + v_1^2 + w_1^2$$
$$c_2^2 = u_2^2 + v_2^2 + w_2^2$$
$$c_3^2 = u_3^2 + v_3^2 + w_3^2$$
$$\vdots$$
$$c_N^2 = u_N^2 + v_N^2 + w_N^2$$

228

Adding all the equations, we have
$$(c_1^2 + \dots + c_N^2) = (u_1^2 + \dots + u_N^2) + (v_1^2 + \dots + v_N^2) + (w_1^2 + \dots + w_N^2)$$
This equation can be simplified by using average values

i.e. mean square speed $<c^2> = \dfrac{c_1^2 + \dots + c_N^2}{N}$

Hence $c_1^2 + \dots + c_N^2 = N<c^2>$

Similarly
$$u_1^2 + \dots + u_N^2 = N<u^2>$$
$$v_1^2 + \dots + v_N^2 = N<v^2>$$
$$w_1^2 + \dots + w_N^2 = N<w^2>$$

i.e. $N<c^2> = N<u^2> + N<v^2> + N<w^2>$

or $<c^2> = <u^2> + <v^2> + <w^2>$

Molecules move randomly and they do not of their own accord have a preference to move in one specific direction. Hence it follows that
$$<u^2> = <v^2> = <w^2>$$

Hence $<c^2> = 3<u^2>$

$$\therefore <u^2> = \frac{1}{3}<c^2>$$

The equation in (b) can be modified to

$$P = \frac{1}{3}\frac{M}{V}<c^2>$$

KINETIC ENERGY OF A MOLECULE

The Relationship Between Molecular Kinetic Energy and Temperature

From kinetic theory,

$$p = \frac{1}{3}\rho<c^2>$$

Multiply both sides of the equation by V, the volume of gas

$$pV = \frac{1}{3}\rho V<c^2>$$

Since $m' = $ mass of gas in volume V
$$= \rho V$$
we have

$$pV = \frac{1}{3}m'<c^2>$$

$$pV = \frac{1}{3}Nm<c^2> \quad\text{————— (5)}$$

where N is the total number of molecules in volume V, and m is the mass of one molecule.

Rewriting equation (5)

$$pV = \frac{2}{3}N\left(\frac{1}{2}m<c^2>\right) \quad\text{————— (6)}$$

The equation of state for n moles of gas at pressure p, volume V and absolute temperature T is given by
$$pV = nRT \quad\text{————— (7)}$$

229

Equating equation (6) and (7)

$$\frac{2}{3}N\left(\frac{1}{2}m<c^2>\right) = nRT$$

$$\frac{1}{2}m<c^2> = \frac{3}{2}\frac{nR}{N}T$$

$$\frac{1}{2}m<c^2> = \frac{3}{2}\frac{R}{N_A}T$$

$$\left[\text{since Avogadro constant } N_A = \frac{N}{n}\right]$$

or $\qquad \frac{1}{2}m<c^2> = \frac{3}{2}kT$ ———— (8)

where $k = \dfrac{R}{N_A}$, the Boltzmann constant

Equation (8) is the basis for the molecular interpretation of temperature. It shows us that the average translational kinetic energy of a molecule (a microscopic quantity) is directly proportional to the absolute temperature (a macroscopic quantity). The faster the molecule is moving, the higher the temperature.

The ideal gas equation is $pV_m = RT$, where V_m is the volume occupied by one mole, R is the molar gas constant and T is the absolute temperature. By comparing this equation with $pV = \frac{1}{3}Nm<c^2>$, show that the r.m.s. speed is given by

$$c_{r.m.s.} = \sqrt{\frac{3RT}{N_A m}}$$

Given $pV_m = RT$ and $pV = \frac{1}{3}Nm<c^2>$,

when $V = V_m$ and $N = N_A$ (Avogadro constant)

$$pV_m = \frac{1}{3}N_A m<c^2> = RT$$

i.e. $<c^2> = \dfrac{3RT}{N_A m}$

$$c_{r.m.s.} = \sqrt{<c^2>} = \sqrt{\frac{3RT}{N_A m}}$$

What is the temperature at which the r.m.s. speed of nitrogen molecules is twice as great as their r.m.s. speed at 300 K?

230

A

Let $c'_{r.m.s.}$ = r.m.s. speed of nitrogen at $T' = 300$ K

Let $c_{r.m.s.}$ = r.m.s. speed of nitrogen at temperature T

$$c_{r.m.s.} = 2\, c'_{r.m.s.}$$

$$\sqrt{<c^2>} = 2\sqrt{<c^2>'}$$

Squaring both sides of the equation

$$<c^2> = 4<c^2>'$$

Multiply both sides of the equation by $\frac{1}{2}m$ where m is the mass of a nitrogen molecule, we have

$$\frac{1}{2}m<c^2> = 4\left[\frac{1}{2}m<c^2>'\right]$$

i.e. $\frac{3}{2}kT = 4\left[\frac{3}{2}kT'\right]$

$\therefore\ T = 4\,(300) = 1200$ K

Q

Oxygen molecules in the Earth's atmosphere have a root mean square speed of about 500 m s^{-1}. If the relative molecular masses of oxygen and helium are 32 and 4 respectively, what is the root mean square speed of a helium molecule in the atmosphere?

A

Since temperature T for oxygen and helium are the same

$$\frac{1}{2}m_O<c^2>_O = \frac{3}{2}kT$$

and

$$\frac{1}{2}m_H<c^2>_H = \frac{3}{2}kT$$

where m_O and m_H are the masses of one oxygen and one helium molecule respectively, and $<c^2>_O$ and $<c^2>_H$ are the mean square speeds of oxygen molecule and helium molecule rspectively, i.e.

$$m_O<c^2>_O = m_H<c^2>_H$$

$$<c^2>_H = \left(\frac{m_O}{m_H}\right)<c^2>_O$$

r.m.s. speed of helium molecule $= \sqrt{<c^2>_H}$

$$= \left(\sqrt{\frac{m_O}{m_H}}\right)\sqrt{<c^2>_O}$$

$$= \left(\sqrt{\frac{N_A m_O}{N_A m_H}}\right)\sqrt{<c^2>_O}$$

$$= \left(\sqrt{\frac{M_O}{M_H}}\right)\sqrt{<c^2>_O}$$

$$= \left(\sqrt{\frac{32}{4}}\right)500$$

$$= 1414$$

$$\approx 1400 \text{ m s}^{-1}$$

The two curves shown below are isotherms for a fixed mass of an ideal gas.
What is the ratio

$$\frac{\text{r.m.s. speed of the molecules at temperature } T_2}{\text{r.m.s. speed of the molecules at temperature } T_1}?$$

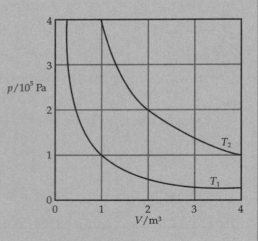

Since $<c^2> \propto T$

$$c_{\text{r.m.s.}} = \sqrt{T}$$

Hence $\dfrac{(c_{\text{r.m.s.}})_{T2}}{(c_{\text{r.m.s.}})_{T1}} = \sqrt{\dfrac{T_2}{T_1}} = \sqrt{\dfrac{p_2 V_2}{p_1 V_1}}$

$$= \sqrt{\frac{(2)(2)}{(1)(1)}}$$

$$= 2$$

(a) Define the term *density*.

(b) Outline how molecular movement causes the pressure exerted by a gas.

(c) One mole of oxygen has a mass of 32 g. Assuming oxygen behaves as an ideal gas, calculate
   (i) the volume occupied by one mole of oxygen gas when at temperature 273 K and pressure 1.01×10^5 Pa,
   (ii) the density of oxygen gas at this temperature and pressure.

(d) (i) Explain what is meant by the root-mean-square speed $\sqrt{<c^2>}$ of gas molecules.
   (ii) Calculate the root-mean-square speed of four molecules travelling with speeds 300 m s^{-1}, 400 m s^{-1}, 500 m s^{-1} and 600 m s^{-1}.

(e) Assuming ideal gas behaviour, calculate for oxygen at 273 K
   (i) the root-mean-square speed of its molecules,
   (ii) the average kinetic energy of a molecule.

(f) Oxygen has a boiling point of 90 K and a melting point of 55 K. Describe qualitatively how oxygen at 273 K and oxygen at 27 K differ in respect of
   (i) density,
   (ii) spacing of the molecules,
   (iii) order in the pattern of molecules,
   (iv) motion of the molecules.

(a) Density is defined as the mass per unit volume.

(b) Gas molecules collide with molecules of the wall continously. For each of these collisions, there is a change of momentum for the gas molecule and hence a force is exerted on the molecule of the wall. The sum total of these forces exerted by gas molecules on unit area is the pressure exerted by a gas.

(c) (i) Using $pV = nRT$

where $p = 1.01 \times 10^5$ Pa, $n = 1$ mole
$R = 8.31$ JK^{-1} mol^{-1}, $T = 273$ K

Hence $(1.01 \times 10^5)V = (1)(8.31)(273)$

$$V = \frac{(1)(8.31)(273)}{(1.01 \times 10^5)}$$

$$= 0.02246$$
$$= 0.0225 \text{ m}^3$$

(ii) Density of oxgyen $= \dfrac{\text{mass}}{\text{volume}}$

$$= \frac{0.032}{0.02246}$$
$$= 1.425$$
$$= 1.4 \text{ kg m}^{-3}$$

(d) (i) The root-mean-square speed $\sqrt{<c^2>}$ is the square root of the mean square speed of the gas molecules.

(ii) $c_{\text{r.m.s.}} = \sqrt{\dfrac{300^2 + 400^2 + 500^2 + 600^2}{4}}$

$$= 463.68$$
$$= 464 \text{ m s}^{-1}$$

(e) (i) Using $p = \dfrac{1}{3}\rho<c^2>$

$$c_{\text{r.m.s.}} = \sqrt{<c^2>}$$

$$= \sqrt{\frac{3p}{\rho}}$$

$$= \sqrt{\frac{(3)(1.01 \times 10^5)}{1.425}}$$

$$= 461.1$$
$$= 461 \text{ m s}^{-1}$$

(ii) Average KE of a molecule $= \dfrac{3}{2}KT$

$$= \frac{3}{2}(1.38 \times 10^{-23})(273)$$

$$= 5.651 \times 10^{-21}$$
$$= 5.65 \times 10^{-21} \text{ J}$$

A comparision between oxygen at 273 K (a gas) with oxygen at 27 K (a solid)

233

(f)	Oxygen at 27 K (A solid)	Oxygen at 273 K (A gas)
Density	Much greater (about 1000 times greater than gaseous oxygen)	Small (about a 1000 times smaller than solid oxygen)
Spacing of the molecules	Molecules are closely packed with very small inter-molecular distances	Molecules are generally far apart except when they collide with each other. Inter-molecular distances are large.
Order in the patterns of molecules	Rigid and unchanging	Random and constantly changing
Motion of the molecules	Slower than gaseous oxygen. There is only vibrational motion and no translational motion	Much faster than molecules in solid. Motion is translational and rotational

Exercise 9

Multiple Choice Questions

1. One way of expressing the equation of state for an ideal gas is by the equation
$$pV = NkT$$
What do N and k represent?

	N	k
A	Avogadro constant	molar gas constant
B	total number of molecules	Boltzmann constant
C	total number of molecules	molar gas constant
D	total number of moles	Boltzmann constant

2. In deriving the equation
$$p = \frac{1}{3}\rho <c^2>$$
in the simple kinetic theory of gases, which of the following is NOT taken as a valid assumption?

A Attractive forces between the molecules are negligible.

B The duration of collision is negligible compared with the time between collisions.

C Collisions with the walls of the container and with other molecules cause no change in the average kinetic energy of the molecules.

D The molecules suffer negligible change of momentum on collision with the walls of the container.

3. The molecules of an ideal gas at thermodynamic (absolute) temperature T have a root-mean-square speed c_{rms}. The gas is heated to temperature $2T$. What is the new root-mean-square speed of the molecules?

A $\sqrt{2}\,c_{rms}$ B $2\sqrt{2}\,c_{rms}$

C $2\,c_{rms}$ D $4\,c_{rms}$

4. A fixed mass of gas undergoes changes of pressure and volume starting at L, as shown.

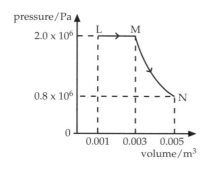

Which graph shows how temperature (measured in kelvin) changes with volume?

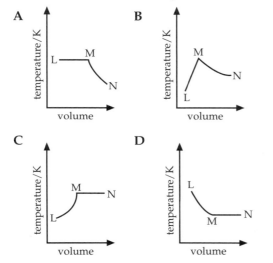

5   Four gas molecules have the speeds shown.

Speed/10^2 m s^{-1}			
1.0	3.0	5.0	7.0

What is their root-mean-square speed?

A 2×10^2 m s^{-1}

B 2.3×10^2 m s^{-1}

C 4.0×10^2 m s^{-1}

D 4.6×10^2 m s^{-1}

6   In the diagram the volume of bulb X is twice that of bulb Y. The system is filled with an ideal gas and a steady state is established with the bulbs held at 200 K and 400 K.

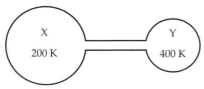

There are x moles of gas in X.
How many moles of gas are in Y?

A $\dfrac{x}{4}$ B $\dfrac{x}{2}$

C x D $2x$

7   What is the approximate number of atoms in a cubic metre of an ideal monatomic gas at a temperature of 27°C and a pressure of 1×10^5 Pa?

A 1×10^{22} B 6×10^{23}

C 2×10^{25} D 3×10^{26}

Structured Question

1   (a) The pressure p of an ideal gas of density ρ is related to the mean-square speed $<c^2>$ of its molecules by the expression

$$p = \frac{1}{3}\rho<c^2>$$

   (i) State three basic assumptions of the kinetic theory of gases, which lead to a model of an ideal gas.

   (ii) Write down the equation of state for an ideal gas.

   (iii) Show that the average kinetic energy of a molecule of an ideal gas is proportional to the thermodynamic temperature T.

   (b) Free neutrons in the core of a fission reactor are sometimes referred to as a 'neutron gas'. These free (thermal) neutrons may be assumed to behave as molecules of an ideal gas at a temperature of 35°C.

   (i) Calculate for a free neutron of mass 1.67×10^{-27} kg,
      1. its mean kinetic energy.
      2. its root-mean-square (r.m.s.) speed.

   (ii) Determine the temperature of helium gas, assumed to be an ideal gas, at which helium molecules (each of mass $4u$) would have the same r.m.s. speed as the free neutrons.

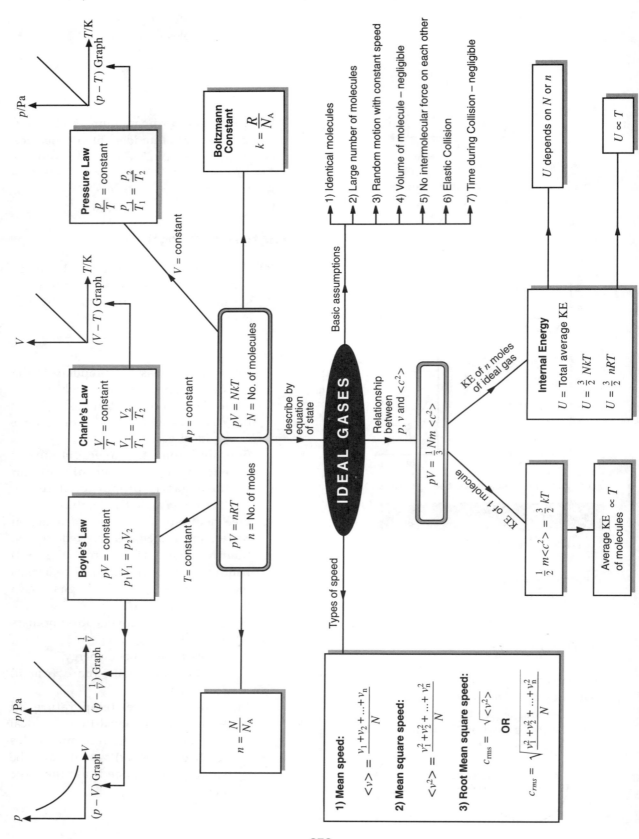

IDEAL GASES

Pressure Law
$\frac{p}{T}$ = constant
$\frac{p_1}{T_1} = \frac{p_2}{T_2}$

$(p - T)$ Graph

Boltzmann Constant
$k = \frac{R}{N_A}$

Charle's Law
$\frac{V}{T}$ = constant
$\frac{V_1}{T_1} = \frac{V_2}{T_2}$

$(V - T)$ Graph

Boyle's Law
pV = constant
$p_1 V_1 = p_2 V_2$

$(p - \frac{1}{V})$ Graph

$(p - V)$ Graph

V = constant

p = constant

T = constant

$pV = NkT$
N = No. of molecules

$pV = nRT$
n = No. of moles

$n = \frac{N}{N_A}$

describe by equation of state

Basic assumptions

1) Identical molecules
2) Large number of molecules
3) Random motion with constant speed
4) Volume of molecule – negligible
5) No intermolecular force on each other
6) Elastic Collision
7) Time during Collision – negligible

Relationship between p, v and $<c^2>$

$pV = \frac{1}{3} Nm <c^2>$

KE of n moles of ideal gas

Internal Energy
U = Total average KE
$U = \frac{3}{2} NkT$
$U = \frac{3}{2} nRT$

U depends on N or n

$U \propto T$

KE of 1 molecule

$\frac{1}{2} m<c^2> = \frac{3}{2} kT$

Average KE $\propto T$ of molecules

Types of speed

1) **Mean speed:**
$<v> = \frac{v_1 + v_2 + ... + v_n}{N}$

2) **Mean square speed:**
$<v^2> = \frac{v_1^2 + v_2^2 + ... + v_n^2}{N}$

3) **Root Mean square speed:**
$c_{rms} = \sqrt{<v^2>}$

OR

$c_{rms} = \sqrt{\frac{v_1^2 + v_2^2 + ... + v_n^2}{N}}$

10 Temperature

THERMAL EQUILIBRIUM

PRACTICAL THERMOMETERS

TEMPERATURE SCALES

Syllabus Objectives

In this chapter you should be able to:

- show an appreciation that thermal energy is transferred from a region of higher temperature to a region of lower temperature.

- show an understanding that regions of equal temperature are in thermal equilibrium.

- show an understanding that a physical property which varies with temperature may be used for the measurement of temperature and state examples of such properties.

- compare the relative advantages and disadvantages of resistance and thermocouple thermometers as previously calibrated instruments.

- show an understanding that there is an absolute scale of temperature which does not depend on the property of any particular substance (i.e. the thermodynamic scale and the concept of absolute zero).

- convert temperatures measured in kelvin to degrees Celsius:

$$\frac{T}{K} = \frac{\theta}{°C} + 273.15.$$

THERMAL EQUILIBRIUM

- Temperature is a fundamental quantity that measures the degree of hotness of a body as indicated on a calibrated scale.

- When two systems have different temperatures, thermal energy is transferred from a region of higher temperature to a region of lower temperature. (Fig 10.1)

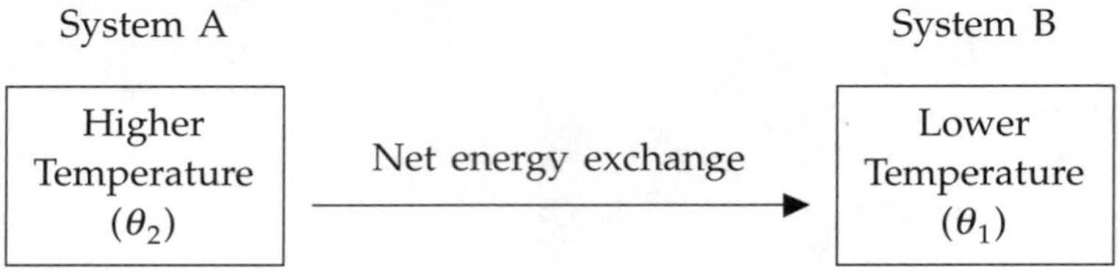

System A   System B

| Higher Temperature (θ_2) | Net energy exchange → | Lower Temperature (θ_1) |

Fig 10.1 Transfer of thermal energy

(a) In a power station, pressurized hot steam from a boiler rotates a turbine to generate electricity. After passing through the turbine the steam condenses to water in a cooling system.
The schematic diagram in Fig 10.2 shows the direction of heat flow from the boiler to the cooling system. The temperature in the boiler (θ_2) must be higher than the temperature in the cooling system (θ_1).

(b) Although the Sun is separated from the Earth by vast distances of empty space, it still can transfer its energy to the Earth through radiation. The temperature of the Sun (θ_2) is much higher than the temperature of the Earth (θ_1).

Boiler (Higher Temperature) θ_2

↓ Thermal energy input

Turbine → generates electricity

↓ Thermal energy output

Cooling system (Lower Temperature) θ_1

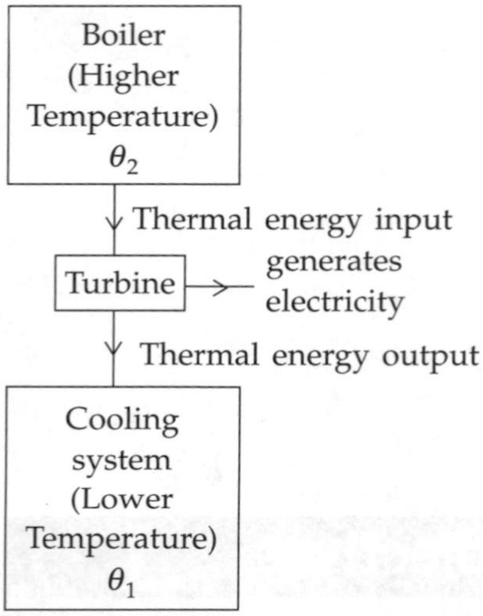

Fig 10.2 Thermal energy transfer in a turbine

- Two systems are in thermal contact with each other if there exists a mechanism for the transfer of thermal energy. Thermal contact does not necessarily mean physical contact and thermal energy can be transmitted through a vacuum as shown in Fig 10.3. There are three types of heat transfer mechanism.

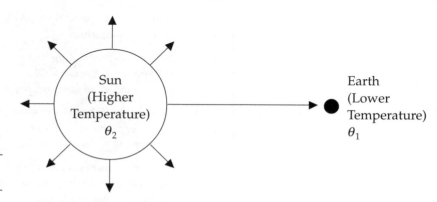

Fig 10.3 Energy is transferred through radiation

- **Thermal Conduction**
Thermal conduction is the process by which heat is transmitted from a region of higher temperature to a region of lower temperature as a result of collisions between atoms, molecules, ions and free electrons of the material. This mechanism of heat

238

transfer is most inefficient in a fluid as it takes time for energy to be transmitted from atom to atom in gases and liquids.

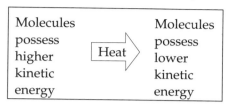

Higher temperature — Molecules possess higher kinetic energy — Heat → Molecules possess lower kinetic energy — Lower temperature

Fig 10.4 Thermal conduction in a solid

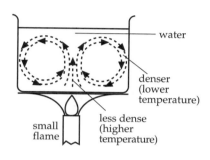

water

denser (lower temperature)

less dense (higher temperature)

small flame

Fig 10.5 Convection current

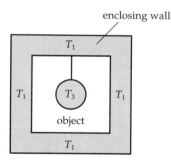

enclosing wall

T_1

T_1 T_3 T_1

object

T_1

Fig 10.6a Heat flows from object to wall

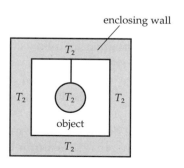

enclosing wall

T_2

T_2 T_2 T_2

object

T_2

Fig 10.6b Net heat flow is zero

- **Convection**
  Convection is the process by which heat is transmitted through a fluid by the movement of that fluid from a region of higher temperature to a region of lower temperature.
  (a) Convection occurs only in a fluid (i.e. liquid or gas). There is no convection in solids or in a vacuum.
  (b) Convection currents are produced whenever there is a temperature difference in a fluid. This is illustrated in Fig 10.5.
  (c) Convection currents are produced when liquid or gas changes its density. In Fig 10.5, water at the bottom of the beaker expands after absorbing heat from a small flame. This expansion is caused by the faster molecules moving further apart from each other. The expanded water rises because it is less dense than the cooler, denser water surrounding it.
  (d) As the fluid moves, it carries heat energy along to the cooler region.

- **Radiation**
  Radiation is the process by which heat is transmitted from a region of higher temperature to a region of lower temperature by means of a net transfer of electromagnetic waves.
  (a) Radiation consists mainly of infra-red electromagnetic waves.
  (b) Radiation is transmitted through a vacuum at a speed of 3×10^8 m s^{-1}.
  (c) All bodies above absolute zero emit radiation.
  (d) All surfaces absorb as well as emit radiation.
    (i) Consider an object with higher temperature T_3 surrounded by walls at lower temperature T_1 (i.e. $T_3 > T_1$, Fig 10.6a). Heat transfer between wall and object causes T_3 to decrease and T_1 to increase.
    (ii) After some time, the temperature of the object and wall will become equal and attain a value T_2 such that $T_1 < T_2 < T_3$ (Fig 10.6b). Thermal equilibrium is achieved and the object and the enclosing wall must each emit and absorb energy at the same rate.

- Two systems in thermal contact are in thermal equilibrium if
  (a) there is no net energy exchange between the two systems,
  (b) their temperatures are identical,
  (c) they have achieved a steady state condition (i.e. their temperatures do not fluctuate).

- The **zeroth law of thermodynamics** states that if two bodies X and Y are separately in thermal equilibrium with a third body T, then X and Y are in thermal equilibrium with each other. We use this as the basis to measure temperature with a thermometer.

- All thermometers are constructed to contain a material that has a thermometric property that changes continuously with temperature. Some common examples are the length of a mercury column, the electrical resistance of wires and the e.m.f. of a thermocouple. The variation of thermometric property with temperature can be linear (Fig 10.7) or non-linear (Fig 10.8).

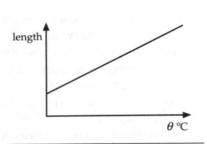

Fig 10.7 Graph of length against temperature θ

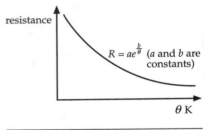

$R = ae^{\frac{b}{\theta}}$ (a and b are constants)

Fig 10.8 Graph of resistance of a thermistor against temperature

- The thermometric property should have the following characteristics:
  (a) It must vary continuously with the degree of hotness.
  (b) It can be measured accurately.
  (c) It should vary over a wide range of temperature.
  (d) It must not change its state as temperature changes.

Establishing a Temperature Scale

- A calibrated temperature scale can be obtained as follows:
  (a) Select a suitable thermometric property.
  (b) Select two fixed points. Measure the values of the thermometric property at the lower (X_L) and the upper fixed points (X_U).
  (c) A calibrated temperature scale can be defined by drawing a graph to relate the variation in thermometric property X with temperature.

Q The calibration curve for the thermistor is shown in Fig 10.9.

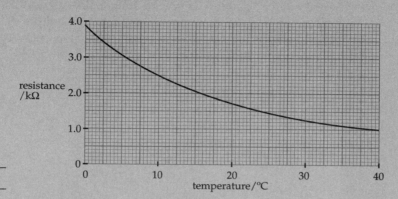

Fig 10.9

(a) The thermistor is used as a probe to measure temperature in the range of 0°C to 30°C.
   Use Fig 10.9 to find the resistance of the thermistor when the probe is at 30°C.
(b) Suggest one disadvantage of using the thermistor for temperature measurement.

A (a) When temperature = 30°C, resistance = 1.26 kΩ
(b) The variation of resistance with each degree change in temperature is not constant.

Q The graph shows the variation with temperature θ of a thermocouple e.m.f. E. Temperature θ is measured on the Celsius scale.
Why is the thermocouple inappropriate for measurement of temperature in the range shown?

Fig 10.10

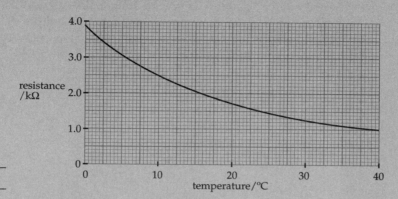

A The thermocouple does not always indicate a unique value of temperature.

Empirical Centigrade Scale

- In the empirical centigrade scale, the two fixed points are defined as the melting point of pure ice (ice point) and the boiling point of pure water (steam point). The interval between the two fixed points is divided into 100 divisions. Fig 10.11 illustrates this.

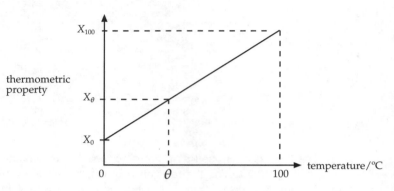

Fig 10.11 Graph of thermometric property against temperature

- From the graph, gradient of the line is constant.

Hence, $\dfrac{X_{100} - X_0}{100} = \dfrac{X_\theta - X_0}{\theta}$

$\therefore \theta = \left(\dfrac{X_\theta - X_0}{X_{100} - X_0}\right) 100°C$

PRACTICAL THERMO- METERS

- Examples of thermometer that has an empirical centigrade scale are the mercury-in-glass thermometer, resistance thermometer and the thermocouple thermometer.

Mercury-In-Glass Thermometer

- The thermometric property is the change in length (l) of a column of mercury as temperature changes. If l_{100}, l_0 and l_θ are are the lengths of mercury column at steam-point, ice-point and temperature θ, then

$$\theta = \left(\dfrac{l_\theta - l_0}{l_{100} - l_0}\right) 100°C$$

- The main features of this thermometer are as follows:
  (a) The wall of the mercury-filled glass bulb is made thin. This allows heat to penetrate quickly through the glass wall and reduces the response time for the thermometer.
  (b) The mercury-filled glass bulb is small. The thermometer is lighter and is more responsive to heat.
  (c) The bore of the capillary is narrow. This increases the sensitivity of the thermometer. Small changes in temperature cause the mercury to expand through a greater distance. When the thermometer has high sensitivity, the ratio $\dfrac{\text{change in length}}{\text{change in temperature}} \left(\dfrac{\Delta l}{\Delta \theta}\right)$ is high.

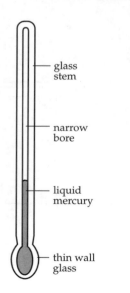

glass stem

narrow bore

liquid mercury

thin wall glass

Fig 10.12 Mercury-in-Glass thermometer

242

(d) The walls of the glass-stem are thick. This makes the thermometer stronger. In addition, the thick glass helps to magnify the narrow capillary tube and makes it easier to read.

An un-calibrated mercury-in-glass thermometer is placed in melting ice, boiling water and a liquid of unknown temperature θ consecutively. The lengths of the mercury column at each of the above temperatures are shown in Fig 10.13.
What is the unknown temperature θ?

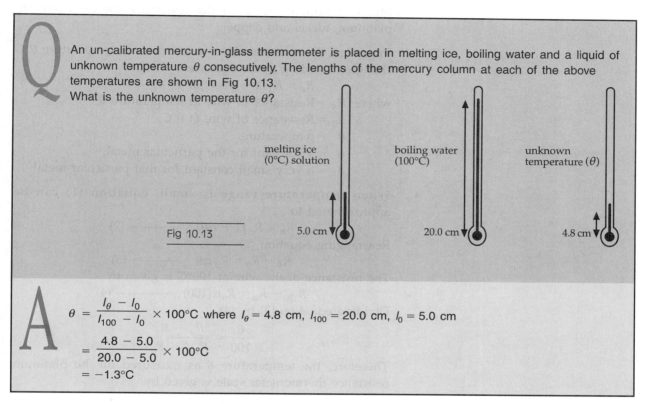

Fig 10.13

melting ice (0°C) solution   5.0 cm

boiling water (100°C)   20.0 cm

unknown temperature (θ)   4.8 cm

$$\theta = \frac{l_\theta - l_0}{l_{100} - l_0} \times 100°C \text{ where } l_\theta = 4.8 \text{ cm}, \ l_{100} = 20.0 \text{ cm}, \ l_0 = 5.0 \text{ cm}$$

$$= \frac{4.8 - 5.0}{20.0 - 5.0} \times 100°C$$

$$= -1.3°C$$

A mercury thermometer is found to have a volume of 0.400 cm³ at 0°C and a volume of 0.425 cm³ at 100°C. What is the temperature on the Celsius scale when the volume of mercury is 0.420 cm³?

$$\theta = \frac{l_\theta - l_0}{l_{100} - l_0} \times 100°C = \frac{(l_\theta - l_0)A}{(l_{100} - l_0)A} \times 100°C$$

where l_θ = length of mercury column at temperature θ,
       l_{100} = length of mercury column at 100°C,
       l_0 = length of mercury column at 0°C,
       A = cross-sectional area of the capillary tube.

$$\therefore \ \theta = \frac{V_\theta - V_0}{V_{100} - V_0} \times 100°C = \frac{0.420 - 0.400}{0.425 - 0.400} \times 100°C = 80.0°C$$

where V_θ = volume of mercury at temperature θ°C,
       V_{100} = volume of mercury at 100°C,
       V_0 = volume of mercury at temperature 0°C

Resistance Thermometer

- The thermometric property is the change in resistance of a wire as temperature changes.

- Metals commonly used in the resistance thermometer are platinum, nickel and copper.

- In general, the resistance R_θ of a conductor at temperature $\theta°C$ changes according to the equation
$$R_\theta = R_0 (1 + \alpha\theta + \beta\theta^2) \quad\text{——— (1)}$$
where R_θ = Resistance of wire at temperature θ,
R_0 = Resistance of wire at $0°C$,
θ = temperature,
α = a constant for the particular metal,
β = a very small constant for that particular metal

- When temperature range is small, equation (1) can be approximated to
$$R_\theta = R_0 (1 + \alpha\theta) \quad\text{——— (2)}$$
Rearranging equation (2)
$$R_\theta - R_0 = R_0 \alpha\theta \quad\text{——— (3)}$$
The resistance of the wire at $100°C$ is given by
$$R_{100} - R_0 = R_0\alpha(100) \quad\text{——— (4)}$$
Dividing equation (3) by (4)
$$\frac{\theta}{100} = \frac{R_\theta - R_0}{R_{100} - R_0}$$
Therefore, the temperature θ as measured on the platinum resistance thermometer scale is given by
$$\theta = \left(\frac{R_\theta - R_0}{R_{100} - R_0}\right)100°C$$

- The graph of resistance against temperature is approximately a straight line over a small range of temperature (Fig 10.14).

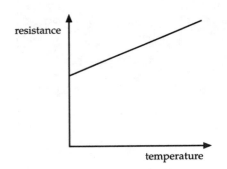

Fig 10.14 Linear relationship between resistance and temperature

- The main features of this thermometer are as follows:
  (a) The resistance of the platinum wire (R) is measured by Wheatstone bridge circuit shown below (Fig 10.15). When the Wheatstone bridge circuit is balanced, the resistance R can be calculated.
  (b) The platinum wire is coiled around a mica strip and connected to the Wheatstone bridge by thick copper leads.
  (c) To offset the change in resistance in the copper leads as temperature changes, a pair of identical leads is connected to the other arm of the Wheatstone bridge.
  (d) Both dummy leads and platinum are enclosed in a silica tube.
  (e) This thermometer is very accurate and has high sensitivity. This means that the ratio $\dfrac{\text{change in resistance}}{\text{change in temperature}}\left(\dfrac{\Delta R}{\Delta \theta}\right)$ is large.

244

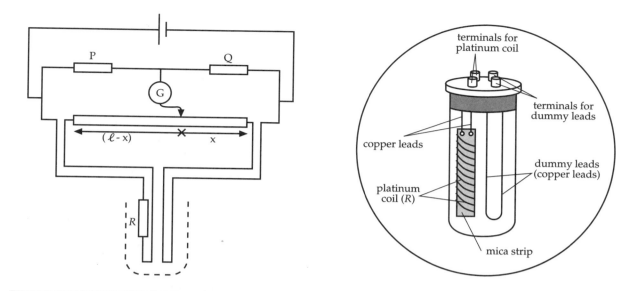

Fig 10.15 Platinum Resistance Thermometer

Q The resistance of a platinum wire is 3.129 Ω at the ice-point and 4.620 Ω at the steam point. It is used to measure an unknown temperature θ and its resistance is 3.547 Ω. What is the unknown temperature θ on the centigrade scale of this thermometer?

A $\theta = \dfrac{R_\theta - R_0}{R_{100} - R_0} \times 100°C$ where $R_\theta = 3.547 \ \Omega$, $R_0 = 3.129 \ \Omega$, $R_{100} = 4.620 \ \Omega$

$= \dfrac{3.547 - 3.129}{4.620 - 3.129} \times 100°C$

$= 28.03°C$

Thermocouple Thermometer

• A constantan wire is soldered to two pieces of copper wire (Fig 10.16) at C (reference junction) and H (test junction). The free ends of the copper wire are connected to a sensitive millivoltmeter. If C is kept at ice-point (0°C) and H at a higher temperature (θ), a deflection can be seen on the millivoltmeter. This is because electrons migrate across the boundary between two dissimilar metals. This produces the contact potential difference E_0 and E_θ at C and H respectively. The millivoltmeter gives the net thermal electric e.m.f. between the two junctions. This arrangement is known as a thermocouple.

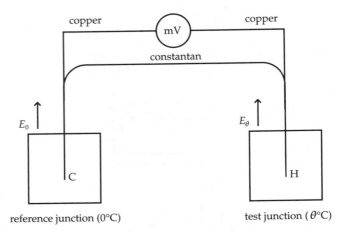

copper · mV · copper

constantan

E_0

E_θ

C

H

reference junction (0°C)

test junction (θ°C)

Fig 10.16 Thermocouple

- The production of an e.m.f. in a thermocouple by heating one junction and keeping the other cold is known as the Seebeck effect.

- The thermoelectric property is the change in e.m.f. in the thermocouple as temperature changes.

- If we assume that the thermoelectric e.m.f. increases linearly with the temperature difference between the test and reference junctions, the temperature θ on the thermoelectric thermometer scale can be found from:

$$\theta = \left(\frac{E_\theta - E_0}{E_{100} - E_0} \right) 100°C$$

where E_0, E_{100} and E_θ are the thermoelectric e.m.f. of the test junctions at ice point, stream point and temperature θ°C.

- The main features of this thermometer are as follows:
  (a) The small size of junction H enables the thermometer to respond to small temperature changes rapidly. This is due to its small heat capacity and good conductivity of heat.
  (b) The thermocouple can measure temperature at a point or in cracks or crevices on the surface.
  (c) It can measure a wide range of temperature. With suitable choice of dissimilar metals at the two junctions, temperatures from $-200°C$ to $1700°C$ can be obtained.
  (d) Thermocouple e.m.f. varies smoothly with temperatures.
  (e) A potentiometer can be used to measure the e.m.f. instead of a millivoltmeter.

246

Q When one junction X of a thermocouple is placed in melting ice and the junction Y in steam at 100°C, the e.m.f is 6.0 mV. Junction X is removed from the melting ice and is placed in a liquid bath at a constant temperature, junction Y remaining in steam. The e.m.f. is now −1.5 mV. What is the temperature of the bath on the centigrade scale of this thermocouple?

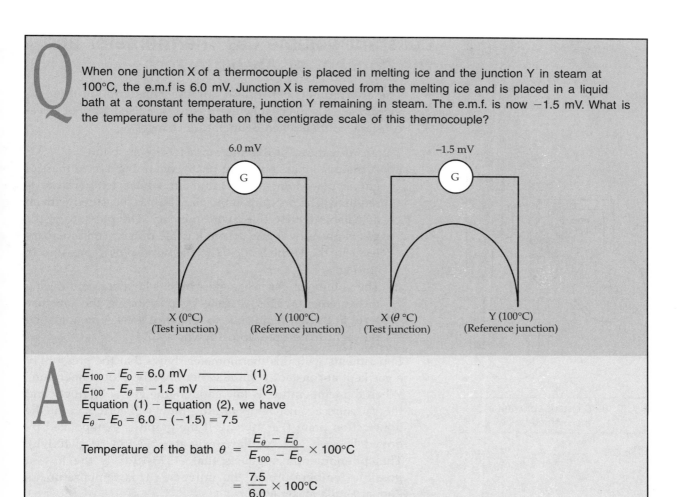

A

$E_{100} - E_0 = 6.0$ mV ———— (1)

$E_{100} - E_\theta = -1.5$ mV ———— (2)

Equation (1) − Equation (2), we have

$E_\theta - E_0 = 6.0 - (-1.5) = 7.5$

Temperature of the bath $\theta = \dfrac{E_\theta - E_0}{E_{100} - E_0} \times 100°C$

$= \dfrac{7.5}{6.0} \times 100°C$

$= 125°C$

Limitations of the Centigrade Temperature Scale

- When the same temperature is measured on the Centigrade temperature scale by different types of thermometer, the reading obtained will differ from each other. There is no exact agreement except at the fixed points which in the first place were obtained by definition. This is because the assumption that the thermometric property varies linearly with temperature is only an approximation. Different thermometers with different properties do not respond to temperature in the same way. In view of this deficiency, a new scale known as the Ideal Gas Temperature Scale or the Absolute Scale was introduced. The constant volume gas thermometer is used to define temperatures on this scale.

Constant Volume Gas Thermometer and the Concept of Absolute Zero

- The thermometric property in the constant volume gas thermometer is the change in pressure of a fixed mass of gas at constant volume when temperature changes.

- The main features of this thermometer are as follows:
  (a) A thin wall glass bulb (Fig 10.18) containing a fixed mass of gas is placed in an environment whose temperature is required. The pressure in the glass bulb is measured with an adjustable U-tube filled with mercury. The pressure of the gas is given by $h + H$ where h is the difference in mercury level in the U-tube, and H is the atmospheric pressure in cm Hg.
  (b) The volume of gas in the glass bulb is kept constant during measurements. This is done by positioning the mercury level in the left hand tube to reference level A by adjusting the right hand tube up or down.

- Experiments with this thermometer shows that the pressure of a gas kept at constant volume varies linearly with temperature. When the temperature is low enough, the gas will liquefy and the pressure against temperature graph will terminate at the liquefaction point (Fig 10.19a). If the graph is extrapolated by dotted lines, it will cut the x-axis at $-273.15°C$ (Fig 10.19b). This phenomenon suggests that $-273.15°C$ is the lowest possible temperature in the universe. This temperature is known as the absolute zero.

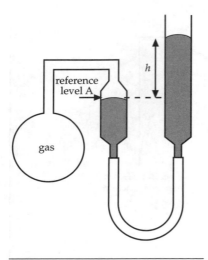

Fig 10.18   Constant Volume Gas thermometer

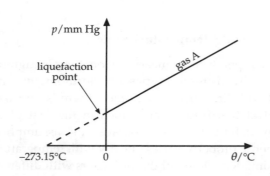

Fig 10.19a   A graph of p against θ

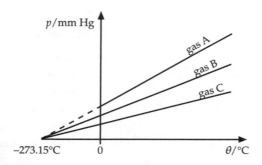

Fig 10.19b   Extrapolation of lines in a p against θ graph

248

TEMPERATURE SCALES

The Absolute Scale of Temperature (The Ideal Gas Scale)

- Lord Kelvin in 1848 proposed the absolute scale of temperature on the basis of the existence of an absolute zero and the relationship between the pressure and temperature of an ideal gas.

- The two fixed points on the absolute scale are defined as follows:
  (a) Lower fixed point is the absolute zero and is denoted by 0 kelvin (or 0 K). This is the temperature at which thermal energy is zero.
  (b) Upper fixed point is the temperature of the triple point of pure air-free water. Triple point is the temperature at which ice, water and water vapour co-exist in equilibrium. This occurs at 0.01°C or 273.16 K and is a unique point which can be more accurately determined experimentally.

- The unit of temperature on this scale is called the kelvin (K) and the symbol for the temperature is represented by T. One kelvin (K) is defined as $\dfrac{1}{273.16}$ of the temperature of the triple point of water. This figure makes its size the same as the commonly used Celsius temperature scale.

- An ideal gas obeys the equation of state

$$\frac{\text{Pressure} \times \text{Volume}}{\text{Temperature}} = \text{constant}$$

- A constant volume gas thermometer is used to measure the pressure and temperature of a gas at an unknown temperature and at triple point.
  Pressure at an unknown temperature $= p$
  Unknown temperature on the scale $= T$
  Pressure at triple point $= p_{tr}$
  Temperature at triple point $= 273.16$ K
Since volume is the same for both measurements

$$\frac{p}{T} = \frac{p_{tr}}{273.16}$$

$$T = 273.16 \times \left(\frac{p}{p_{tr}}\right)$$

Based on the ideal gas scale, the temperature in kelvins is directly proportional to the pressure of the gas (Fig 10.20).

- Since ideal gas do not exist in nature, real gases are used. However, real gases behave like an ideal gas only at low pressures. Hence in practice, the pressure of a real gas in a constant volume thermometer is reduced progressively towards

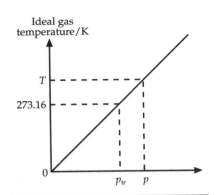

Fig 10.20   Ideal gas temperature scale

249

zero and the corresponding temperatures are measured. In Fig 10.21, the straight line graphs of temperature against pressure for O_2, air, N_2, He and H_2 are obtained. All of them converge at the vertical axis to indicate the Ideal Gas Temperature or Thermodynamic Temperature.

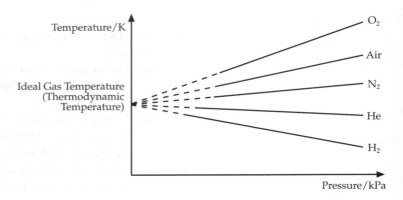

Fig 10.21   Ideal gas temperature

Q At the triple point of water the pressure of a fixed mass of gas is 2680 Pa. The temperature is changed to T while the volume of the gas is kept constant. The pressure is then 4870 Pa.
(a) Find the value of T.
(b) What is the advantage of making this determination at such a low pressure?

A (a) Since $T = 273.16 \left(\dfrac{P}{P_{tr}} \right)$ where $P = 4870$ Pa and $P_{tr} = 2680$ Pa

$$\therefore T = 273.16 \left(\frac{4870}{2680} \right) = 496 \text{ K}$$

(b) At low pressure, the value of T approaches the ideal gas temperature.

The Celsius Scale

- The Celsius scale is obtained by adjusting the temperature interval of the Kelvin scale to agree with the temperature interval on the Centigrade scale. The temperature in degree Celsius is given by

$$\frac{\theta}{°C} = \frac{T}{K} - 273.15$$

To convert temperatures in kelvin to degree Celsius, we use

$$\frac{T}{K} = \frac{\theta}{°C} + 273.15.$$

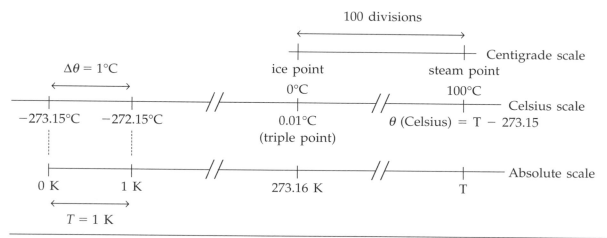

Fig 10.22 A comparison of the Centigrade scale, Celsius scale and the Absolute scale

	Centigrade	Celsius	Kelvin
Absolute zero	−273.15	−273.15	0.00
Freezing point of water	0.00	0.00	273.15
Triple point of water	0.01	0.01	273.16
Boiling point of water	100.00	100.00	373.15

The above table gives the numerical values of the temperature, to 2 decimal places, of four reference points on three different temperature scales. In each column, two of the values are exact by definition and two are found by experiment. Which, for each scale, are exact temperatures?

	Centigrade	Celsius	Kelvin
Boiling point of water	100°C	100.00°C	373.15 K
Triple point of water	0.01°C	0.01°C	273.16 K
Freezing point of water	0°C	0.00°C	273.15 K
Absolute zero	−273.15°C	−273.15°C	0 K

From the above illustration, the exact temperatures are
1) Centigrade scale: 0°C and 100°C
2) Celsius scale: −273.15°C and 0.01°C
3) Kelvin scale: 0 K and 273.16 K

251

Any physical quantity which varies with temperature can, in theory, be used to measure temperature. Three such quantities are — the volume of a sample of water, the resistance of platinum wire and the resistance of a sample of silicon. The table gives the values of these quantities at different temperatures.

Temperature/°C	Volume of water/cm³	Resistance of platinum/Ω	Resistance of silicon/Ω
0	3.47	5.26	2800
8	3.47	5.41	2710
30	3.49	5.84	2310
50	3.52	6.22	1800
80	3.58	6.80	620
100	3.63	7.19	72

Use data from this table where necessary to respond to parts (a), (b), (c), (d), (e) and (f) which follow.

(a) Describe the principal features of a thermometer which makes use of the variation in the resistance of a platinum wire.

(b) What advantage would be gained by using a quantity which varies linearly with thermodynamic temperature?

(c) Give one advantage and one disadvantage of using the variation in the resistance of a sample of silicon.

(d) In what ways does the table make it clear that water is unsuitable as a thermometric liquid?

(e) A constant α, called the temperature coefficient of resistance, is defined by the equation
$$R_t = R_0 (1 + \alpha t)$$
where R_t is the resistance of a wire at $t°C$, R_0 is the resistance of the wire at 0°C and t is the Celsius temperature. Find the average value of α for the platinum wire between 0°C and 100°C.

(f) A microbiologist needs accurate measurements of a temperature which varies between 90°C and 91°C. Which type of thermometer would you advice? Explain your choice.

Cambridge

(a) The principle features of a platinum-resistance thermometer are as follows:
  (i) The resistance of platinum wires varies continuously as temperature changes. When temperature increases from 0°C to 100°C, the resistance changes from 5.26 Ω to 7.19 Ω.
  (ii) The resistance of the platinum wire is measured by a Wheatstone bridge circuit. A pair of dummy leads is connected to the other arm of the Wheatstone bridge to offset the change in resistance in the copper leads as temperature changes. (See Fig 10.15). Both dummy leads and platinum wire are enclosed in a silica tube.

252

(iii) Within the range of 0°C to 100°C, the resistance against temperature graph is approximately linear. The gradients of 3 arbitrarily chosen intervals on the graph are approximately the same.

$$\text{Gradient 1} = \frac{6.22 - 5.26}{50 - 0} = 0.0192$$

$$\text{Gradient 2} = \frac{7.19 - 5.26}{100 - 0} = 0.0193$$

$$\text{Gradient 3} = \frac{6.80 - 5.41}{80 - 8} = 0.0193$$

(iv) The thermometer is bulky and cannot measure localised or rapidly varying temperature. It is however accurate and capable of measuring small temperature differences.

(b) The temperature scale can be divided into regular intervals that correspond to the thermodynamic temperature scale. This makes conversion from one scale to the other easy.

(c) The advantage of using silicon is its high sensitivity. The ratio

$$\frac{\text{change in resistance}}{\text{change in temperature}}\left(\frac{\Delta R}{\Delta \theta}\right) = \frac{2800 - 72}{0 - 100} = -27.3 \ \Omega/°C$$

The disadvantage is the non-linearity of the resistance against temperature graph. The gradients of 3 arbitrarily chosen intervals on the graph are different.

$$\text{Gradient 1} = \frac{2800 - 1800}{0 - 50} = -20 \ \Omega/°C$$

$$\text{Gradient 2} = \frac{2710 - 620}{8 - 80} = -29.0 \ \Omega/°C$$

$$\text{Gradient 3} = \frac{2710 - 72}{8 - 100} = -28.7 \ \Omega/°C$$

(d) From 0°C to 8°C, the volume of water do not change as temperature increases. This irregular behaviour makes the change in volume of water an unsuitable thermometric property.

(e) $R_{100} = 7.19 \ \Omega$, $R_0 = 5.26 \ \Omega$, $t = 100°C$
$\therefore R_{100} = R_0 (1 + \alpha t)$
$7.19 = 5.26 (1 + \alpha(100))$
$\therefore \alpha = 3.67 \times 10^{-3} \ °C^{-1}$

(f) Silicon resistance thermometer should be chosen because it has high sensitivity between 90°C and 91°C.

253

Exercise 10

Multiple Choice Questions

1 An advantage of the platinum resistance thermometer is that
   A it may be used to measure rapidly changing temperatures.
   B it has a linear scale, because the resistance of a piece of platinum varies directly as thermodynamic temperature.
   C it may be used to measure steady temperatures with very high accuracy.
   D it absorbs energy from its surroundings very slowly so that it does not disturb the condition of the body under test when placed in contact with it.

2 Which of the following instruments would be most suitable to measure a rapidly changing temperature in the range 25°C to 50°C assuming that they had all been previously calibrated to give direct read-outs?
   A an alcohol-in-glass thermometer
   B a clinical thermometer
   C a mercury-in-glass thermometer
   D a thermocouple

3 Which combination of thermometers would be most appropriate for measuring the following three temperatures?

	1 temperature at various positions in a flame	2 boiling point of sulphur (717 K)	3 boiling point of liquid nitrogen (80 K)
A	liquid-in-glass	resistance	thermocouple
B	resistance	liquid-in-glass	thermocouple
C	resistance	thermo-couple	liquid-in-glass
D	thermocouple	resistance	resistance

4 Which one of the following thermometers would be most suitable for monitoring the temperature of gases in a factory chimney if the temperature can vary over a range of 200 K in a minute?
   A alcohol in glass
   B mercury in glass
   C constant-volume gas
   D thermoelectric

5 What is 273.00 K on the Celsius scale of temperature?
   A -0.15°C
   B 0.00°C
   C 0.15°C
   D 273.15°C

6 What thermodynamic temperature is equivalent to 501.85°C?
   A 775.01 K   B 775.00 K
   C 774.85 K   D 228.85 K

Structured Questions

1 (a) Describe the principle features of a thermocouple and state a suitable indicating instrument to use with it.
   (b) State why the thermodynamic scale of temperature is called an absolute scale.
   (c) Name types of thermometers that would be suitable for measuring each of the following:
      (i) the boiling point of oxygen (about 90 K),
      (ii) a rapidly changing temperature,
      (iii) the temperature of a very small quantity of a liquid.
      Give a reason for your choice of thermometer in (ii).

Cambridge

2 (a) Outline how a physical property which varies with temperature may be used for the measurement of temperature.
   (b) How does the absolute (thermo-dynamic) scale of temperature differ from that described in (a)?

(c) Suggest types of thermometer (one in each case) which would be suitable for measuring each of the following:
  (i) the melting point of ethanol (about 160 K
  (ii) the temperature inside a blast furnace (about 1800 K).
(d) Briefly discuss whether a thermistor could be used to monitor the variation with time of the temperature in a room.
Cambridge

3 (a) State **two** physical properties which may be used for the measurement of temperature.
(b) Express 273 K as a temperature measured on the Celsius scale.
(c) Comment on the statement "Today the temperature is 40°C and yesterday it was 20°C so it is twice as hot today as it was yesterday.'

4 (a) By reference to thermal energy transfer, explain what is meant by
  (i) two bodies having the same temperature,
  (ii) body H having a higher temperature than body C.

(b) (i) Briefly describe how a physical property may be used to measure temperature on its empirical centigrade scale.
  (ii) Hence explain why two thermometers measuring temperature on their empirical centigrade scale do not agree at all temperatures.

5 (a) A resistance thermometer is placed in a bath of liquid at 0°C and its resistance is found to be 3740 Ω. At 100°C, its resistance is 210 Ω. The bath is now cooled until the resistance of the thermometer is 940 Ω.
  (i) What is the temperature of the bath, as measured using the resistance thermometer?
  (ii) The reading taken at the same time on a mercury-in-gass thermometer placed in the bath is 40°C. Suggest a reason for the difference between this reading and the value calculated in (a)(i).
(b) What do you understand by the absolute (thermodynamic) scale of temperature?

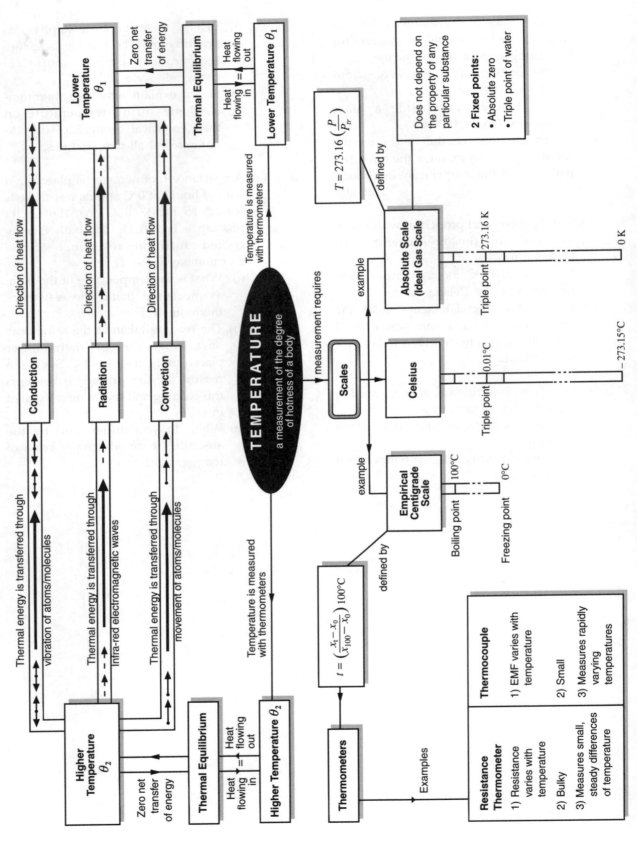

TEMPERATURE — a measurement of the degree of hotness of a body

Higher Temperature θ_2

Lower Temperature θ_1

Conduction — Thermal energy is transferred through vibration of atoms/molecules — Direction of heat flow

Radiation — Thermal energy is transferred through Infra-red electromagnetic waves — Direction of heat flow

Convection — Thermal energy is transferred through movement of atoms/molecules — Direction of heat flow

Thermal Equilibrium — Zero net transfer of energy

Heat flowing out / Heat flowing in — **Higher Temperature θ_2**

Heat flowing in = Heat flowing out — **Lower Temperature θ_1**

Temperature is measured with thermometers

measurement requires — **Scales**

example — **Empirical Centigrade Scale**

Boiling point 100°C — Freezing point 0°C

defined by — $t = \left(\dfrac{x_t - x_0}{x_{100} - x_0}\right) 100°C$

example — **Celsius**

Triple point 0.01°C — $-273.15°C$

example — **Absolute Scale (Ideal Gas Scale)**

Triple point 273.16 K — 0 K

Does not depend on the property of any particular substance

2 Fixed points:
- Absolute zero
- Triple point of water

defined by — $T = 273.16 \left(\dfrac{P}{P_{tr}}\right)$

Temperature is measured with thermometers — **Thermometers**

Examples

Resistance Thermometer
1) Resistance varies with temperature
2) Bulky
3) Measures small, steady differences of temperature

Thermocouple
1) EMF varies with temperature
2) Small
3) Measures rapidly varying temperatures

256

11

Thermal Properties of Materials

THREE STATES OF MATTER

SPECIFIC LATENT HEAT

SPECIFIC HEAT CAPACITY

FIRST LAW OF THERMODYNAMICS

Syllabus Objectives

In this chapter you should be able to:

- explain, using a simple kinetic model for matter, why
  — melting and boiling take place without a change in temperature,
  — the specific latent heat of vaporisation is higher than specific latent heat of fusion for the same substance,
  — a cooling effect accompanies evaporation.

- define and use the concept of specific latent heat, and identify the main principles of its determination by electrical methods.

- define and use the concept of specific heat capacity, and identify the main principles of its determination by electrical methods.

- relate a rise in temperature of a body to an increase in its internal energy.

- show an understanding that internal energy is determined by the state of the system and that it can be expressed as the sum of a random distribution of kinetic and potential energies associated with the molecules of a system.

- recall and use the first law of thermodynamics expressed in terms of the change in internal energy, the heating of the system and the work done on the system.

257

THREE STATES OF MATTER

- The three states of matter are solid, liquid and gas. Table 11.1 illustrates the differences between the three states

State of Matter	Structure and Characteristics	Motion of Molecules
Solid	Atoms or molecules are very closely packed. (a) Crystalline solid — atoms or molecules are compactly arranged in a regular and orderly lattice structure. Crystals have a high density. (b) Non-crystalline solid — atoms or molecules are arranged in a more random way. Density is still high but generally lower than many crystalline solid.	Atoms and molecules are locked in and constrained by attractive and repulsive intermolecular forces. They vibrate about their equilibrium positions continually as long as temperature is above absolute zero. All molecular motion ceases at zero kelvin. As temperature rises, molecular motion and kinetic energy increases.
	Has fixed shape and volume. They are not easily compressed or stretched by mechanical means.	When solids are stretched, atoms/molecules move further apart but are opposed by attractive forces. When solids are compressed, atoms/molecules move closer together but are opposed by repulsive forces.
	A typical inter-atomic separation in a crystalline solid is about 3×10^{-10} m	At melting point, kinetic energy is high enough to enable atoms/molecules to escape from their fixed positions and exchange places with their neighbours. Bonds are broken and lattice structure collapsed.
Liquid	Atoms or molecules are only slightly further apart than in solids. Density remains high.	Atoms or molecules continue to vibrate but in addition, have random and restricted translational motion.
	Volume is constant but has variable shape. They are not easily compressed by mechanical means.	Attractive forces between atoms or molecules are weaker. This allows for greater mobility which in turn explains why liquid can take the shape of any container. Attractive forces manifest themselves as surface tension and viscosity of a liquid.

	Evaporation occurs at the surface of a liquid.	Kinetic energy of atoms or molecules varies. Those with higher speeds are energetic enough to overcome the forces of attraction and escape from the surface. Atoms or molecules left behind have lower kinetic energy. This explains why evaporation causes cooling in a liquid.
	Atomic or molecular separation in a liquid is about the same as that of solid. The difference between liquids and solids is a difference of structure.	There is no structure in a liquid because atoms or molecules move randomly and haphazardly.
Gas	Atoms or molecules are very far apart. Densities of gases are very low.	Atoms or molecules move randomly at very high speed. The average kinetic energy is directly proportional to temperature.
	Gases do not have fixed volume or shape. They are highly compressible.	Atoms or molecules will occupy any available space in a container. Intermolecular forces between them are negligible except during random collisions with each other. Large repulsive forces are exerted during collisions.
	Atomic or molecular separations at s. t .p. (standard temperature pressure) are on average about 10 molecular diameters. The average distance travelled between collisions is roughly 300 molecular diameters.	The average distance travelled between collisions is roughly 300 molecular diameters.

Table 11.1 A summary of the characteristics of solids, liquids and gases

- The description of the properties of solid, liquid and gas in terms of the random and continuous motion of atoms and molecules is known as the kinetic theory of matter.

Melting and Boiling

- Heat (Q) is a form of energy that is transferred from one region to another as a result of a temperature difference.

259

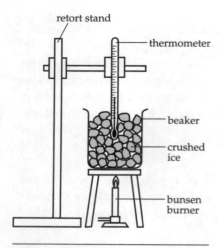

Fig 11.1   Experimental set-up

Fig 11.2   Graph of temperature against time

- When heat is transferred from one point to another, it could produce a change in state in the material through which it flows. This can be illustrated by heating ice in a beaker. (Fig 11.1) Readings of temperature are taken every minute with a thermometer. Fig 11.2 shows a typical temperature against time graph for the melting and boiling of ice and water respectively.

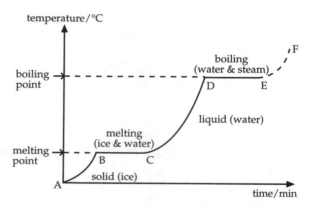

- Melting is the process in which a substance changes its state from solid to liquid at a definite temperature.
  - (a) When ice melts (BC), there is no change in temperature even though heat is being absorbed continually.
  - (b) When heat is supplied to ice, molecules vibrate with increasing energy in fixed positions in an ordered lattice structure. At the melting point (BC), bonds between molecules are broken progressively. The orderly structure of ice breaks down into a disordered phase. Intermolecular distances do not increase significantly but the increase in thermal agitation allows molecules to vibrate and rotate about variable positions. This increases the potential energies of the molecules without changing the average molecular kinetic energy. The temperature remains constant until ice has turned completely into water at $0°C$. The energy that is supplied to change a solid into a liquid is known as latent heat of fusion.

- Boiling is the process in which a liquid changes into vapour at a definite temperature.
  - (a) When water boils (DE), there is no change in the average molecular kinetic energy even though heat is being absorbed continually. The temperature remains constant.
  - (b) Part of the heat supplied is used to overcome intermolecular forces of attraction and to increase the potential energy of the molecules. The rest is used to do external work in pushing back the surrounding atmosphere. More energy is required to change liquid to the gaseous

260

state during boiling. The total amount of energy needed is known as the latent heat of vaporisation.

SPECIFIC LATENT HEAT

- The specific latent heat of fusion (l_f) of a substance is the quantity of heat required to change 1 kg of the substance from solid state to liquid state without a change in temperature. Mathematically,

$$l_f = \frac{Q}{m}$$

where Q is the latent heat of fusion,
m is the mass of solid, and
l_f is the specific latent heat of fusion.

The unit for l_f is J kg^{-1}.

- Determination of specific latent heat of fusion of ice

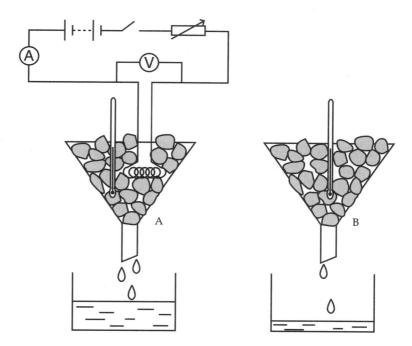

Fig 11.3 Apparatus used to determine the specific latent heat of ice

(a) A heater connected to a power supply is immersed in ice at 0°C in funnel A (Fig 11.3). When a steady current is switched on, the stopwatch is started at the same time. The heat produced by the heater melts the ice and the water that trickles down funnel A is collected in a beaker of known mass. Ammeter and voltmeter readings are recorded and if necessary, the rheostat adjusted to maintain constant current and voltage. After a time t, the mass of water collected (m_1) is determined.

(b) A control experiment is set up side by side with funnel A. This is to determine the mass of ice (m_2) that will melt in time t at room temperature. Equal amount of ice at 0°C are placed in funnel B and the water collected with a beaker of known mass.

261

(c) Mass of water from funnel A $= m_1$ kg

Mass of water from funnel B $= m_2$ kg

Mass of ice melted by the heater $= (m_1 - m_2)$ kg

Specific latent heat of fusion of ice $= l_f \, J \, kg^{-1}$

Reading of ammeter $= I$ A

Reading of voltmeter $= V$ V

Time for which heater was switched on $= t$ sec

Hence, heat needed to melt the ice

= Electrical energy given out by the heater

$(m_1 - m_2) \, l_f = IVt$

$$\therefore l_f = \frac{IVt}{(m_1 - m_2)}$$

- The specific latent heat of vaporisation (l_v) of a liquid is the quantity of heat required to change 1 kg of the liquid to vapour without a change in temperature.

Mathematically, $l_v = \dfrac{Q}{m}$

where Q is the latent heat of vaporisation,

m is the mass of liquid,

l_v is the specific latent heat of vaporisation.

The unit for l_v is $J \, kg^{-1}$.

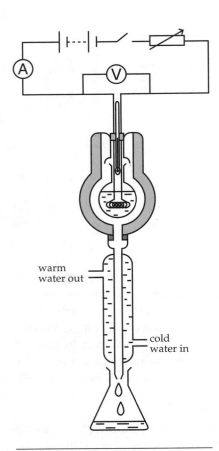

- Determination of specific latent heat of vaporisation of water.

(a) A heater connected to a power supply is used to boil water in a flask (Fig 11.4). The vapour produced forms a jacket around the flask before entering a condenser.

(b) After a prolonged period of continuous boiling, a steady state is reached when the rate of vaporisation equals the rate of condensation. All electrical energy is used to supply the latent heat of vaporisation of the water.

(c) The ammeter reading (I_1), voltmeter reading (V_1) and the mass (m_1) of water collected in t seconds are recorded.

(d) Electrical energy supplied by heater = Latent heat of vaporisation + Heat lost

$I_1 V_1 t = m_1 l + h$ ——— (1)

(e) The rheostat is adjusted to obtain a significantly different ammeter reading (I_2), voltmeter reading (V_2) and mass (m_2) of water in the same time t.

Hence

$I_2 V_2 t = m_2 l + h$ ——— (2)

Since h remains the same for equations (1) and (2), it can be eliminated and l determined.

Evaporation

- Evaporation is a phenomenon that occurs at the surface of a liquid and involves the change in state of the liquid to a gas at any temperature.

Fig 11.4 Set up for determining the specific latent heat of vaporisation of water

warm water out

cold water in

262

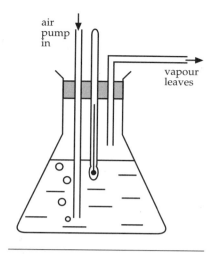

air pump in

vapour leaves

Fig 11.5 Cooling effect of evaporation

- Evaporation causes cooling. This is illustrated in Fig 11.5. Air from a pump is bubbled through ether continuously. This increases the surface area through which evaporation can take place and increases the rate of evaporation. The thermometer immersed in the ether show a continuous decrease in temperature as long as air is bubbled through the liquid.

- This phenomenon can be explained in terms of kinetic theory. Molecules within the liquid collide randomly with each other, exchanging momentum continuously. Molecular speed and kinetic energy change on every impact. The result is a wide distribution of kinetic energies from the very small to the very large at any instant. At the surface of the liquid, fast moving molecules can easily escape from the liquid-vapour boundary. Slower molecules remain in the liquid, as they could not overcome the forces of attraction between the liquid molecules. As molecules of high kinetic energies are lost continuously, the average kinetic energy of ether molecules decreases and therefore the temperature falls.

- The rate of evaporation of a liquid is affected by the following factors:
  (a) Temperature – higher temperature increases the rate
  (b) Area of exposure – larger exposed surface area increases the rate
  (c) Humidity of the surrounding air – low humidity increases the rate
  (d) Wind – high wind speed increases the rate
  (e) Pressure – lower pressure increases the rate
  (f) Nature of liquid – liquid with a lower boiling point evaporates faster

Q A thermally insulated vessel containing liquid water and water vapour is connected to a vacuum pump which removes water vapour continuously. When the temperature reaches 0°C, the vessel contains 110 g of liquid water. What mass of ice has been formed when no liquid remains?
(Specific latent heat of fusion of water = 3.40×10^5 J kg^{-1},
Specific latent heat of vaporisation of water = 2.52×10^6 J kg^{-1})

Cambridge

A Let m be the mass of ice formed when no liquid remains.
Water of mass $(110 - m)$ must be evaporated to form ice of mass m.
i.e. Latent heat of fusion = Latent heat of vaporisation
$m(3.40 \times 10^5) = (110 - m)(2.52 \times 10^6)$
$\therefore m = 96.9$ g

Heat Capacity

- The heat capacity (C) of an object is defined as the amount of heat required to raise the temperature of the object by 1 K or 1°C.
  Mathematically,

  $$C = \frac{Q}{\theta_f - \theta_i}$$

  where Q is the amount of heat transferred,
  θ_f is the final temperature of the object,
  θ_i is the initial temperature of the object.

- The S. I. Unit for heat capacity (C) is J K^{-1} or J°C^{-1}.

SPECIFIC HEAT CAPACITY

- The specific heat capacity (c) of an object is defined as the amount of heat required to raise the temperature of 1 kg of the substance through 1 K or 1°C.
  Mathematically,

  $$c = \frac{Q}{m(\theta_f - \theta_i)}$$

  $$= \frac{C}{m}$$

  where m is the mass of the object.

- The S.I. unit for specific heat capacity (c) is J kg^{-1} K^{-1} or J kg^{-1} °C^{-1}.

A piece of copper of mass 0.275 kg is heated from 14.0°C to 100.0°C. By how much does its internal energy increase?
(Specific heat capacity of copper = 380 J kg^{-1} K^{-1})

Cambridge

The heat transferred (Q) to the copper is given by
$Q = mc\,(\theta_f - \theta_i)$
   = (0.275) (380) (100.0 − 14.0)
   = 8987 J
Increase in internal energy = 8987 J = 8990 J

A bullet of mass 3.0 g travelling with a speed of 300 m s^{-1} is brought to a rest after hitting a wooden block. During impact, 70% of the bullet's kinetic energy is converted to thermal energy. What is the rise in temperature of the bullet?
[Specific heat capacity of the bullet = 400 J kg^{-1} K^{-1}]

A

$$mc\,\Delta\theta = \frac{70}{100}\left(\frac{1}{2}\,mv^2\right)$$

where m = 3.0 g, c = 400 J kg^{-1} K^{-1}, v = 300 m s^{-1},
$\Delta\theta$ = rise in temperature of the bullet

$$\Delta\theta = \frac{70v^2}{200c}$$

$$= \frac{70(300)^2}{200(400)}$$

$$= 79°C$$

Q

In a certain waterfall, water falls through a vertical distance of 24 m as illustrated in the figure. The water is brought to rest at the base of the waterfall.
Calculate

(i) the change in gravitational potential energy of 18 kg of water when it descends the waterfall,

(ii) the difference in temperature between the top and the bottom of the waterfall if all of the potential energy is converted into thermal energy. The specific heat capacity of water is 4.2 kJ kg^{-1} K^{-1}.

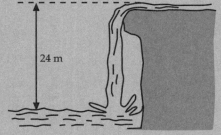

Cambridge

A

(i) Change in potential energy $\Delta PE = mgh$
where m = 18 kg,
g = 9.81 m s^{-2},
h = 24 m
$\therefore \Delta PE$ = (18) (9.81) (24)
= 4237.9
= 4200 J

(ii) Since $mc\,(\theta_T - \theta_B) = \Delta PE$
where m = 18 kg,
c = 4.2 kJ kg^{-1} K^{-1}
θ_T = temperature at the top of the waterfall
θ_B = temperature at the bottom of the waterfall

$$\therefore \theta_T - \theta_B = \frac{\Delta PE}{mc}$$

$$= \frac{4237.9}{(18)(4200)}$$

$$= 0.056 \text{ K}$$

265

Q Cooling water enters the heat exchanger in the turbine of a nuclear power station at 6°C and leaves at 14°C. The specific heat capacity of water is 4200 J kg^{-1} K^{-1}. If the rate of heat removal by the water is 6.72×10^9 J per minute, what is the rate of water flow?

Cambridge

A

$$Q = mc\Delta\theta$$

$$P = \frac{Q}{t} = \frac{mc\Delta\theta}{t}$$

i.e. $\dfrac{m}{t} = \dfrac{P}{c\Delta\theta}$

$$= \frac{6.72 \times 10^9}{4200 \times (14 - 6)}$$

$$= 2 \times 10^5 \text{ kg min}^{-1}$$

Determination of specific heat capacity by electrical methods

• **Solids**

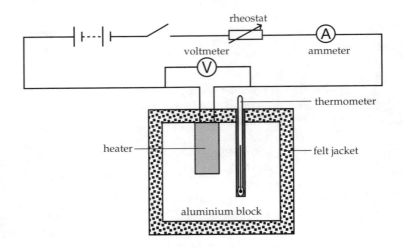

Fig 11.6   Electrical Method to Determine the Specific Heat Capacity of a Solid

(a) An immersion heater is placed in the central hole of a cylindrical aluminium block of known mass m_1 and unknown specific heat capacity c_1. The temperature of the block is measured with a thermometer as shown in Fig 11.6. Both heater and thermometer must maintain good contact with the aluminium block.

(b) The initial temperature θ_1 is first recorded. A steady current is then switched on and the stopwatch started at the same time. After a time t, the current is stopped and the final temperature θ_2, voltmeter reading V_1 and ammeter reading I_1 are recorded.

266

(c) To reduce heat loss, the block is lagged with a felt jacket. In general,

Electrical energy supplied by heater $=$ Heat recieved by aluminium block $+$ Heat lost to the surroundings

$$I_1 V_1 t = m_1 c_1 (\theta_2 - \theta_1) + h \quad \text{———} \quad (1)$$

(d) To eliminate h, the experiment is repeated with another similar metal block of known mass m_2 and known specific heat capacity c_2. Adjust the rheostat such that the temperature changes from θ_1 to θ_2 in time t. If the ammeter and voltmeter readings are I_2 and V_2, then

$$I_2 V_2 t = m_2 c_2 (\theta_2 - \theta_1) + h \quad \text{———} \quad (2)$$

• Since the change in temperature in time t remains the same for both experiments, the heat lost to the surroundings h will also be the same. This can be eliminated by subtracting equation (2) from (1).

$$m_1 c_1 (\theta_2 - \theta_1) - m_2 c_2 (\theta_2 - \theta_1) = I_1 V_1 t - I_2 V_2 t$$

$$\therefore c_1 = \frac{(I_1 V_2 - I_2 V_2)t + m_2 c_2 (\theta_2 - \theta_1)}{m_1 (\theta_2 - \theta_1)}$$

• **Liquids**

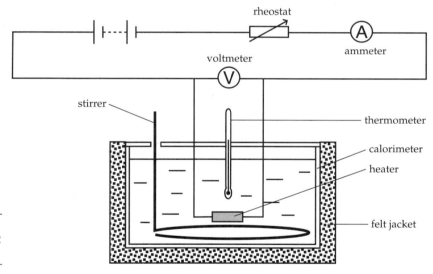

Fig 11.7 Electrical Method to Determine the Specific Heat Capacity of a Liquid

(a) The electrical method in Fig 11.7 can be modified to measure the specific heat capacity of a liquid. Heat given out by the heater is now absorbed by the calorimeter, stirrer and liquid.

(b) Some heat is lost to the environment. To minimise this, the calorimeter should be fitted with a felt jacket. (Fig 11.9) To ensure uniform heat distribution, the liquid must be stirred continuously throughout the experiment.

267

(c) Electrical = Heat + Heat received + Heat lost
    energy   received   by calorimeter   to the
    supplied   by water   & stirrer   environment
    by heater

$$I_1V_1t = m_1c_1(\theta_2 - \theta_1) + H + h \quad\text{———— (5)}$$

where c_1 = the specific heat capacity of the liquid to be determined,

m_1 = mass of the liquid,
θ_2 = final temperature,
θ_1 = initial temperature,
I_1 = ammeter reading,
V_1 = voltmeter reading,
t = time taken for temperature to change from θ_1 to θ_2,
H = heat received by calorimeter and stirrer,
h = heat lost to the environment.

(d) To eliminate H and h the experiment is repeated with another liquid of known mass m_2 and known specific heat capacity c_2. The same volume of liquid is placed in the calorimeter. The rheostat is adjusted to obtain the same change in temperature (i.e. from θ_1 to θ_2) in time t. If the ammeter and voltmeter readings are I_2 and V_2, then

$$I_1V_1t = m_2c_2(\theta_2 - \theta_1) + H + h \quad\text{———— (6)}$$

Since H and h remain the same for equation (5) and (6), they can be eliminated and c_1 determined.

- **Determination of specific heat capacity by Callendar and Barnes Continuous flow method**

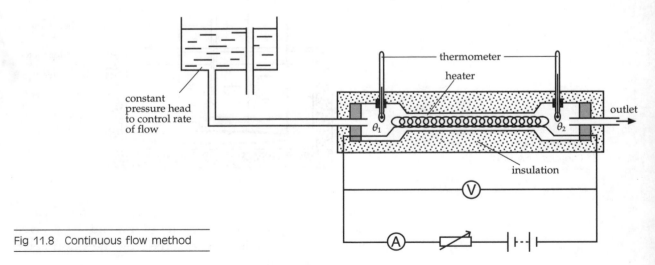

Fig 11.8 Continuous flow method

(a) A liquid is passed through the continuous flow apparatus (Fig 11.8) until steady condition is achieved. Voltmeter reading (V_1), ammeter reading (I_1), temperature at the inlet and outlet (θ_1, θ_2) and the rate of flow of liquid m_1 in time t are recorded.

268

Electrical supplied $=$ Heat absorbed $+$ Heat lost by liquid

$$V_1 I_1 t = m_1 c(\theta_2 - \theta_1) + Q \quad \text{------ (3)}$$

where $c =$ the specific heat capacity of the liquid

(b) The experiment is repeated with new values of V_2, I_2 and m_2 such that θ_1 and θ_2 remain unchanged.

For the same time t,

$$V_2 I_2 t = m_2 c(\theta_2 - \theta_1) + Q \quad \text{------ (4)}$$

The energy lost, Q, in equation (3) and (4) remains the same, as temperatures θ_1 and θ_2 are unaltered. This can be eliminated by the subtraction technique and c evaluated.

FIRST LAW OF THERMO-DYNAMICS

- The first law of thermodynamics states that the increase in the internal energy (ΔU) of a closed system is equal to the heat (Q) that enters a system and the work done (W) on the system, i.e.
$$\Delta U = Q + W$$

- A closed system has a boundary or barrier that separates it from its surroundings. The first law of thermodynamics is a statement of the conservation of energy in the closed system.

- Heat (Q) is the energy in transit from a region of higher temperature to a region of lower temperature.

  (a) Q is positive when heat is transferred to a system (Fig 11.9).

  (b) Q is negative when heat is removed from a system (Fig 11.10).

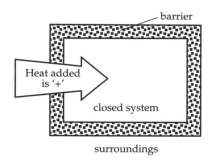

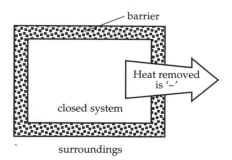

Fig 11.9   Heat is added to the system

Fig 11.10   Heat is removed from the system

- Work (W) is the energy that is transferred from one system to another by a force and is numerically equal to the product of the displacement and the component of the force that is in the direction of the displacement.

  (a) Work done on system is positive if it is compressed (Fig 11.11).

  (b) Work done on system is negative if it expands.

  (c) Work done by system is positive of it expands.

  (d) Work done by system is negative if is compressed (Fig 11.12)

269

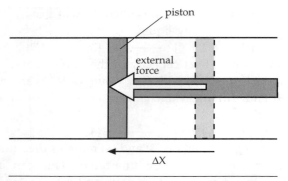

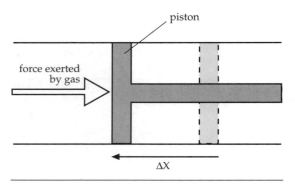

Fig 11.11 Work done on gas is positive

Fig 11.12 Work done by the gas is negative

- The internal energy U of a system is the sum of all the kinetic energies (E_k) and potential energies (E_p) of atoms and molecules moving randomly within the system, i.e.
$$U = E_k + E_p$$
 (a) E_k is dependent on the absolute temperature T.
 (b) E_p is dependent on the separation of the molecules for a real gas.
 (c) E_p is negligible for an ideal gas as intermolecular forces are negligible.

Q A fixed mass of an ideal gas absorbs 1000 J of heat and expands under constant pressure of 20 kPa from a volume of 25×10^{-3} m^3 to a volume of 50×10^{-3} m^3. What is the change in internal energy of the gas?

Cambridge

A
$$\Delta Q = 1000 \text{ J}$$
Work done by the system, $W = p\Delta V$
$$= (20\ 000)\ (50 \times 10^{-3} - 25 \times 10^{-3})$$
$$= 500 \text{ J}$$
Work done on the system, $\Delta W = -500$ J
Increase in internal energy = Heat absorbed + Work done on the system
$\therefore\ \Delta U = Q + W$
$$= 1000 + (-500)$$
$$= 500 \text{ J}$$

An ideal gas is allowed to expand suddenly, with no thermal energy entering or leaving the gas. The temperature of the gas is observed to change.

(i) Explain, by reference to the first law of thermodynamics, what happens to the internal energy of the gas.

(ii) Explain why the change in the internal energy of the gas will give rise to a change in the r.m.s. speed of the molecules of the gas.

(iii) Hence explain whether the temperature of the gas will rise or fall as a result of this expansion.

Cambridge

(i) Since no thermal energy enters or leaves the gas,

$$\Delta Q = 0$$

From the first law of thermodynamics,

$$\Delta U = \Delta Q + \Delta W$$

i.e. $\Delta U = \Delta W$

Since work done on the system is negative when it expands, the internal energy of the ideal gas decreases.

(ii) The internal energy U of an ideal gas is the sum of the translational kinetic energies of its molecules. If there are N molecules of a gas, each of mass m, moving randomly with velocities $(v_1, v_2 \ldots v_N)$, the internal energy is given by:

$$U = \frac{1}{2}mv_1^2 + \frac{1}{2}mv_2^2 + \ldots + \frac{1}{2}mv_N^2$$

$$= \frac{1}{2}m[v_1^2 + v_2^2 + \ldots + v_N^2]$$

$$= \frac{1}{2}Nm<c^2> \text{ where mean square speed } <c^2> = \frac{v_1^2 + v_2^2 + \ldots + v_N^2}{N}$$

$$= \frac{1}{2}Nmc^2_{r.m.s.} \text{ where } c_{r.m.s} = \sqrt{<c^2>}$$

Hence the change in the internal energy of the gas will give rise to a change in the r.m.s. speed of the molecules of the gas.

(iii) As internal energy of the gas decreases, the average kinetic energy decreases. This means the temperature of the gas will decrease as the temperature is proportional to average kinetic energy.

Exercise 11

Multiple Choice Questions

1 What is the internal energy of a system?
   A the maximum amount of work that can be extracted from the system
   B the sum of kinetic energies and potential energies of the molecules
   C the total amount of work which has been done on the system
   D the thermal energy needed to raise the temperature of the system by one kelvin

2 The first law of thermodynamics is a statement which implies that
   A no heat enters or leaves the system.
   B the change in internal energy equals the external work done.
   C the temperature remains constant.
   D energy is conserved.

3 A fixed mass of an ideal gas absorbs 2000 J of heat and expands under a constant pressure of 10 kPa from a volume of 20×10^{-3} m^3 to a volume of 40×10^{-3} m^3. What is the change in internal energy of the gas?
   A -2000 J   B -1800 J
   C zero   D $+1800$ J

4 In a heating experiment, it was noted that the temperature of liquid in a beaker rose at 4.0 K per minute just before it began to boil, and that 40 minutes later all the liquid had boiled away.
   For this liquid, what is the numerical ratio
   $$\frac{\text{specific heat capacity}}{\text{specific latent heat of vaporisation}}?$$

   A $\dfrac{1}{10}$ B $\dfrac{1}{40}$

   C $\dfrac{1}{160}$ D $\dfrac{1}{640}$

5 The graph shows the variation of temperature change $\Delta\theta$ with time t for 1 kg of a substance, initially solid at room temperature. The substance receives heat at a uniform rate of 2000 J min^{-1}.

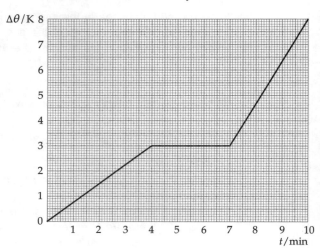

What can be deduced from this graph?
   A The specific heat capacity of the substance is greater than when solid.
   B The specific latent heat of fusion of the substance is 6000 J kg^{-1}.
   C After 4 min of heating the substances is all liquid.
   D After 10 min of heating the substance is all gaseous.

6 The specific heat capacity of water is approximately 4×10^3 J K^{-1} kg^{-1} and the specific latent heat of fusion of ice and of vaporisation of water are approximately 3×10^5 J kg^{-1} and 2×10^6 J kg^{-1} respectively. A constant power supply is used to melt 1 kg of ice, to heat the water produced and finally to turn all the water to steam. Which one of the following graphs shows how the temperature T varies with the time t for this sequence?

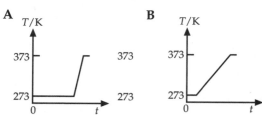

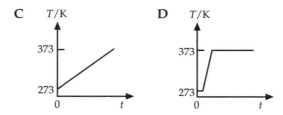

7   Cooling water enters the heat exchanger in the turbine hall of a nuclear power station at 6°C and leaves at 14°C. The specific heat capacity of water is 4200 J kg^{-1} K^{-1}. If the rate of heat removal by the water is 6.72×10^9 J per minute, what is the rate of water flow?

A $\dfrac{6.72 \times 10^9 \times 60}{4200 \times 8}$ kg s^{-1}

B $\dfrac{6.72 \times 10^9}{4200 \times 8 \times 60}$ kg s^{-1}

C $\dfrac{4200 \times 8}{6.72 \times 10^9 \times 60}$ kg s^{-1}

D $\dfrac{4200 \times 8 \times 60}{6.72 \times 10^9}$ kg s^{-1}

Long Questions

1   (a) Describe in molecular terms the process of *melting*. Your answer should make reference to the spacing, ordering, motion and energies of the molecules.
     (b) Define *specific latent heat of fusion*.
     (c) A heating coil is placed in a large funnel and surrounded by lumps of melting ice as shown in Fig 11.13.

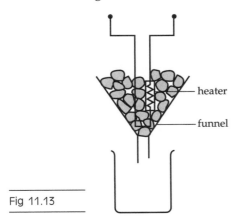

Fig 11.13

The coil is connected to a power supply.
(i) Briefly outline how the apparatus may be used to determine L, the specific latent heat of fusion of ice.
(ii) Show how the readings you would take may be used to calculate L.
(d) The first law of thermodynamics may be expressed in terms of the equation
$$\Delta U = q + w.$$
(i) Identify each of the terms in this equation.
(ii) Some solids contract and some solids expand when they melt. Copy Fig 11.14 on to your answer paper.

	Solids which *contracts* on melting	Solid which *expands* on melting
ΔU		
q		
w		

Fig 11.14

Complete the table with the symbols + or − to indicate the *signs* of the thermodynamic quantities for each of the two types of solids when the solids melt at constant pressure.

Cambridge

2   (a) Define *specific heat capacity*.
     (b) Outline the principles involved in measuring the specific heat capacity of a liquid using an electrical method.
     (c) Write down a word equation relating the increase in the internal energy of a system to the amount of energy put in by heating and working on the system.
     (d) A hot air balloon contains 850 m^3 of air at an assumed constant temperature of 390 K. The density of the air at this temperature is 0.903 kg m^{-3} and the specific heat capacity of the air under the conditions in which it is heated is 1000 J kg^{-1} K^{-1}. Calculate

(i) the mass m of air in the balloon at 390 K,

(ii) the heat energy required to raise the temperature of the air from 275 K to 390 K,

(iii) the density of air at 275 K, given that the density of a gas at constant pressure is inversely proportional to the Kelvin temperature,

(iv) the volume which mass m occupies at 275 K.

(e) The balloon referred to in (d) is illustrated in Fig 11.15.

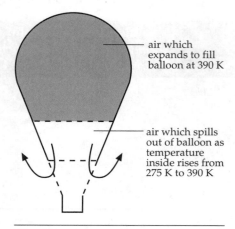

air which expands to fill balloon at 390 K

air which spills out of balloon as temperature inside rises from 275 K to 390 K

Fig 11.15

The diagram shows that during the heating process, air which was originally within the balloon spills out from the balloon. Calculate the work done on the atmosphere during this process. Atmospheric pressure is 1.03×10^5 Pa.

(f) Apply the equation from (c), together with your answers from (d) (ii) and (e), to find the change in the internal energy of the mass m of air when heated from its initial temperature of 275 K to its final temperature of 390 K.

Cambridge

274

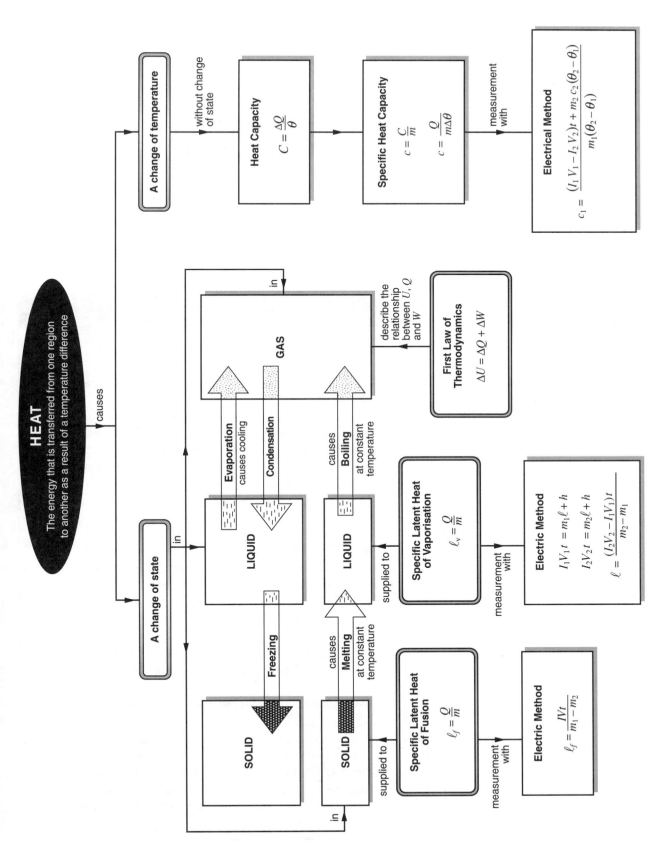

HEAT

The energy that is transferred from one region to another as a result of a temperature difference

causes

A change of temperature

without change of state

Heat Capacity

$$C = \frac{\Delta Q}{\theta}$$

Specific Heat Capacity

$$c = \frac{C}{m}$$

$$c = \frac{Q}{m\Delta\theta}$$

measurement with

Electrical Method

$$c_1 = \frac{(I_1 V_1 - I_2 V_2)t + m_2 c_2 (\theta_2 - \theta_1)}{m_1 (\theta_2 - \theta_1)}$$

A change of state

in

GAS

Evaporation causes cooling

Condensation

causes **Boiling** at constant temperature

LIQUID

describe the relationship between U, Q and W

First Law of Thermodynamics

$$\Delta U = \Delta Q + \Delta W$$

LIQUID

Freezing

causes **Melting** at constant temperature

supplied to

Specific Latent Heat of Vaporisation

$$\ell_v = \frac{Q}{m}$$

measurement with

Electric Method

$$I_1 V_1 t = m_1 \ell + h$$
$$I_2 V_2 t = m_2 \ell + h$$
$$\ell = \frac{(I_2 V_2 - I_1 V_1)t}{m_2 - m_1}$$

SOLID

SOLID

supplied to

Specific Latent Heat of Fusion

$$\ell_f = \frac{Q}{m}$$

measurement with

Electric Method

$$\ell_f = \frac{IVt}{m_1 - m_2}$$

in

275

12 Oscillations

SIMPLE HARMONIC
MOTION

ENERGY IN SIMPLE
HARMONIC MOTION

DAMPED AND
FORCED OSCILLATION:
RESONANCE

Syllabus Objectives

In this chapter you should be able to:

- describe simple examples of free oscillations.

- investigate the motion of an oscillator, using experimental and graphical methods.

- understand and use the terms amplitude, period, frequency, angular frequency and phase difference and express the period in terms of both frequency and angular frequency.

- recognise and use the equation $a = -\omega^2 x$ as the defining equation of simple harmonic motion.

- recall and use $x = x_0 \sin \omega t$ as a solution to the equation $a = -\omega^2 x$.

- recognise and use $v = v_0 \cos \omega t$ and $v = \pm\omega \sqrt{(x_0^2 - x^2)}$.

- describe, with graphical illustrations, the changes in displacement, velocity and acceleration during simple harmonic motion.

- describe the interchange between kinetic energy and potential energy during simple harmonic motion.

- describe practical examples of damped oscillations with particular reference to the effects of the degree of damping and the importance of critical damping in cases such as a car suspension system.

- describe practical examples of forced oscillations and resonance.

- describe graphically how the amplitude of a forced oscillation changes with frequency near to the natural frequency of the system, and understand qualitatively the factors which determine the frequency response and sharpness of the resonance.

- show an appreciation that there are some circumstances in which resonance is useful and other circumstances in which resonance should be avoided.

SIMPLE HARMONIC MOTION

- Periodic motion is the regular, repetitive motion of a body which continually retraces its path at equal time intervals. The motions of orbiting planets, simple pendulum and oscillating springs are examples of periodic motion.

- An oscillation is a special periodic motion in which the oscillator moves to and fro about an equilibrium position. This is also called harmonic motion. There are three types:
  (a) Simple harmonic motion
     (i) Linear simple harmonic motion
     (ii) Angular simple harmonic motion
  (b) Damped harmonic motion
  (c) Forced harmonic motion

Definition of Linear Simple Harmonic Motion

- Linear simple harmonic motion is defined as the to and fro linear motion of a particle about an equilibrium position such that its acceleration is directly proportional to the displacement from the equilibrium position and is always directed towards that position.

  Mathematically, $\dfrac{d^2x}{dt^2} \propto -x$

  i.e. $\dfrac{d^2x}{dt^2} = -\omega^2 x$

  where x is the displacement from the equilibrium position and ω^2 is a positive constant.

- Angular velocity is used because linear SHM (simple harmonic motion) can always be associated with circular motion.

- $\dfrac{d^2x}{dt^2}$ is the acceleration of the particle.

- Uniform circular motion can be translated into linear simple harmonic motion and vice-versa. Fig 12.1 shows a wheel of radius r rotating with uniform angular velocity ω. A rod connects a peg on the rim of the wheel to a slider which moves along an axis passing through the centre of the wheel. The rotary motion of the wheel is converted to linear simple harmonic motion about the point O (the mid-point of the SHM). When the displacement of the slider from O is plotted against t, a sine curve is obtained.

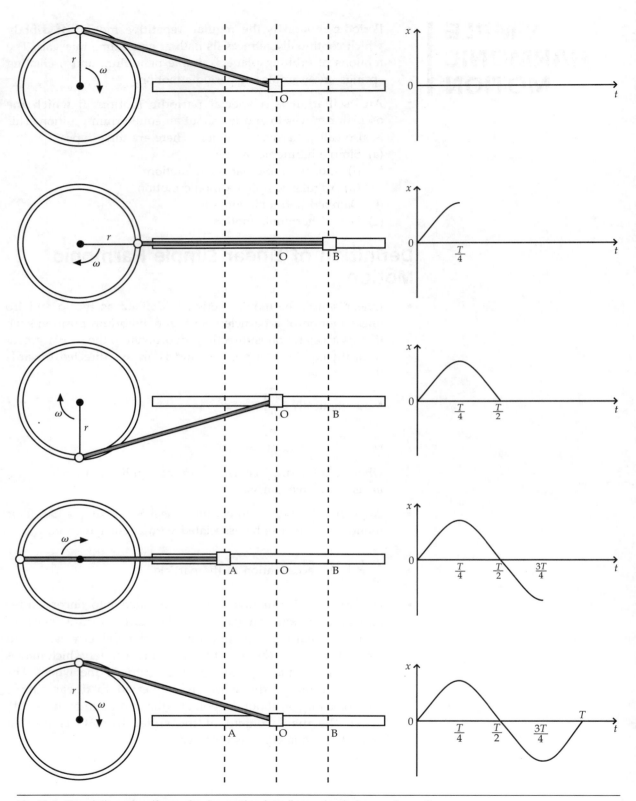

Fig 12.1 Translation of uniform circular motion into linear simple harmonic motion

Characteristics of linear Simple Harmonic Motion

- Fig 12.2 shows the path taken by an object moving with linear simple harmonic motion. It has the following characteristics:

  $|OA| = |OB| = x_o$ = amplitude;

  x – displacement from O (the equilibrium position);

  $\dfrac{d^2x}{dt^2}$ – acceleration

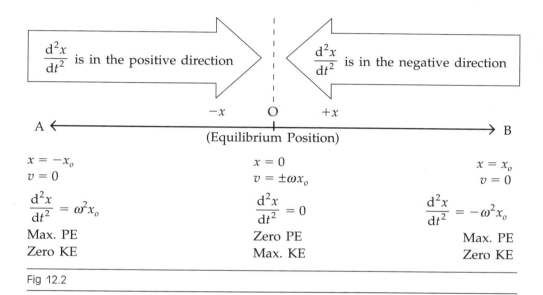

$\dfrac{d^2x}{dt^2}$ is in the positive direction

$\dfrac{d^2x}{dt^2}$ is in the negative direction

$-x$ O $+x$

A ← → B

(Equilibrium Position)

$x = -x_o$
$v = 0$

$\dfrac{d^2x}{dt^2} = \omega^2 x_o$

Max. PE
Zero KE

$x = 0$
$v = \pm\omega x_o$

$\dfrac{d^2x}{dt^2} = 0$

Zero PE
Max. KE

$x = x_o$
$v = 0$

$\dfrac{d^2x}{dt^2} = -\omega^2 x_o$

Max. PE
Zero KE

Fig 12.2

(a) The path traced out is a straight line.
(b) Motion is symmetrical about the equilibrium position O.
(c) The distance from the equilibrium position to the extremity is known as the amplitude (i.e. OA and OB).
(d) The period T is the time taken to describe a complete oscillation or cycle (e.g. OBOAO).

   Hence $T = \dfrac{2\pi}{\omega}$ where ω is the angular velocity.

(e) The frequency f is the number of oscillations (cycles performed in one second). Thus $f = \dfrac{1}{T}$; unit: Hz.

(f) The velocity at the equilibrium position is a maximum. The velocity at the extremity is zero.
(g) Acceleration is always directed towards the equilibrium position.
(h) The acceleration is zero at the equilibrium position. The acceleration is a maximum at both extremities.

- Relationship between velocity and displacement

$$\frac{d^2x}{dt^2} = -\omega^2 x$$

$$v\frac{dv}{dx} = -\omega^2 x \qquad \left[\frac{d^2x}{dt^2} = \frac{dv}{dt} = \frac{dx}{dt} \times \frac{dv}{dx} = v\frac{dv}{dx}\right]$$

By separation of variables

$$v\,dv = -\omega^2 x\,dx$$

$$\int v\,dv = -\int \omega^2 x\,dx$$

$$\frac{v^2}{2} = -\frac{\omega^2 x^2}{2} + c \qquad\qquad \text{------- (1)}$$

where c is a constant.

When $x = \pm x_o$ (where x_o is the amplitude), $v = 0$

Hence equation (1) becomes

$$0 = -\frac{\omega^2 x_o{}^2}{2} + c$$

$$\therefore c = \frac{\omega^2 x_o{}^2}{2}$$

Hence,

$$\frac{v^2}{2} = -\frac{\omega^2 x^2}{2} + \frac{\omega^2 x_o{}^2}{2}$$

$$\text{or} \quad v^2 = \omega^2 (x_o{}^2 - x^2)$$

$$v = \pm\omega\sqrt{x_o{}^2 - x^2}$$

- The graphs of $\dfrac{d^2x}{dt^2}$ and $\dfrac{dx}{dt}$ against x are shown in Fig 12.3.

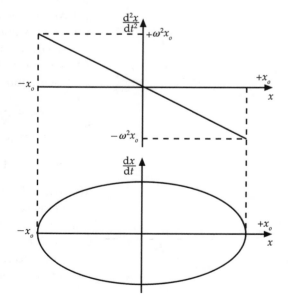

Fig 12.3 Graph of $\dfrac{d^2x}{dt^2}$ against x

and $\dfrac{dx}{dt}$ against X

280

- Relationship between displacement and time

$$v = \omega \sqrt{x_o^2 - x^2}$$

$$\frac{dx}{dt} = \omega \sqrt{x_o^2 - x^2}$$

$$\int \frac{dx}{\sqrt{x_o^2 - x^2}} = \int \omega \, dt$$

$$\sin^{-1} \frac{x}{x_o} = \omega t + \delta \text{ (where } \delta \text{ is the phase constant)}$$

$$\frac{x}{x_o} = \sin (\omega t + \delta)$$

$$\text{or } x = x_o \sin (\omega t + \delta)$$

Alternatively,

$$x = x_o \sin \left(\frac{2\pi}{T} t + \delta \right)$$

$$x = x_o \sin (2\pi f t + \delta)$$

- The phase constant indicates the starting point of the simple harmonic motion. Consider the equation

$$x = x_o \sin (\omega t + \delta) \text{ where } \delta = \frac{\pi}{2}$$

If $t = 0$, the oscillatory motion starts at $x = x_o$. Fig 12.4 shows the displacement-time graph of the simple harmonic motion.

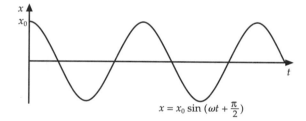

$$x = x_0 \sin \left(\omega t + \frac{\pi}{2} \right)$$

Fig 12.4 $x = x_0 \sin \left(\omega t + \frac{\pi}{2} \right)$

- Variation of x, v, x_o with time

$$x = x_o \sin (\omega t + \delta) \qquad \text{———— (1)}$$

Differentiating x w.r.t. t

$$\frac{dx}{dt} = x_o \omega \cos (\omega t + \delta)$$

i.e. $\quad v = x_o \omega \cos (\omega t + \delta)$

Differentiating v w.r.t. t

$$\frac{d^2x}{dt} = -x_o \omega^2 \sin (\omega t + \delta)$$

or $\quad \dfrac{d^2x}{dt^2} = -\omega^2 x$

281

If $\delta = 0$, equation (1) becomes
$$x = x_o \sin \omega t$$
$$v = x_o \omega \cos \omega t$$
$$\frac{d^2x}{dt^2} = -x_o \omega^2 \sin \omega t$$

- The above equations are represented graphically in Fig 12.5.

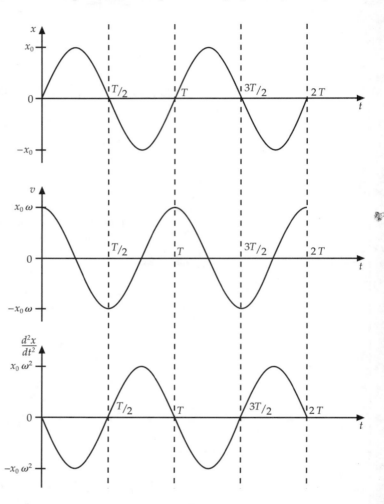

Fig 12.5 Graph of x, v and $\dfrac{d^2x}{dt^2}$ against t

- A summary of the characteristics of linear simple harmonic motion is shown in Table 12.1.

Quantity	Variation with x	Variation with t
x	—	$x = x_o \sin (\omega t + \delta)$
$\dfrac{dx}{dt}$	$v = \pm \omega \sqrt{x_o^2 - x^2}$	$\dfrac{dx}{dt} = x_o \omega \cos (\omega t + \delta)$
$\dfrac{d^2x}{dt^2}$	$\dfrac{d^2x}{dt^2} = -\omega^2 x$	$\dfrac{d^2x}{dt^2} = -x_o \omega^2 \sin (\omega t + \delta)$

Table 12.1 Characteristics of SHM

The pendulum bob of a particular clock oscillates so that its displacement from a fixed point is shown in Fig 12.6.

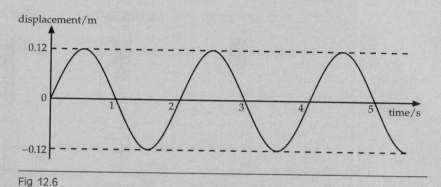

Fig 12.6

By taking the necessary readings from the graph, determine for these oscillations
(a) the amplitude;
(b) the period;
(c) the frequency;
(d) the angular frequency;
(e) the acceleration
  (i) when the displacement is zero,
  (ii) when the displacement is at its maximum;
(f) the maximum velocity of the pendulum bob. $\left[\text{Hint}: v = \pm\omega\sqrt{x_0^2 - x^2}\right]$

Cambridge

(a) Amplitude = 0.12 m
(b) Period $T = 2.0$ s
(c) Frequency $f = \dfrac{1}{T}$

$$= \dfrac{1}{2.0}$$
$$= 0.5 \text{ Hz}$$

(d) Angular frequency $\omega = 2\pi f$
$$= 2\pi\ (0.50)$$
$$= 3.14 \text{ rad s}^{-1}$$

(e) (i) When $x = 0$, $\left|\dfrac{d^2x}{dt^2}\right| = \omega^2\ (0) = 0$

  (ii) When $x = 0.12$ m, $\left|\dfrac{d^2x}{dt^2}\right| = \omega^2 x$

$$= (3.14)^2\ (0.12)$$
$$= 1.18 \text{ m s}^{-2}$$

(f) Maximum velocity occurs when $x = 0$, i.e. $v_{max} = \omega x_o$
$$= (3.14)\ (0.12)$$
$$= 0.38 \text{ m s}^{-1}$$

283

The Period of a Simple Spring-Mass System

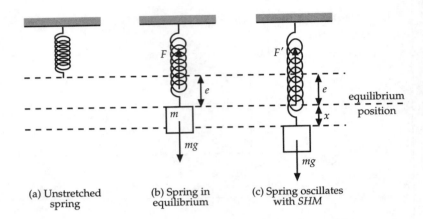

(a) Unstretched spring

(b) Spring in equilibrium

(c) Spring oscillates with *SHM*

Fig 12.7   Oscillation of a spring-mass system

- Consider a spring or elastic cord suspended as shown in Fig 12.7a. A mass m attached to the spring will extend the spring by e (Fig 12.7b). If the elastic limit is not exceeded,

$$F = ke = mg \qquad \text{———— (1)}$$

where k is the spring constant.

If the mass is pulled down a little and released, it oscillates with simple harmonic motion about the equilibrium position (Fig 12.7c). According to Hooke's law, the tension F' is equal to $k(e + x)$. The restoring force on the mass is given by

$$m\frac{d^2x}{dt^2} = mg - F' = mg - k(e + x) \qquad \text{———— (2)}$$

Substituting $ke = mg$ into equation (2), we have

$$m\frac{d^2x}{dt^2} = mg - mg - kx$$

Hence $\quad m\dfrac{d^2x}{dt^2} = -kx$

$$\frac{d^2x}{dt^2} = -\left(\frac{k}{m}\right)x$$

The mass m is oscillating with SHM and its angular velocity is given by $\omega^2 = \dfrac{k}{m}$ or $\omega = \sqrt{\dfrac{k}{m}}$.

Hence $T = \dfrac{2\pi}{\omega}$

$$\therefore T = 2\pi\sqrt{\frac{m}{k}}$$

From equation (1), $\dfrac{m}{k} = \dfrac{e}{g}$

284

The period T can also be written as $T = 2\pi\sqrt{\dfrac{e}{g}}$

The derivation of the period makes the following assumptions:
(a) The mass of the spring is negligible.
(b) Displacement $(x) <$ extension (e)
(c) The elastic limit is not exceeded.

The Period of a Series Connected Spring-Mass System

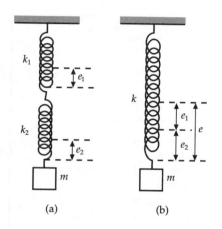

Fig 12.8 Series connection of spring-mass system

- Two springs of spring constants k_1 and k_2 are joined together and attached to a mass m as shown in Fig 12.8a. When the mass is displaced and released, it oscillates vertically with simple harmonic motion.

- The configuration in Fig 12.8a is equivalent to the configuration in Fig 12.8b where the mass m is connected to a single spring of spring constant k.

  The tension in Fig 12.8a is the same for both springs. The total extension (e) in Fig 12.8b is given by
  $$e = e_1 + e_2 \quad\text{————— (3)}$$
  According to Hooke's law, the tension is
  $$T = k_1 e_1 = k_2 e_2 = ke$$

  i.e. $e_1 = \dfrac{T}{k_1}$, $e_2 = \dfrac{T}{k_2}$ and $e = \dfrac{T}{k}$.

  Substituting for e, e_1 and e_2 in equation (3), we have
  $$\frac{T}{k} = \frac{T}{k_1} + \frac{T}{k_2}$$

  Hence, $\quad \dfrac{1}{k} = \dfrac{1}{k_1} + \dfrac{1}{k_2}$

  The period of oscillation is given by
  $$T = 2\pi\sqrt{\frac{m}{k}}$$
  $$= 2\pi\sqrt{m\left(\frac{1}{k_1} + \frac{1}{k_2}\right)}$$

  or $\quad T = 2\pi\sqrt{\dfrac{m(k_1 + k_2)}{k_1 k_2}}$

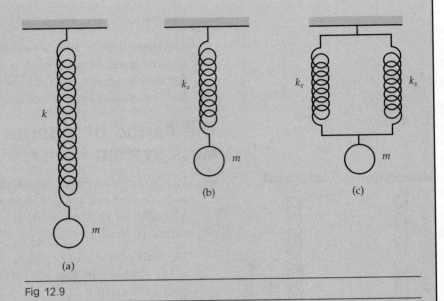

(a)

Fig 12.9

The period of the vertical oscillation of a mass m at the end of a light helical spring of force constant k (Fig 12.9a) is T_1. (The force constant is the force per unit extension of the spring.) Write down the relation between T_1, m and k. If the spring was cut into two pieces of equal length and one portion was used to support the same mass (Fig 12.9b), what would be the period T_2? If both portions of the spring were used in parallel (Fig 12.9c), what would be the period T_3? (Give your answers for T_2 and T_3 in terms of T_1.)

Cambridge

Relation between T_1, m and k in Fig 12.9a is given by:

$$T_1 = 2\pi\sqrt{\frac{m}{k}}$$

The spring constant k_x in Fig 12.9b is given by:

$$k_x = 2k$$

The period T_2 is given by:

$$T_2 = 2\pi\sqrt{\frac{m}{k_x}}$$

$$= 2\pi\sqrt{\frac{m}{2k}} = \frac{T_1}{\sqrt{2}}$$

The mass supported by each spring in Fig 12.9c is $\frac{m}{2}$.

The period T_3 is given by:

$$T_3 = 2\pi\sqrt{\frac{\left(\frac{m}{2}\right)}{2k}}$$

$$= 2\pi\sqrt{\frac{m}{4k}} = \frac{T_1}{2}$$

286

The Period of a Simple Pendulum

- A mass m attached to a rigid support by a light inelastic string oscillates with angular simple harmonic motion about P. The motion approaches linear simple harmonic motion if
  (a) θ is very small ($<5°$),
  (b) the length of the spring (l) is large.

  In Fig 12.10, $\sin \theta = \dfrac{x}{l}$

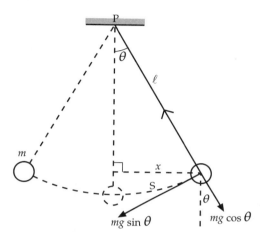

Fig 12.10 Simple Pendulum

As $\sin \theta \simeq \theta$ when θ is very small, $\theta = \dfrac{x}{l}$.

When the mass m is displaced, the tangential force ($mg \sin \theta$ causes it to move with simple harmonic motion. Hence, from Newton's law of motion,

$$m\frac{d^2x}{dt^2} = -mg \sin \theta$$

$$= -mg\,\theta$$

$$= -\frac{mg}{l}x$$

- The negative sign indicates that the tangential force is in the opposite direction to the angular displacement.

$$\frac{d^2x}{dt^2} = -\frac{g}{l}x \qquad \text{——— (4)}$$

Comparing equation (4) with $\dfrac{d^2x}{dt^2} = -\omega^2 x$, we have

$$\omega^2 = \frac{g}{l} \text{ or } \omega = \sqrt{\frac{g}{l}}.$$

- The period (T) of a simple pendulum is given by

$$T = 2\pi\sqrt{\frac{l}{g}}$$

287

ENERGY IN SIMPLE HARMONIC MOTION

- Consider the oscillation of a spring as shown in Fig 12.11a. The potential energy of the spring is given by:

$$U = \frac{1}{2} kx^2$$

$$= \frac{1}{2} kx_0^2 \sin^2 (\omega t + \delta)$$

The kinetic energy of the mass is given by

$$K = \frac{1}{2} mv^2$$

$$= \frac{1}{2} mx_0^2 \omega^2 \cos^2 (\omega t + \delta)$$

$$= \frac{1}{2} kx_0^2 \cos^2 (\omega t + \delta) \text{ as } \omega^2 = \frac{k}{m}$$

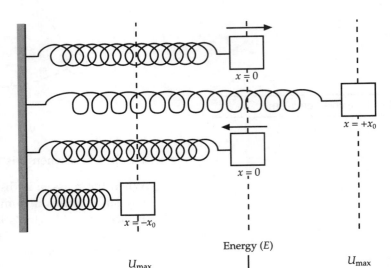

Fig 12.11a   Oscillation of a spring-mass system

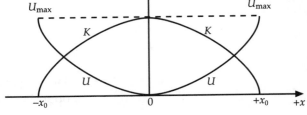

Fig 12.11b   Graph of energy against displacement

The total mechanical energy (E) is given by the sum of the kinetic and potential energy of the spring-mass system.

$$E = U + K$$

$$= \frac{1}{2} kx_0^2 \sin^2 (\omega t + \delta) + \frac{1}{2} kx_0^2 \cos^2 (\omega t + \delta)$$

$$= \frac{1}{2} kx_0^2 (\sin^2 (\omega t + \delta) + \cos^2 (\omega t + \delta))$$

$$= \frac{1}{2} kx_0^2$$

The total mechanical energy is constant and is independent of the time.

Fig 12.11b shows how the potential and kinetic energy of the spring-mass system varies with displacement

Fig 12.11c shows how the potential and kinetic energy of the spring-mass system varies with time

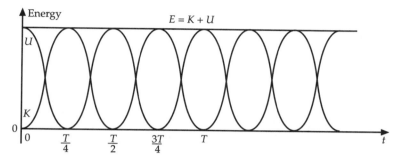

Fig 12.11c Variation of the potential and kinetic energy of a spring-mass system with time

DAMPED AND FORCED OSCILLATIONS: RESONANCE

- Damping is the process whereby energy is taken away from the oscillating system (Fig 12.12). For example, the vibration of a guitar string will die away after some time. Energy is removed from the vibrating string in two ways:
  (a) Radiation of sound energy from the vibrating string (Fig 12.13)
  (b) Work done against air resistance

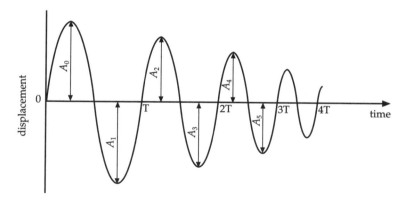

Fig 12.12 Damped Oscillations

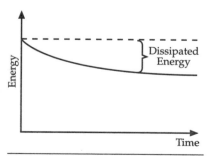

Fig 12.13 Energy of an oscillating system

- A displacement-time graph of the system (Fig 12.12) shows an exponential decay of the amplitude with time. The ratio of the adjacent amplitude is a constant known as decrement δ.

$$\delta = \frac{A_0}{A_1} = \frac{A_1}{A_2} = \frac{A_2}{A_3} = \ldots$$

- Fig 12.14 shows three types of damping:
  (a) Light damping (curve A) — The system oscillates about the equilibrium position with decreasing amplitude over a period of time. An example is the oscillation of a mass and spring in air or in a liquid.

289

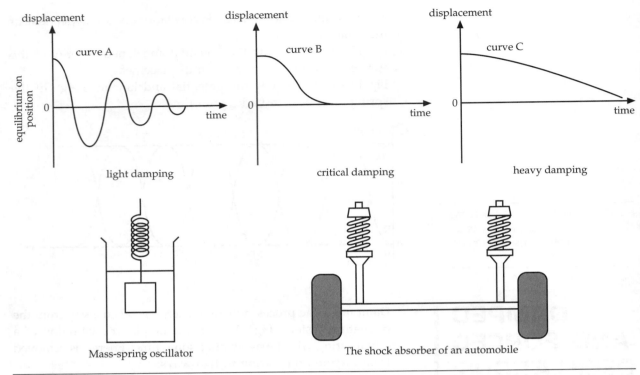

light damping   critical damping   heavy damping

Mass-spring oscillator   The shock absorber of an automobile

Fig 12.14 Damping curves of three types of system

(b) Critical damping (curve B) — The system does not oscillate but returns to the equilibrium position in the shortest time. The suspension system of a car is critically damped. This will ensure a smoother ride in the car and minimise discomfort. Voltmeters and ammeters are also critically damped. The needle will not oscillate unnecessarily and the final reading can be read quickly.

(c) Heavy damping (curve C) — The system does not oscillate and damping is so large that it will take a long time to reach the equilibrium position.

Forced Oscillations and Resonance

- Forced oscillations are produced when a body is subjected to an oscillatory external force. The force is usually called a driving force or driver and the oscillating body is known as a responder.

Barton's Pendulums

- Barton's pendulums shown in Fig 12.15 can be used to illustrate forced oscillations.

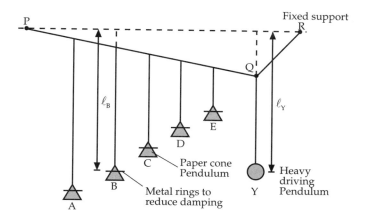

Fig 12.15   Barton's pendulum

- It consists of six simple pendulums attached to a common inextensible string suspended from two fixed supports at P and R. Five of the pendulums are made of paper cones and loaded with metal rings to reduce damping. When the heavy driving pendulum (Y) is set oscillating in a plane perpendicular to the diagram, small rhythmic oscillations are produced along the string PQR. This is sufficient to set the five paper cone pendulums into a steady state of forced oscillations after a short time.

- Barton's pendulum illustrates the concept of resonance
  (a) Measurements show that the period of the five paper cones corresponds to the period of the driving pendulum (Y). This shows that the five pendulums are forced to oscillate at the natural frequency of the driver rather than their natural frequencies.
  (b) The amplitudes of oscillation are different for the five paper cones. It is a maximum when l_y is equal to l_B but decreases when the length of the paper cone pendulum is either larger or smaller than the length of the driving pendulum. We say that pendulum B resonates with the driver or B shows the effects of resonance. In this state, the applied frequency is always in phase with the oscillating pendulum and the accumulated effect is an increase in the amplitude of oscillation to a maximum.
  (c) Resonance occurs when a system oscillates with maximum amplitude when it is subjected to an oscillatory force whose driving frequency is equal to the natural frequency of the system.

- The effects of damping on resonance can be investigated by removing the metal rings placed on the paper cone pendulum in Fig 12.15. As the mass decreases, the damping increases. The driving frequency is varied and the corresponding steady state amplitude of a chosen pendulum is measured. Fig 12.16 shows

291

graphically how the amplitude of forced oscillation changes with the applied frequency when the pendulum is subjected to different degrees of damping.

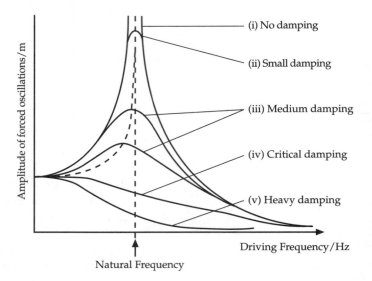

Fig 12.16 Graph of amplitude against driving frequency

- The sharpness of resonance is determined by the degree of damping:
  (a) When damping is zero (Fig 12.16(i)), the amplitude of resonance becomes infinite.
  (b) When damping is small (Fig 12.16(ii)), the amplitude is large but falls off rapidly when the driving frequency of the body differs slightly from the natural frequency of the body. The resonance is sharp.
  (c) When damping is medium (Fig 12.16(iii)), the amplitude at resonance decreases. The curve falls off gradually and maximum amplitude occurs at a frequency that is slightly different from the natural frequency of the pendulum.
  (d) When damping is critical or heavy the resonance is flat.

- Further examples of resonance are illustrated below:
  (a) Resonance in an a.c. circuit
    (i) The magnitude of the alternating current flowing through the a.c. circuit with resistance R, inductance L and capacitance C depends on the frequency of the alternating e.m.f.(Fig 12.17).
    (ii) Maximum current flows at the resonant frequency of the circuit. This frequency is given by:

$$f = \frac{1}{2\pi\sqrt{LC}}$$

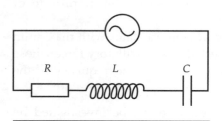

Fig 12.17 Series a.c. circuit

292

(b) Resonance in an air column
(i) The length of the air column in the tube (Fig 12.18) can be varied by adjusting the tube higher or lower with respect to the reservoir.
(ii) A vibrating tuning fork can set the air column into oscillations.
(iii) Resonance occurs and a loud note can be heard if the frequency of the tuning fork is equal to the natural frequency of the air column.

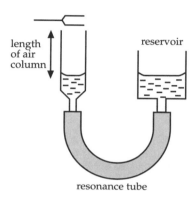

length of air column

reservoir

resonance tube

Fig 12.18 Resonance tube

(c) Resonance at the molecular level
(i) Common salt (NaCl) is an ionic crystal and has a lattice structure shown in Fig 12.19.
(ii) Sodium (Na^+) and chloride (Cl^-) ions vibrate about fixed positions in the lattice structure.
(iii) Resonance occurs when the crystal is exposed to electromagnetic radiation of frequency equal to the natural frequency of vibrations of the ions. Maximum energy is absorbed.

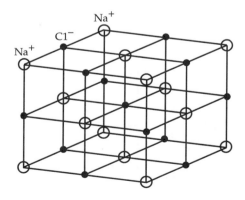

Na^+

Cl^-

Na^+

Fig 12.19 Lattice structure of sodium chloride

293

(a) (i) Give an account of the energy transformations which occur during one complete oscillation of an undamped simple pendulum. Illustrate your answer with sketch graphs wherever appropriate.

(ii) Explain why a lightly damped oscillatory system experiences a progressive decrease in its amplitude.

(b) The acceleration of a particle undergoing simple harmonic motion is given by the expression $a = -bx$, where x is the displacement and b is a positive constant.

How is b related to the period of the oscillation?

(c) A vertical rod is fixed near the rim of a horizontal turntable which is rotating at exactly 33 revolutions per minute. A horizontal beam of light casts a shadow of the rod onto a screen in front of which is suspended a simple pendulum as shown in Fig 12.20.

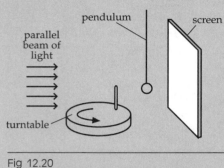

Fig 12.20

If the shadows of the rod and the pendulum bob move in phase on the screen, what must be the effective length of the pendulum?

(d) The speed of the turntable in (c) suddenly increases to $33\frac{1}{3}$ revolutions per minute.

(i) Briefly describe what will be observed subsequently on the screen.

(ii) Calculate the number of oscillations made by the pendulum before the two shadows are next in phase.

(iii) How long does this take?

Cambridge

(a) (i)

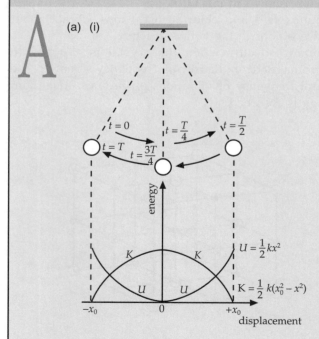

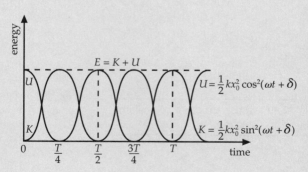

The above graphs show the energy transformation which occurs during one complete oscillation of an undamped simple pendulum.

294

At $t = 0$, kinetic energy $= 0$ and potential energy $= \frac{1}{2}kx_o^2$ where x_o is the amplitude of the periodic motion.

At $t = \frac{T}{4}$, kinetic energy $= \frac{1}{2}kx_o^2$ and potential energy $= 0$

At $t = \frac{T}{2}$, kinetic energy $= 0$ and potential energy $= \frac{1}{2}kx_o^2$

At $t = \frac{3T}{4}$, kinetic energy $= \frac{1}{2}kx_o^2$ and potential energy $= 0$

At $t = T$, kinetic energy $= 0$ and potential energy $= \frac{1}{2}kx_o^2$

The total energy of the simple pendulum at any instant remains constant and is given by:

$$E = K + U = \frac{1}{2}kx_o^2$$

(ii) Energy is removed continuously from a lightly damped oscillating system when air resistance and friction oppose the oscillation. The result is a progressive decrease in the total energy and amplitude of the oscillatory motion.

(b) Comparing $a = -bx$ with $a = -\omega^2 x$, we have

$$\omega^2 = b \quad \text{or} \quad \omega = \sqrt{b}$$

Since $T = \frac{2\pi}{\omega}$ where T is the period of oscillation

$$T = \frac{2\pi}{\sqrt{b}} \quad \text{or} \quad b = \frac{4\pi^2}{T^2}$$

(c) The period (T) of the SHM of the shadow and pendulum is

$$T = \frac{60}{33}\,\text{s} = 1.82\ \text{s}$$

If l is the effective length of the simple pendulum,

$$T = 2\pi\sqrt{\frac{l}{g}}$$

$$= 1.82$$

$$\therefore l = \frac{1.82^2 \times 9.81}{4\pi^2}$$

$$= 0.823\ \text{m}$$

(d) (i) The shadow will oscillate faster and move out of phase with the simple pendulum.

(ii) When the pendulum and shadow are next in phase, the pendulum would have gone through n oscillations while the shadow would have covered $(n + 1)$ oscillations in the same time.

Thus $nT_p = (n + 1)T_s$

where T_p = period of simple pendulum $= \frac{60}{33}\,\text{s}$

and T_s = period of shadow

$$= \frac{\frac{60}{33}}{3^{\frac{1}{3}}}$$

$$= \frac{180}{100}\,\text{s}$$

$$n\left(\frac{60}{33}\right) = (n+1)\left(\frac{180}{100}\right)$$

$$n = (n+1)\left(\frac{99}{100}\right)$$

$$100n = 99n + 99$$

$$\therefore n = 99$$

(iii) Time taken for the pendulum and the shadow to be next in phase is given by:

$$t = \frac{\theta}{\omega}$$

where θ = angle turned through in 99 oscillations = $99 \times 2\pi$

and ω = angular velocity = $\dfrac{2\pi}{\frac{60}{33}} = \dfrac{2\pi(33)}{60}$

$$\therefore t = \frac{99 \times 2\pi}{2\pi\frac{(33)}{60}} = 180 \text{ s}$$

(a) In the preparation of tide tables for coastal resorts and harbours, use is made of a graph of depth of water against time for a particular place. One such graph is shown in Fig 12.21.

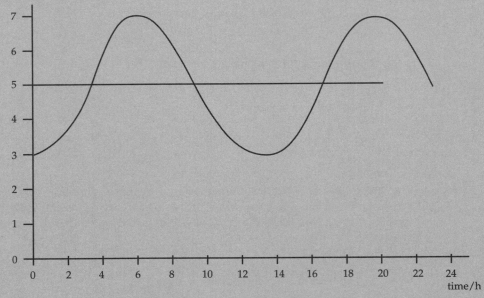

Fig 12.21

(i) Describe the steps you would take to obtain such a graph practically for a particular harbour.

(ii) What is the period of this oscillation?

(iii) What is the amplitude of this oscillation?

(b) In some harbours, the rise and fall of the water level is simple harmonic. What does *simple harmonic* mean?

(c) In one harbour, the equation for the depth h of water is

$$h = 5.0 + 3.0 \sin \frac{2\pi t}{45600},$$

where h is given in metres and t is the time in seconds.

$$\left(\text{The angle } \frac{2\pi t}{45600} \text{ is in radians.} \right)$$

For this harbour, calculate
(i) the maximum depth of water,
(ii) the minimum depth of water,
(iii) the time interval between high- and low-water,
(iv) two values of t at which the water is 5.0 m deep,
(v) the length of time for each tide during which the depth of water is more than 7.0 m deep.

Cambridge

A

(a) (i) The following are practical steps to obtain a graph of depth of water against time for coastal resorts and harbours.

1) Choose a suitable location to conduct observations. The place chosen must be easily accessible and the water surface should be reasonably calm and free from surface turbulence.
2) Fix firmly to the seabed a vertical rod that is calibrated in metres. The numbers on the rod should be large so that the depth of water can be read off easily from it.
3) Readings are taken at intervals of 30 minutes for 24 hours. To minimise errors due to wave movements, three values of the depth of water are recorded and an average value determined. A tabulation of these values are shown in Table 12.2.

Depth of water				Time/h
d_1/m	d_2/m	d_3/m	Average d/m	

Table 12.2 Variation of depth with time

4) A graph of average depth (d) against time (t) can be plotted from table 12.2.

(ii) Period = $19.5 - 6.0 = 13.5$ h

(iii) Amplitude = 2.0 m

(b) Simple harmonic motion is the to and fro motion of a particle about an equilibrium position such that its acceleration is directly proportional to the displacement from the equilibrium position and is always directed towards that position.

(c) (i) $h = 5.0 + 3.0 \sin \dfrac{2\pi t}{45600}$

At maximum depth, $\sin \dfrac{2\pi t}{45600} = 1$

$\therefore h_{max} = 5.0 + 3.0$
$= 8.0$ m

297

(ii) At minimum depth, $\sin \dfrac{2\pi t}{45600} = -1$

$$\therefore h_{min} = 5.0 + 3.0(-1)$$
$$= 2.0 \text{ m}$$

(iii) If t_H is the time at high tide (maximum depth),

$$\frac{2\pi t_H}{45600} = \frac{\pi}{2}$$
$$t_H = 11400 \text{ s}$$

If t_L is the time at low tide (minimum depth),

$$\frac{2\pi t_H}{45600} = \frac{3\pi}{2}$$
$$t_L = 34200 \text{ s}$$

Time interval between high and low tide $= t_L - t_H$
$$= 34200 - 11400$$
$$= 22800 \text{ s}$$

(iv) When $h = 5.0$ m,

$$5.0 = 5.0 + 3.0 \sin \frac{2\pi t}{45600}$$

$$\therefore \sin \frac{2\pi t}{45600} = 0$$

or $\dfrac{2\pi t_1}{45600} = 0$ and $\dfrac{2\pi t_2}{45600} = \pi$

Hence $t_1 = 0$ and $t_2 = 22800$ s

(v) When $h = 7.0$ m,

$$7.0 = 5.0 + 3.0 \sin \frac{2\pi t}{45600}$$

$$\sin \frac{2\pi t}{45600} = \frac{2}{3}$$

$$\therefore \sin \frac{2\pi t}{45600} = \frac{2}{3}$$

or $\dfrac{2\pi t_1}{45600} = 0.7297$ and $\dfrac{2\pi t_2}{45600} = 2.412$

Hence $t_1 = 5296$ s and $t_2 = 17505$ s

Length of time for which the depth is more than 7.0 m

$$= t_2 - t_1$$
$$= 12209 \text{ s}$$
$$= 12200 \text{ s (to 3 significant fig.)}$$

Exercise 12

Multiple Choice Questions

1   In which group below do all three quantities remain constant when a particle moves in simple harmonic motion?

A	acceleration	force	total energy
B	force	total energy	amplitude
C	total energy	amplitude	angular frequency
D	amplitude	angular frequency	acceleration

2   The diagram shows a displacement-time graph for a body performing simple harmonic motion.

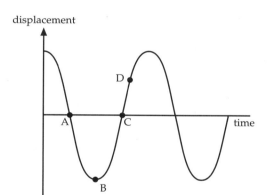

At which labelled point are the velocity and acceleration in opposite directions?

3   In a fair ground shooting game, a gun fires at a moving target. The gun fires by itself at random times. The player has to point the gun in a fixed direction, and the target moves from side to side with simple harmonic motion.

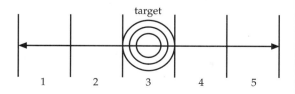

At which region should the player take a fixed aim to score the greatest number of hits?

A	3	**B**	either 1 or 5
C	either 2 or 4	**D**	any of 1, 3 or 5

4   Which graph shows the relationship between the acceleration, a, and the displacement x of a particle performing simple harmonic motion?

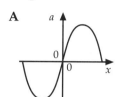
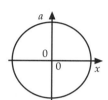
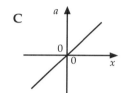
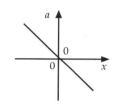

5   The rise and fall of water in a harbour is simple harmonic. The depth varies between 1.0 m at low tide and 3.0 m at high tide. The time between successive low tides is 12 hours.

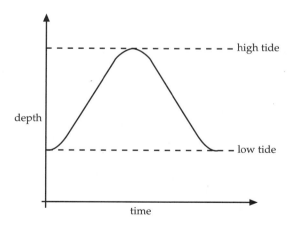

A boat, which requires a minimum depth of 1.5 m, approaches the harbour at low tide. How long will the boat have to wait before entering?

A	0.5 hours	**B**	1.0 hours
C	1.5 hours	**D**	2.0 hours

6   The cone of a loudspeaker sounding a note of frequency f executes simple harmonic motion of amplitude a.

Which of the following expressions gives the maximum acceleration of the cone?

A fa **B** $2\pi fa$

C $(fa)^2$ **D** $(2\pi f)^2 a$

7   The bob of a simple pendulum of period 2 s is given a small displacement and then released at time $t = 0$.

Which diagram shows the variation with time of the bob's kinetic energy E_k and its potential energy E_p?

A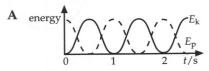

B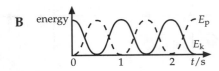

C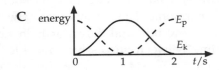

D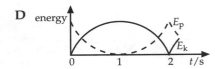

8   It is important that a car suspension system should be critically damped.

The equilibrium height above the ground of the bodywork of such a car is H_0. The body of the car is raised to a greater height H and released at time $t = 0$. Assume that the car tyres remain in contact with the ground throughout and there is critical damping.

Which graph shows how the height of the car body above the ground varies with time?

A 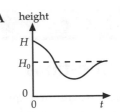   **B**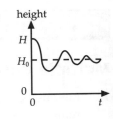

C 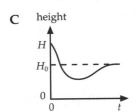   **D**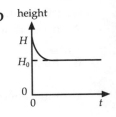

9   Which graph best shows how the velocity v of an object performing simple harmonic motion of amplitude a varies with displacement x for one complete oscillation?

A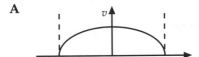

B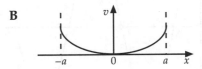

C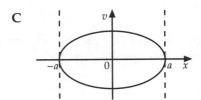

D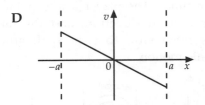

10 Simple harmonic motion is **defined** as the motion of a particle such that

A its displacement x is always given by the expression $x = x_o \sin \omega t$.

B its displacement x is related to its velocity v by the expression $v = \omega x$.

C its acceleration is always $\omega^2 x_0$ and is directed at right angles to its motion.

D its acceleration is proportional to, and in the opposite direction to, the displacement.

Structured Question

1 A mass of 0.100 kg oscillates with simple harmonic motion of amplitude 0.0030 m and period 0.020 s.

(a) Find the frequency of the oscillation.

(b) Find ω, the angular frequency of the oscillation.

(c) Write down the equation representing the variation with time, t, of the displacement, x, for this oscillation.

(d)

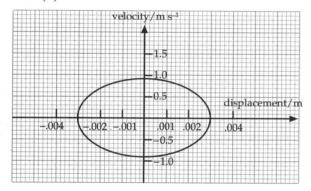

Fig 12.22

A graph of velocity against displacement for this oscillation is shown in Fig 12.22.

(i) Read from the graph the maximum value of the velocity.

(ii) Explain why there are two values of velocity for zero displacement.

(iii) Explain why there are two values of displacement for zero velocity.

(e) (i) Calculate the maximum kinetic energy of the mass.

(ii) Sketch on Fig 12.23, a graph of the kinetic energy of the mass against displacement.

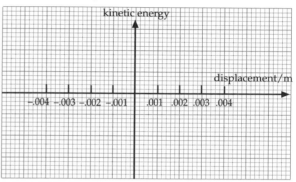

Fig 12.23

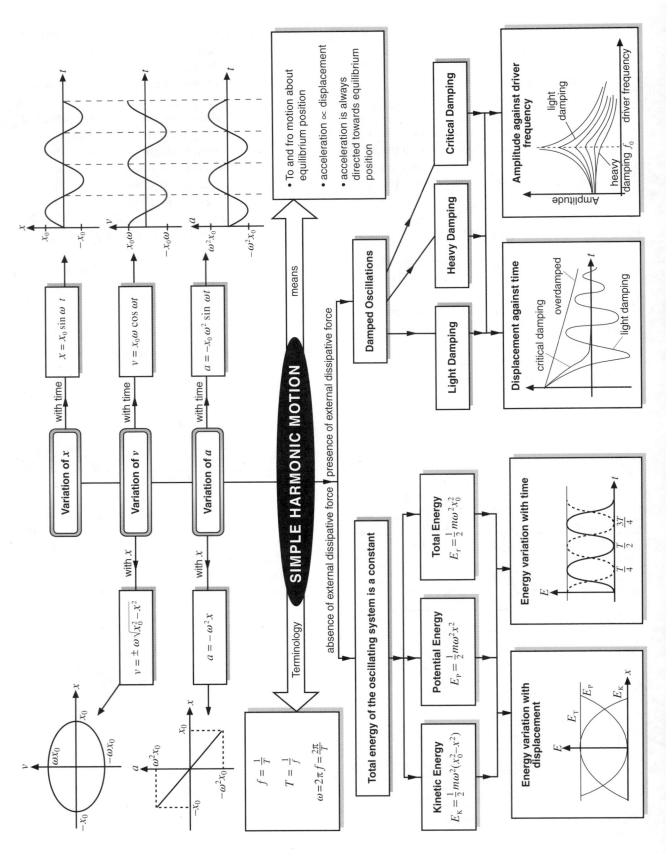

SIMPLE HARMONIC MOTION

- To and fro motion about equilibrium position
- acceleration $\propto$ displacement
- acceleration is always directed towards equilibrium position

means

Variation of x — with time — $x = x_0 \sin \omega t$

Variation of v — with time — $v = x_0 \omega \cos \omega t$

Variation of a — with time — $a = -x_0 \omega^2 \sin \omega t$

with x: $v = \pm \omega \sqrt{x_0^2 - x^2}$

with x: $a = -\omega^2 x$

Terminology
$$f = \frac{1}{T}$$
$$T = \frac{1}{f}$$
$$\omega = 2\pi f = \frac{2\pi}{T}$$

presence of external dissipative force

Damped Oscillations

- Light Damping
- Heavy Damping
- Critical Damping

Displacement against time

Amplitude against driver frequency

absence of external dissipative force

Total energy of the oscillating system is a constant

Kinetic Energy
$$E_{\mathrm{K}} = \frac{1}{2}m\omega^2(x_0^2 - x^2)$$

Potential Energy
$$E_{\mathrm{P}} = \frac{1}{2}m\omega^2 x^2$$

Total Energy
$$E_{\mathrm{T}} = \frac{1}{2}m\omega^2 x_0^2$$

Energy variation with displacement

Energy variation with time

13 Waves

PROGRESSIVE WAVES

TRANSVERSE AND
LONGITUDINAL WAVES

POLARISATION

Syllabus Objectives

In this chapter you should be able to:

- describe what is meant by wave motion as illustrated by vibration in ropes, springs and ripple tanks.

- show an understanding and use the terms displacement, amplitude, phase difference, period, frequency, wavelength and speed.

- deduce, from the definitions of speed, frequency and wavelength, the equation $v = f\lambda$.

- recall and use the equation $v = f\lambda$.

- show an understanding that energy is transferred due to a progressive wave.

- recall and use the relationship, *intensity* $\propto$ *(amplitude)*^{2}.

- compare transverse and longitudinal waves.

- analyse and interpret graphical representations of transverse and longitudinal waves.

- show an understanding that polarisation is a phenomenon associated with transverse waves.

- state that all electromagnetic waves travel with the same speed in free space and recall the orders of magnitude of the wavelengths of the principal radiations from radio waves to γ-rays.

PROGRESSIVE WAVES

- A progressive wave is one in which the wave profile carries energy and momentum away from the source of disturbance.

- Fig 13.1 shows a taut, horizontal rope held at A and fixed to the wall at the other end. A is moved vertically upwards with simple harmonic motion. This causes the next section to move in the same manner but at a latter time. The motion is transmitted along the rope and the successive repetition of simple harmonic motion produces a progressive wave moving to the right in the figure. It should be noted that there is no physical transfer of the material medium (i.e. the rope) to the right. What is seen moving is the wave profile.

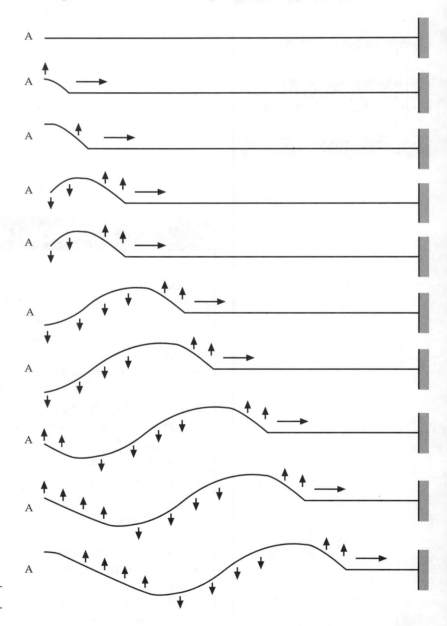

Fig 13.1 Transverse waves

304

- Progressive wave can also be produced by a ripple tank. A dipper attached to a motor can generate continuous circular waves. These waves are illuminated by light from an overhead-projector. Dark and bright fringes representing the crest and trough of the waves can be projected on a screen (Fig 13.2a). They are seen as expanding concentric circles moving away from the dipper (Fig 13.2b).

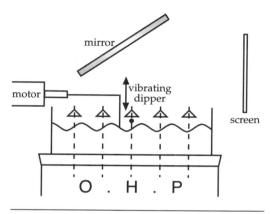

Fig 13.2a   Progressive wave in a ripple tank

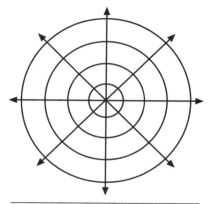

Fig 13.2b   Concentric circle of bright and dark fringes moving away from the centre of disturbance

- **Description of Wave Motion**

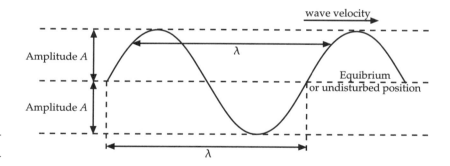

Fig 13.3   Wave motion

(a) The displacement of a particle in a wave motion is the distance travelled in a specific direction from its equilibrium position.

(b) The amplitude A is the distance from the equilibrium position to the crest or trough of the wave motion (i.e. its maximum displacement).

(c) The wavelength λ is the distance between 2 consecutive particles which have the same phase or state of disturbance.

(d) The period T is the time taken for a point on the wave to complete one cycle. The unit for period is second.

(e) The frequency f of the wave is the number of cycles produced in each second and, is thus the number of crests that pass a fixed point in each second. The unit for frequency is Hertz. Frequency and period are related,

$$f = \frac{1}{T}$$

(f) The phase of a particular point in an oscillation is the fraction of the oscillation measured from an initial chosen point. Oscillation motion is closely related to circular motion. In Fig 13.4, one complete revolution of the radius vector OP propagates one cycle of a sinusoidal wave.

In general, the phase at S measured from R is given by ϕ, where

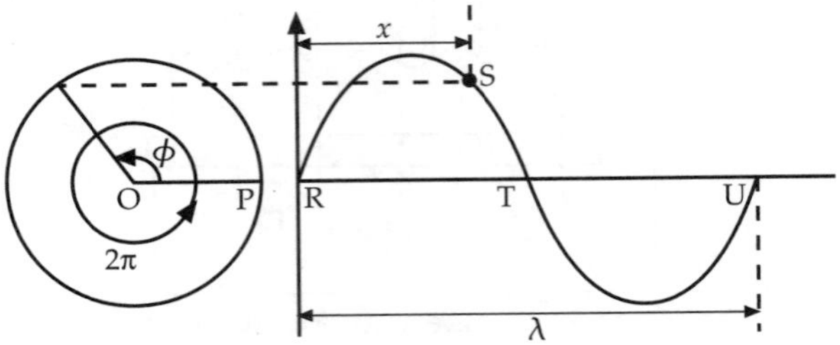

Fig 13.4   Concept of phase

2 π rad – they are in phase

π rad out of phase with each other.

$$\frac{\phi}{2\pi} = \frac{x}{\lambda} \qquad \text{or} \qquad \phi = \frac{2\pi}{\lambda} x$$

ϕ = 2π

From the diagram, R and U are in phase with each other and R and T are 180° or π radian out of phase with each other.

In Fig 13.5, W and X are 2 points on different sinusoidal waves. Although they are at the same position, they are at different phases. Phase difference is given by

$$\Delta\phi = \phi_2 - \phi_1 = 90° - 0° = 90° \qquad \text{or} \qquad \frac{\pi}{2} \text{ radian}$$

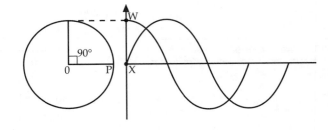

Fig 13.5   Two different sinusoidal waves

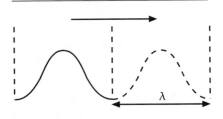

Fig 13.6   Speed of a wave

(g) The wavefront is a surface over which the disturbance has the same phase at all points.

(h) The speed of a wave is the distance travelled by a wave profile per unit time. Fig 13.6 shows a wave profile moving to the right. It moves a distance of λ in time T where λ is the wavelength and T is the period.

$$\text{Speed of wave } v = \frac{\text{Distance}}{\text{Time}}$$

$$= \frac{\lambda}{T}$$

$$v = f\lambda$$

$$\text{as } f = \frac{1}{T}$$

TRANSVERSE AND LONGITUDINAL WAVES

- There are two types of progressive waves.

(a) Transverse progressive waves.

A transverse wave is propagated by vibrations that are perpendicular to the direction of travel of the wave. Examples of transverse waves are electromagnetic waves, water waves in a ripple tank and the oscillation of spiral spring as shown in Fig 13.7.

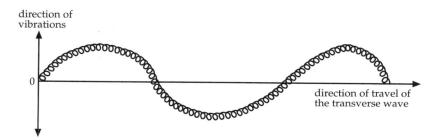

Fig 13.7   Transverse wave propagated with a spiral spring.

The above motion can be represented by a displacement-distance graph (Fig 13.8). This graph represents the displacement of every point on the transverse wave at one instant in time.

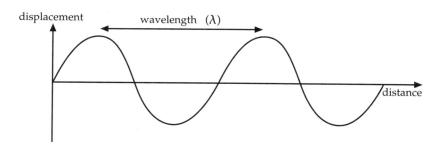

Fig 13.8   Displacement-distance graph

Transverse waves can also be represented by a displacement-time graph (Fig 13.9). This graph shows the displacement of one particle in time. The oscillatory motion is a sinusoidal wave.

307

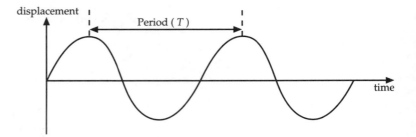

displacement

Period (T)

time

Fig 13.9 Displacement-time graph

(b) Longitudinal progressive waves

A longitudinal wave is propagated by vibrations that are parallel to the direction of travel of the wave. An example is sound wave. This is summarised by the displacement-distance graph in Fig 13.10.

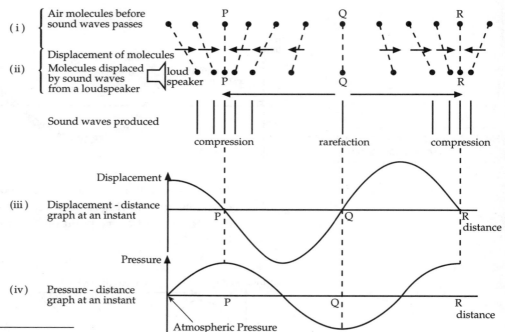

(i) Air molecules before sound waves passes

(ii) Displacement of molecules
Molecules displaced by sound waves from a loudspeaker

loud speaker

Sound waves produced

compression   rarefaction   compression

(iii) Displacement - distance graph at an instant

Displacement

distance

(iv) Pressure - distance graph at an instant

Pressure

Atmospheric Pressure

distance

Fig 13.10 Propagation of sound wave

In the absence of any disturbance, air molecules on the average are about equal distance from each other. This is depicted in Fig 13.10(i) as a series of dots positioned at regular intervals. When the diaphragm of a loudspeaker are set into vibration, the layer of air nearest to it oscillate with simple harmonic motion. This in turn causes successive layers further away to oscillate but with different phases (Fig 13.10(ii)). The result is the formation of compression and rarefaction at regular intervals. Compressions are regions where molecules are gathered towards a momentary stationery layer such as P and R. It's displacement is zero (Fig 13.10(iii)) and pressure is at its highest (Fig 13.10(iv)). Rarefaction are regions where molecules are moving away from the momentary stationary layer such as Q. The displacement is zero and pressure is at its lowest. The position of all molecules in Fig 13.10 will change at the next instant and the series of compression and rarefaction move to the right as longitudinal progressive wave.

Energy and Power in Waves

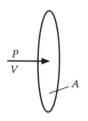

Fig 13.11   Intensity of a wave

- All waves carry energy and momentum. The power of a wave (P) is defined as the rate at which energy (E) is transported by the wave.

$$P = \frac{E}{t}$$

- The intensity of a wave (I) is defined as the power per unit area inclined perpendicularly to the wave's velocity (Fig 13.11).

- Wave Intensity $I = \dfrac{P}{A}$ where P is power and A is area. The S.I. units are watts per m^2.

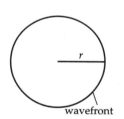

Fig 13.12

- For a spherical wave of radius r (Fig 13.12), the intensity is given by

$$I = \frac{P}{A} = \frac{P}{4\pi r^2}$$

- For a fixed source, P is constant hence

$$I \propto \frac{1}{r^2}$$

This is known as the inverse square law.

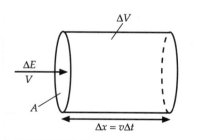

Fig 13.13

- Fig 13.13 shows a quantity of energy ΔE flowing into the volume ΔV in a time Δt.

$$\Delta V = A\Delta x = Av\Delta t$$

- The energy density u of the wave is the wave energy per unit volume, i.e.

$$u = \frac{\Delta E}{\Delta V} = \frac{\Delta E}{Av\Delta t} = \frac{P}{Av}$$

i.e. $u = \dfrac{I}{v}$

Since $I = \dfrac{P}{A}$

$\therefore I = uv$

or $I =$ (Energy density) (wave velocity)

309

- Consider the propagation of a sound wave through a metal rod. The maximum velocity of the vibrating element is ωA where ω is the angular frequency of oscillation and A is the amplitude of the motion. If Δm and ΔV are the masses and volume of the elements undergoing this motion, the maximum kinetic energy (ΔE) is given by

$$\Delta E = \frac{1}{2}mv^2$$

$$= \frac{1}{2}\Delta m(\omega A)^2$$

$$= \frac{1}{2}\Delta m\omega^2 A^2 \quad\quad\text{———— (1)}$$

Dividing equation (1) by ΔV

$$\frac{\Delta E}{\Delta V} = \frac{1}{2}\frac{\Delta m}{\Delta V}\omega^2 A^2 = \frac{1}{2}\rho\omega^2 A^2$$

Hence Energy Density $= \dfrac{1}{2}\rho\omega^2 A^2$

also, $I = $ (Energy density) $\times v$

$$= \frac{1}{2}\rho\omega^2 A^2 v$$

$$= 2\pi^2 f^2 \rho v A^2$$

Intensity $\propto$ (amplitude)^2 since $2\pi^2 f^2 \rho v = $ constant

Sound wave of frequency 512 Hz travels from a rod into air. The speed of sound is 4800 m s^{-1} in the rod and 330 m s^{-1} in the air. Find the wavelength of sound in the rod and in air.

Wavelength in rod $\lambda_r = \dfrac{v_r}{f} = \dfrac{4800}{512} = 9.38$ m.

Since frequency remains unchanged as sound waves leave the rod and enter the air,

Wavelength in air $\lambda_a = \dfrac{v_a}{f} = \dfrac{330}{512} = 0.64$ m.

Sound waves radiate from a point source with a speed of 330 m s^{-1} and frequency of 256 Hz. The power of the waves is 40 watts. Find the intensity of the wave at a distance of 10m. What is the amplitude of the wave at that point. [Density of air $= 1.29$ kg m^{-3}]

The sound waves radiate from the point source in concentric spheres. Energy from the source is spread over a spherical surface of radius r and area $4\pi r^2$. When r is 10m, the intensity of the wave is,

$$I = \frac{P}{A} = \frac{P}{4\pi r^2} = \frac{40}{4\pi(10)^2}$$
$$= 3.18 \times 10^{-2} \text{ Wm}^{-2}$$

The amplitude of the wave at $r = 10$ m is given by

$$A^2 = \frac{I}{2\pi^2 f^2 \rho v}$$

$$= \frac{3.18 \times 10^{-2}}{2\pi^2 (256)^2 (1.29)(330)}$$

$$= 5.77 \times 10^{-11}$$

$$A = 7.6 \times 10^{-6} \text{ m}$$

(a) What is meant by the amplitude of a wave? Intensity is defined as the rate of transfer of energy per unit area normal to the direction of propagation of the wave. Given that intensity I is related to amplitude A by
$$I = cA^2,$$
show that the constant c may have the units W m^{-4}.

(b) A wave of amplitude A and intensity I is coincident with a second wave of amplitude $3A$. Both waves have the same frequency. Calculate, in terms of A and c, the resultant amplitude and intensity when the phase difference is
(i) zero,
(ii) π rad.

(c) A radar transmitter produces pulses of microwaves each with a mean power P which are emitted uniformly in all directions. A small spherical target of effective area S is placed at a distance d from the transmitter. The target reflects a fraction k of the energy incident on it uniformly in all directions as shown below.

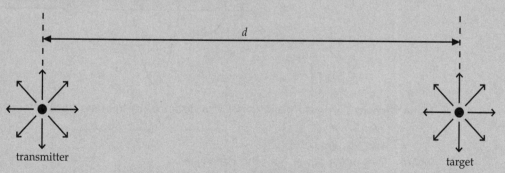

Show that the mean intensity I_t, of the reflected pulse when it is received back at the transmitter is given by

$$I_t = \frac{PkS}{16\pi^2 d^4}$$

[The surface area of a sphere of radius r is $4\pi r^2$.]
If the mean power P is 2 MW and the pulse duration is 3 μs, calculate
(i) the energy in each emitted pulse,
(ii) the mean intensity of the emitted pulse at a range of 50 km,

311

(iii) the mean intensity of the reflected pulse when received back at the transmitter if the range is 50 km and the product $kS = 1$ m^2,

Briefly discuss the effect on your answer to (iii) if the pulses were emitted in an almost parallel beam.

Cambridge

(a) The amplitude of a wave is the maximum displacement from an equilibrium position.

$$c = \frac{I}{A^2} = \frac{P}{(\text{Area})\,A^2} \quad \text{where } P = \text{Power and } A = \text{amplitude}$$

$$\text{Units of } c = \frac{W}{(m^2)(m)^2} = W\ m^{-4}$$

(b) By the principle of superposition (see chapter 14).

Resultant amplitude $= A + 3A$
$$= 4A$$
Intensity $= c(4A)^2$
$$= 16cA^2$$

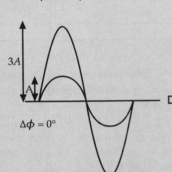

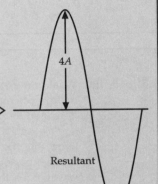

Resultant amplitude $= 3A - A$
$$= 2A$$
Intensity $= c(2A)^2$
$$= 4cA^2$$

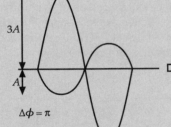

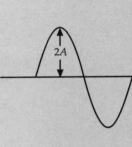

(c) Mean intensity (I) reaching the target at a distance (d) from the transmitter is given by

$$I = \frac{P}{4\pi d^2} = \frac{P'}{S}$$

where P = mean power from the transmitter.
  P' = mean power reaching surface S of the target.
  S = effective surface area S.

Rearranging, $P' = \dfrac{PS}{4\pi d^2}$

If P_t is the reflected power from S, then

$$P_t = kP' = \frac{PkS}{4\pi d^2}$$

The mean intensity I_t, of the reflected pulse when it is received back at the transmitter is,

$$I_t = \frac{P_t}{4\pi d^2}$$

$$= \frac{\left(\frac{PkS}{4\pi d^2}\right)}{4\pi d^2}$$

$$= \frac{PkS}{16\pi^2 d^4}$$

(i) Energy in each emitted pulse $= Pt$
$$= (2 \times 10^6)(3 \times 10^{-6})$$
$$= 6 \text{ J}$$

(ii) The mean intensity of the emitted pulse at a range of 50 km is

$$I = \frac{P}{4\pi d^2}$$

$$= \frac{2 \times 10^6}{4\pi(50000)^2}$$
$$= 6.4 \times 10^{-5} \text{ Wm}^{-2}$$

(iii) The mean intensity of the reflected pulse when $d = 50$ km and $kS = 1$ s.

$$I = \frac{PkS}{16\pi^2 d^4}$$

$$= \frac{(2 \times 10^6)(1)}{16\pi^2(50000)^4}$$

$$= 2.0 \times 10^{-15} \text{ W m}^{-2}$$

If the pulses emitted were almost parallel, the intensity will be almost the same as the initial intensity when it arrived at the target. This means that the intensity of the reflected pulse received by the transmitter would be higher than the value calculated in part (iii).

POLARISATION | Polarisation of transverse wave on a spiral spring.

- Transverse waves generated on a long spiral spring cause elements on the spring to oscillate vertically. They are said to be polarised in the vertical plane known as the plane of polarisation. Such plane polarised waves are illustrated in Fig 13.14.

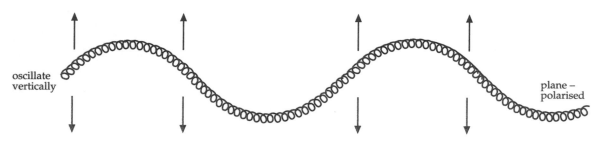

oscillate vertically

plane – polarised

Fig 13.14 Plane-Polarised transverse wave.

313

Such a wave could pass through the vertical slit of a cardboard with ease (Fig 13.15a). However, if the cardboard is turned through 90° (Fig 13.15b) such that the slit is perpendicular to the vibration of the spring elements, the transverse wave is eliminated. Polarisation is unique to transverse waves.

Longitudinal waves do not exhibit any effects of polarisation. This is illustrated in Fig 13.15c where the different orientations of the two cardboards do not affect the transmission of longitudinal waves.

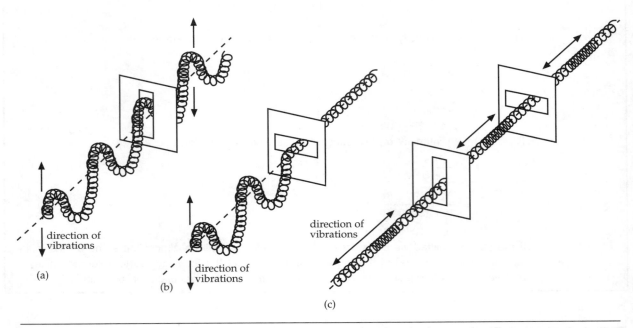

Fig 13.15

Polarisation of Electromagnetic Waves

- Electromagnetic waves such as visible light can be polarised. The vibration of a light wave consists of the vibration of an electric field E and a magnetic field B (Fig 13.16). However, the plane of polarisation of a light wave is regarded as the plane of vibration of an electric field. This is due to the dominant effects of an electric field when they interact with matter. Visible light normally oscillates randomly for most light sources and will occupy a large number of orientations. This results in a symmetric distribution of the plane of polarisation represented by Fig 13.17a. Plane-polarised light are illustrated in Fig 13.17b. The electric field vibrates predominantly in one plane.

314

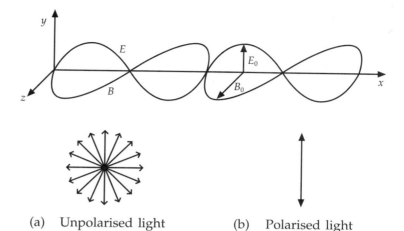

Fig 13.16 Electromagnetic waves

Fig 13.17 Illustrations of unpolarized light and polarized light

(a) Unpolarised light   (b) Polarised light

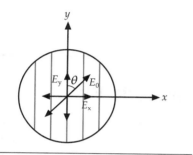

Fig 13.18 Polaroid

- Plane-polarised light can be produced by using Polaroid. This material consists of long chains of molecules that are aligned parallel to each other. Plane-polarised light parallel to the long chains will be absorbed while those that are perpendicular to the chains will pass through. If the plane of vibration represented by E_o is oriented as shown in Fig 13.18, the horizontal component E_x will be cut off while the vertical component E_y will pass through unimpeded. Long chains of molecules are parallel to the x-axis while vertical lines represent axes through which polarised light passes through.

When two polarisers P and Q are placed so that their polarising directions are parallel, the amplitude of the emergent beam is A.

Through what angle must Q be rotated so that the amplitude of the emergent beam is reduced to $\frac{A}{2}$?

What will be the corresponding fractional reduction in the intensity of the emergent beam?

Cambridge

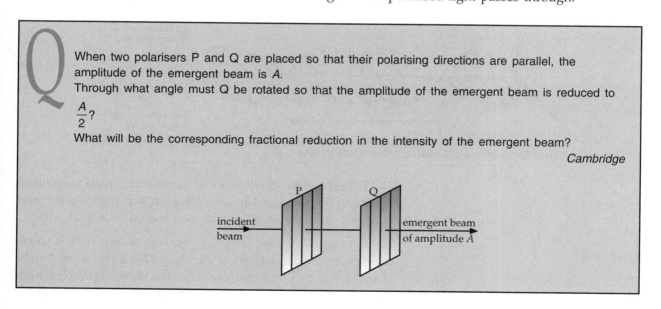

315

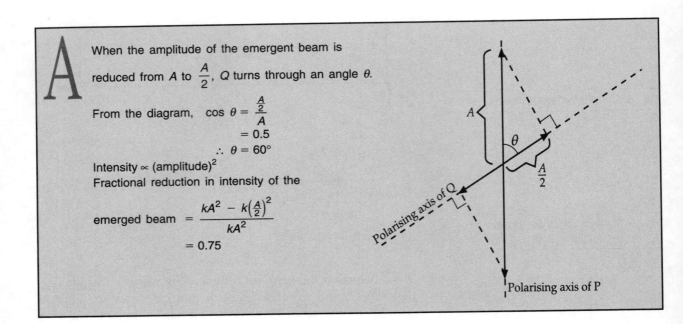

When the amplitude of the emergent beam is reduced from A to $\frac{A}{2}$, Q turns through an angle θ.

From the diagram, $\cos \theta = \dfrac{\frac{A}{2}}{A}$

$$= 0.5$$
$$\therefore \ \theta = 60°$$

Intensity $\propto$ (amplitude)^2

Fractional reduction in intensity of the

emerged beam $= \dfrac{kA^2 - k\left(\frac{A}{2}\right)^2}{kA^2}$

$$= 0.75$$

Properties of Electromagnetic Waves

- Electromagnetic waves consist of oscillating electric E-field, and oscillating magnetic B-field at right angles to each other and, travelling in the same direction in phase with each other (Fig 13.19).

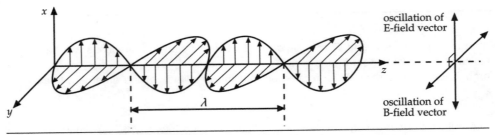

Fig 13.19   E-field and B-field of the electromagnetic waves

- The E-field and the B-field cannot be separated from each other. They can be orientated in any direction but their electric and magnetic fields must always be perpendicular to each other.

- Electromagnetic waves are produced whenever electric charges oscillate or are accelerated or decelerated. Electrons oscillating in an aerial produce radiowaves. The deceleration of high energy electrons when they strike a dense material produces X-rays.

- Electromagnetic waves are transverse waves and they oscillate sinusoidally.

- Electromagnetic waves can be polarised when they pass through a suitable polariser.

316

- Electromagnetic waves do not require a medium for its propagation. They are able to travel through a vacuum at a constant speed of 3×10^8 ms^{-1}. This speed is denoted by c and is related to frequency (f) and wavelength (λ) by the formula $c = f\lambda$.

- When electromagnetic waves travel through a material, the speed v in the material is smaller than c. The frequency of the waves remain unchanged as it travels from one medium to another.

- Electromagnetic waves transmit energy through space or through a material medium. The energy can be absorbed by matter.

- Electromagnetic waves can be reflected or refracted. It exhibits the wave properties of interference and diffraction.

The Electromagnetic Spectrum

- The electromagnetic spectrum shown in Fig 13.20 illustrates the entire frequency range of electromagnetic waves. They all share the same properties as described above and differ only in their frequencies or its corresponding wavelengths.

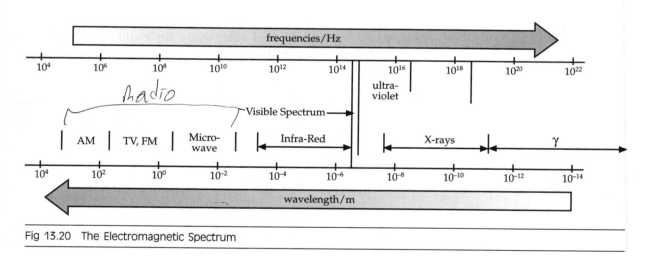

Fig 13.20 The Electromagnetic Spectrum

Radio Waves

- Radio waves are produced when electrons oscillate naturally. They are also transmitted by oscillating circuits connected to radio aerials. When electric current flows up and down the transmitter aerial, electric and magnetic fields are generated. They travel away from the transmitter and can be received by a tuned oscillatory electric circuit (radio receiver).

317

- The frequency range of radiowaves starts from around 1 kHz to 5 GHz. Their wavelengths can be as small as a few centimetres to many kilometres.

- Fig 13.21 shows the frequencies, wavelengths and some common uses of radiowaves.

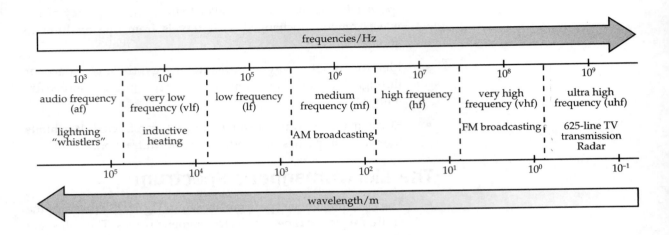

Fig 13.21   Frequency Range of Radiowaves

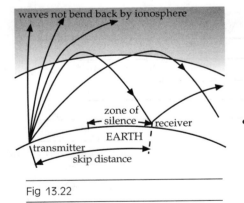

Fig 13.22

- Radio waves are used extensively for radio communications and broadcasting. Two methods are used to transmit radio waves.

  (a) Amplitude modulation (AM)

  This method transmits information varying the amplitude of the radio frequency carrier wave. AM broadcasting uses the low, medium and high frequency bands.

  (b) Frequency modulation (FM)

  This method transmits information by changing the frequency of the radio frequency carrier wave. FM broadcasting uses the very high frequency band.

- Radiowaves can be reflected by a layer of ionized gas known as ionosphere high above the Earth's surface (Fig 13.22). Multiple reflection between this layer and the earth's surface allows radiowaves to be transmitted thousands of kilometres from the transmitter.

Microwaves

- Fig 13.23 shows the frequencies, wavelengths and some common uses of microwaves, infrared, visible and ultraviolet waves.

318

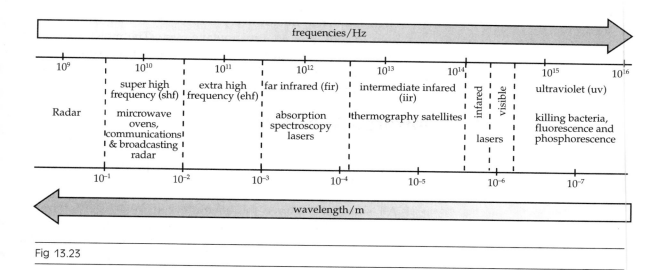

Fig 13.23

- Microwaves can be produced by electrical oscillators like the klystron tube or the magnetron. They can be detected by microwaves bolometer or electrical circuits arranged as microwave receivers.

- Microwaves are actually radiowaves of high frequency and short wavelength (about 10^{-1} to 10^{-3} m). The frequency range is from 10^9 Hz to 3×10^{11} Hz.

- The entire universe is permeated with a unique microwave radiation of the same intensity. If we point our detectors to any part of the sky, we will obtain nearly the same value. This microwave radiation field is known as the cosmic microwave background. This is one of the strongest argument in favour of the Big Bang theory. The microwave background is regarded as the cooled remanant of a hot fire-ball that gave birth to our present universe.

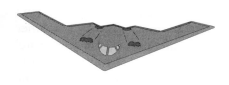

Fig 13.24   Stealth bomber

- Microwaves are commonly used in radar, communications, broadcasting and preparation of food.

  (a) Radar is an acronym for radio detection and ranging. Rapid pulses are sent out continuously from a rotating aerial. These can be reflected back to the transmitter by an airplane. The reflected wave is processed and displayed on a radar screen. Some planes such as the stealth bomber cannot be detected by radar. This is because their planar surfaces reflect pulses away from the transmitter (Fig 13.24).

  (b) Microwaves have higher directivity compared to radiowaves of longer wavelength. This facilitates long distance communications between satellites and deep space probes with earth's stations. In addition, the microwave band has 100 times more frequency space than the radio frequency band. Therefore it is used extensively in communications and broadcasting.

319

- High frequency microwave produced by a magnetron can be used to cook food in a microwave oven. The moisture content of food gains considerable kinetic energy when exposed to the oscillating electric fields of the microwaves. Efficient heating occurs throughout the food.

Infrared Radiation

- Infrared radiation has wavelengths from 7.8×10^{-7} m to 0.5×10^{-3} m. The frequency range is from 6×10^{11} Hz to 4×10^{14} Hz.

- All substances above the absolute zero (0 K) emit infrared radiation. They are generated by vibration and rotation of atoms and molecules. The greater the thermal agitation, the greater the amount of infrared radiation produced. The human body radiates about 200 W m^{-2} while a tungsten lamp can emit as much as 7×10^6 W m^{-2}.

- Infrared radiation can be detected by thermal infrared detectors like thermopile, thermistor and quantum detectors. Other methods include capturing pictorially the natural emission of infrared radiations from an object or person. The variation of the infrared radiation emitted is reproduced to form a thermal image. In this way, an object or person can be seen in the dark. Another important application is the use of special films and cameras to capture thermal images of the earth from a satellite. Vast amounts of information can be collected.

Light or the visible spectrum

- Light has wavelengths from 7.8×10^{-7} m to 3.8×10^{-7} m. The frequency range is from 4×10^{14} Hz to 8×10^{14} Hz.

- Light is produced by atoms and molecules when the outer electrons, after being excited into higher energy levels, return to their unexcited state. Light from a lamp or the sun has a whole range of visible frequencies. This is made possible by the many excited states found in the atom or molecule. On the other hand, when neon and sodium are heated to a high temperature, the total number of excited states are limited. Visible frequencies emitted are also limited. Neon has a characteristic red glow while sodium emits yellow light.

- The colours perceived by the eye when light falls on the rectina depends on the frequency or the wavelength of the electromagnetic wave. Table 13.2 shows the characteristic frequency and wavelength for six colours. Each of the colours is called monochromatic light as their frequency and wavelength are well defined.

320

Colour	Wavelength λ/m	frequency f/Hz
Red	$6.22 - 7.80 \times 10^{-7}$	$4.82 - 3.84 \times 10^{14}$
Orange	$5.97 - 6.22 \times 10^{-7}$	$5.03 - 4.82 \times 10^{14}$
Yellow	$5.77 - 5.97 \times 10^{-7}$	$5.20 - 5.03 \times 10^{14}$
Green	$4.92 - 5.77 \times 10^{-7}$	$6.10 - 5.20 \times 10^{14}$
Blue	$4.55 - 4.92 \times 10^{-7}$	$6.59 - 6.10 \times 10^{14}$
Violet	$3.90 - 4.55 \times 10^{-7}$	$7.69 - 6.59 \times 10^{14}$

Table 13.2 Wavelength and frequency of six colours.

- The study of light phenomena and its applications is so important that a branch of applied physics called optics has evolved from it.

Ultraviolet Radiation

- Ultraviolet radiation has wavelength from 3.8×10^{-7} m to about 6×10^{-10} m. The frequency range is from 8×10^{14} to about 5×10^{17} Hz.

- Ultraviolet radiation is produced when electrons jump from a relatively high excited state to a low excited state within atoms and molecules. Such large energy transitions occur in discharge tubes and incandescent objects of high temperature. Notable examples are the mercury vapour discharge tube and the surface of the sun.

- Ultraviolet radiation ionises atoms readily in the upper atmosphere.
  (a) A layer of ionised gas is formed at about 80 km from the earth's surface. This is commonly known as the ionosphere.
  (b) Ultraviolet radiation that reaches the earth's surface is less energetic. This is because the energetic UV rays are absorbed by the ozone layer in the atmosphere. In recent years, scientists have discovered that ozone depletion above the Arctic and Antartic have increased. The result is the formation of a massive ozone hole that hovers above the two regions. This allows the more energetic UV rays to filter down the earth's surface.
  (c) Ultraviolet radiation causes tanning and the production of vitamin D in the skin cells. Prolong exposure increases the possibility of eye damage and skin cancer.
  (d) Micro-organisms are destroyed when they absorb ultraviolet radiation. For this reason, uv rays are used often in some medical applications and sterilisation processes.
  (e) Ultraviolet radiation is also used extensively in mercury vapour discharge tube. uv rays emitted from mercury vapour are absorbed by fluorescent and phosphorescent materials. The energy absorbed is re-radiated as visible light.

321

X-rays

- Fig 13.25 show the frequencies, wavelengths and some common uses of X-rays and Gamma rays.

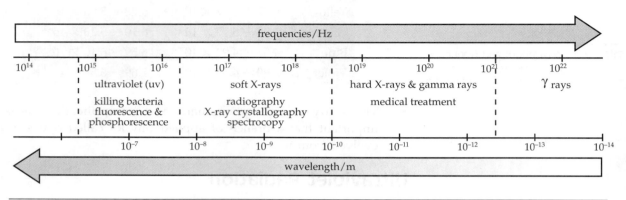

Fig 13.25   The Electromagnetic Spectrum

- X-rays extend from wavelengths of about 10^{-9} m to about 10^{-12} m. The frequency range is from 3×10^{20} Hz.

- X-rays are produced when high velocity electrons strike a metallic target (e.g. tungsten). Electron transitions occur among the inner, tightly bound electrons with the atom. X-rays are emitted in the process.

- The uses of X-rays are as follows:
  (a) They are widely used in medical diagnosis and therapy. Well defined images can be easily captured on photographic film called radiograph. High energy X-rays are used to kill cancer cells and to reduce tumour size.
  (b) X-rays are reflected and diffracted by crystals. It is used to investigate the structure of crystalline material and to determine ionic lattice spacing.

Gamma Rays

- Gamma rays extend from wavelengths of about 10^{-10} m to about 10^{-14} m. The frequency range is from 3×10^{18} Hz to about 3×10^{22} Hz. This is overlapping with the upper limits of the X-ray spectrum.

- Gamma rays are emitted from the excited state of the nucleus of an atom. After the emission, the nucleus rearranges itself into a state of lower excitation.

- The energies of Gamma rays range from a few kiloelectron volts to 100 Mev.

Exercise 13

Multiple Choice Questions

1 The wave disturbance created in a swimming pool moves from right to left. A cork is at point P on the water surface.

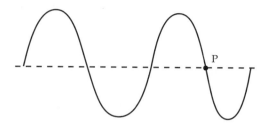

In which direction will the cork move?
A ←　　　　B ↖
C ↑　　　　D ↓

2 Parallel water waves of wavelength 10 m strike a straight sea wall. The wave fronts make an angle of 30° with the wall as shown.

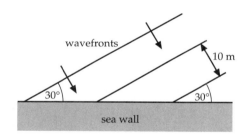

What is the difference in phase at any instant between the waves at two points 5 m apart along the wall?
A 45°　　　　B 55°
C 90°　　　　D 180°

3 The diagram shows two oscillations.

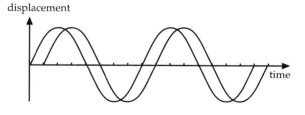

What is the phase difference between the oscillations?

A $\dfrac{\pi}{4}$ rad　　　　B $\dfrac{\pi}{2}$ rad

C $\dfrac{3}{4}\pi$ rad　　　　D π rad

4 The same progressive wave is represented by the following graphs.

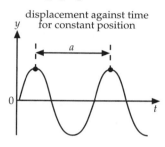

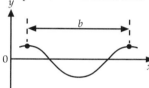

Which of the following gives the speed of propagation of the wave?

A ab　　　　B $\dfrac{a}{b}$

C $\dfrac{b}{a}$　　　　D $\dfrac{1}{b}$

5 A sound wave of frequency 400 Hz is travelling in a gas at a speed of 320 m s^{-1}. What is the phase difference between two points 0.2 m apart in the direction of travel?

A $\dfrac{\pi}{4}$ rad　　　　B $\dfrac{\pi}{2}$ rad

C $\dfrac{2}{5}\pi$ rad　　　　D $\dfrac{4}{5}\pi$ rad

6 If a wave can be polarised, it must be
A a longitudinal wave.
B a progressive wave.
C a stationary wave.
D a transverse wave.

7   Plane-polarised radio waves are transmitted by a vertical aerial. The amplitude of the waves is A when they reach a receiving aerial which is tilted from the vertical at an angle θ in the plane perpendicular to the direction of arrival. The power delivered by the aerial to the receiver is proportional to

   A $A^2 \cos^2 \theta$ **B** $A \cos \theta$
   C zero   **D** $A \sin \theta$

8   A plane wave of amplitude A is incident on a surface of area S placed so that it is perpendicular to the direction of travel of the wave. The energy per unit time intercepted by the surface is E.
   The amplitude of the wave is increased to $2A$ and the area of the surface is reduced to $\dfrac{S}{2}$.

   How much energy per unit time is intercepted by this smaller surface?

   A $4E$ **B** $2E$
   C E **D** $\dfrac{E}{2}$

9   A sound wave of amplitude 0.20 mm has an intensity of 3.0 W m^{-2}. What will be the intensity of a sound wave of the same frequency which has an amplitude of 0.40 mm?

   A 4.2 W m^{-2} **B** 6.0 W m^{-2}
   C 9.0 W m^{-2} **D** 12 W m^{-2}

10 Ultra-violet rays differ from X-rays in that they
   A cannot be diffracted.
   B cannot be polarised.
   C have a lower frequency.
   D are deviated when they pass through a magnetic field.

11 Which one of the following could be the frequency of ultraviolet radiation?
   A 1.0×10^6 Hz   **B** 1.0×10^9 Hz
   C 1.0×10^{12} Hz   **D** 1.0×10^{15} Hz

12 Data transmitted along glass-fibre cables is in the form of pulses of monochromatic red light each of duration 2.5 ns. Which of the following is the best estimate of the number of wavelengths in each pulse?
   A 10^3 **B** 10^6
   C 10^9 **D** 10^{12}

13 In which part of the electromagnetic spectrum does a wave of frequency 500 MHz occur?
   A infra-red   **B** radio
   C ultra-violet   **D** visible

14 Which of the following frequency ranges includes most of the electromagnetic waves emitted by ultra-violet tubes used in a sun bed?
   A 5×10^5 to 5×10^8 Hz
   B 5×10^8 to 5×10^{11} Hz
   C 5×10^{11} to 5×10^{14} Hz
   D 5×10^{14} to 5×10^{17} Hz

15 Typical wavelengths of radio waves and X-rays are in the ratio 10^m: 1. Which of the following is a possible value for m?
   A $+24$ **B** $+12$
   C 1   **D** -12

16 An electromagnetic radiation has a frequency of 10^8 Hz. In which region of the spectrum would such radiation occur?
   A infrared   **B** radio
   C ultraviolet   **D** visible

Structured Questions

1   (a) Explain what is meant by the *frequency* of a wave.
   (b) A certain wave has a wavelength 1.00 m. What is the distance between two points on this wave with a phase difference of $\dfrac{\pi}{4}$ rad?
   (c) Fig 13.26 represents the variation with time t of the displacement y of a point in a sinusoidal wave of frequency 100 Hz.

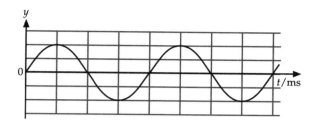

Fig 13.26

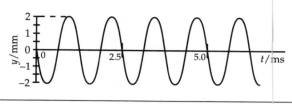

Fig 13.28(a)

(i) Mark the t-axis of Fig 13.27 with values of time measured in milliseconds.

(ii) On the axes of Fig 13.27 and using the same scales as in Fig 13.26, draw a second curve representing the displacement of a point in a second wave of twice the frequency and half the amplitude.

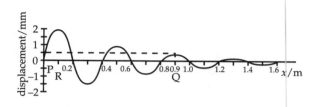

Fig 13.28(b)

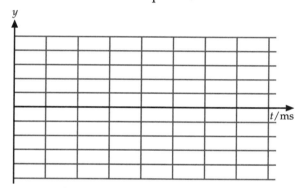

Fig 13.27

Cambridge

2 (a) Explain what is meant by the term *progressive* as applied to a wave.

(b) Starting with the definition of speed, show that the speed of a wave is given by the equation

speed = frequency × wavelength.

(c) A progressive wave moves past two points P and Q, separated by a distance of 0.90 m. A graph showing how the displacement y at P varies with time t is shown in Fig 13.28(a).

Another graph, Fig 13.28(b), shows how the displacement of the wave at time $t = 0$ varies with distance x from point P.

Using data from the graphs, deduce for this wave

(i) the wavelength,

(ii) the frequency,

(iii) the speed,

(iv) the phase difference between the oscillations at P and those at Q,

(v) the ratio $\dfrac{\text{amplitude at R}}{\text{amplitude at Q}}$,

(vi) the ratio $\dfrac{\text{intensity at R}}{\text{intensity at Q}}$.

(d) Light waves, sound waves in air and surface water waves are different forms of waves. Suggest, with a reason, which of these might be the wave being considered in (c).

(e) (i) Suggest an experimental method for obtaining the graph shown in Fig 13.28(a).

(ii) Discuss whether the same method could be used for the graph in Fig 13.28(b).

Cambridge

3

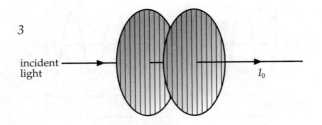

incident light → I_0

Fig 13.29

Two sheets of polariod, P and A, are placed so that their polarising directions are parallel and vertical, as shown in Fig 13.29, the intensity of the emergent beam is then I_0. Through what angle should A be turned for the intensity of the emergent beam to be reduced to $\frac{1}{2}I_0$?

Describe the polarisation of the emergent beam when this operation is carried out.

Cambridge

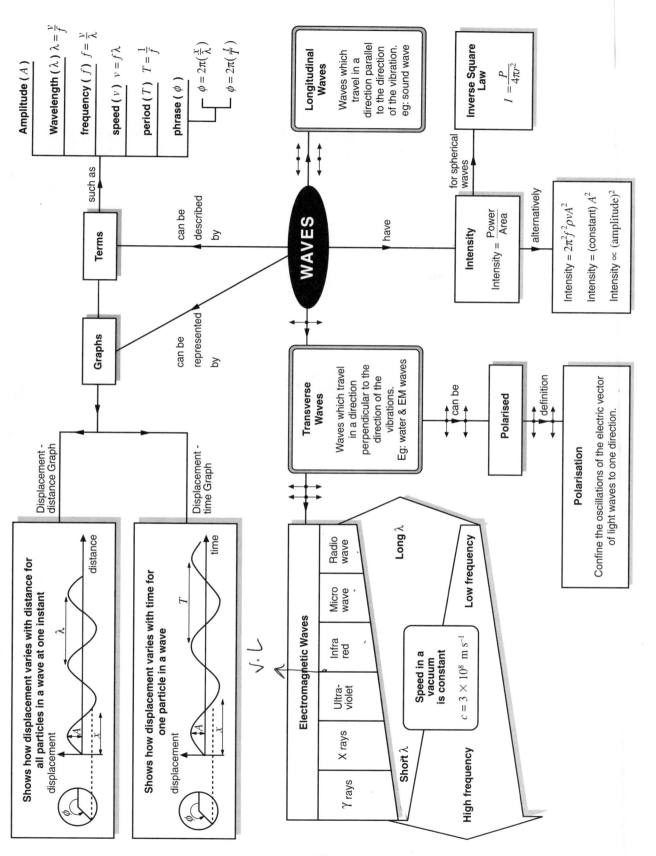

Superposition

PRINCIPLE OF SUPERPOSITION

STANDING WAVES

INTERFERENCE

DIFFRACTION

DIFFRACTION GRATING

Syllabus Objectives

In this chapter you should be able to:

- explain and use the principle of superposition in simple applications.

- show an understanding of experiments which demonstrate stationary waves, using microwaves, stretched strings and air columns.

- explain the formation of a stationary wave, using a graphical method, and identify nodes and antinodes.

- explain the meaning of the term diffraction.

- show an understanding of experiments which demonstrate diffraction, including the diffraction of water waves in a ripple tank both with a wide gap and with a narrow gap.

- show an understanding of the terms interference and coherence.

- show an understanding of experiments which demonstrate two-source interference, using water, light and microwaves.

- show an understanding of the conditions required if two-source interference fringes are to be observed.

- recall and solve problems by using the equation $\lambda = \dfrac{ax}{D}$ for double-slit interference using light.

- recall and solve problems by using the formula $d\sin\theta = n\lambda$ and describe the use of a diffraction grating to determine the wavelength of light. (The structure and use of the spectrometer is not included.)

PRINCIPLE OF SUPER-POSITION

- The principle of superposition states that whenever two or more waves are travelling in the same region simultaneously, the total displacement at any point is equal to the vector sum of their individual displacement at that point. The superposition of two waves with displacements y_1 and y_2 are shown in Fig 14.1. The total displacement is given by $y = y_1 + y_2$.

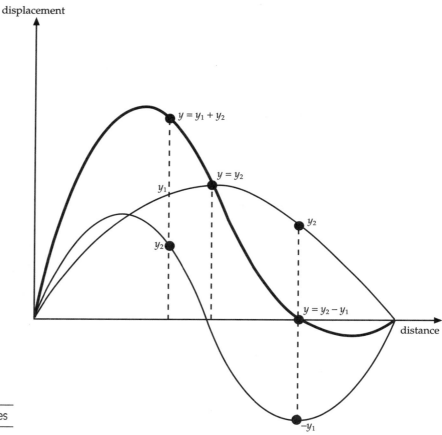

Fig 14.1 Superposition of two waves

- In general, if n waves are superimposed, the total displacement is $y = y_1 + y_2 + \ldots \ldots + y_n$.

- Consider two similar waves travelling towards each other in Fig 14.2a and Fig 14.2b. The principle of superposition can be used to find the resultant waveform when they interact. When the two wave pulses are in phase momentarily (Fig 14.2(a)(iii)), the resultant amplitude is a maximum and is equal to twice the amplitude of the interacting waves. This phenomenon is known as constructive interference. When the two waves are 180° out of phase (Fig 14.2(b)(iii)), total cancellation occurs and no waves can be seen at that moment. This is known as destructive interference. After the brief moment of superposition, the two waves leave each other without any changes to their waveforms.

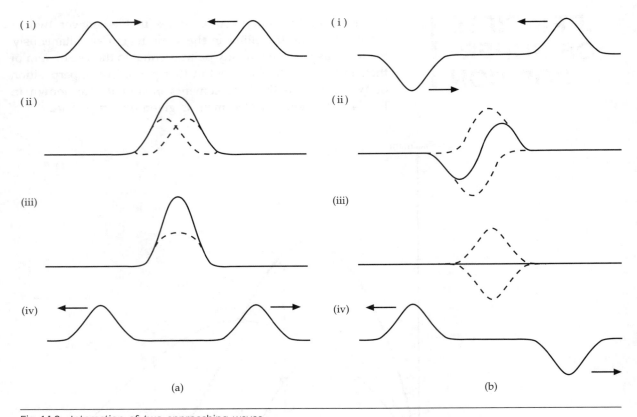

(i)	(i)
(ii)	(ii)
(iii)	(iii)
(iv)	(iv)
(a)	(b)

Fig 14.2   Interaction of two approaching waves

- The application of the principle of superposition to interacting waveforms produces four kinds of phenomena.
  (a) Stationary waves — the superposition of two wave trains with the same speed, frequency and amplitude travelling in opposite directions.
  (b) Beats — the superposition of two wave trains of slightly different frequencies travelling in the same direction. (The phenomenon of beats will not be discussed here.)
  (c) Interference — the superposition of two or more wave trains from coherent sources.
  (d) Diffraction — the spreading of wavefronts through a narrow slit or opening by the superposition of secondary wavelets from the emerging wave front.

STATIONARY WAVES

- A stationary wave is formed when two waves which are travelling in opposite directions, and which have the same speed, frequency and amplitude are superimposed.

- Figure 14.3 shows the formation of a stationary wave on a string that is fixed to the wall at one end. The incident wave on reaching the wall is reflected with a phase change of $180°$.

330

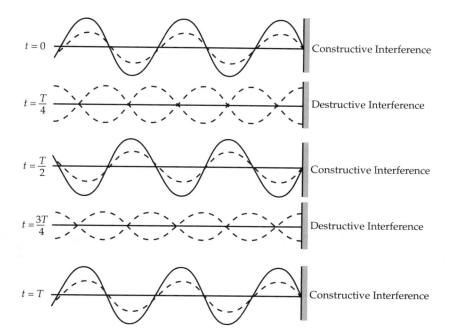

$t = 0$ — Constructive Interference

$t = \dfrac{T}{4}$ — Destructive Interference

$t = \dfrac{T}{2}$ — Constructive Interference

$t = \dfrac{3T}{4}$ — Destructive Interference

$t = T$ — Constructive Interference

Fig 14.3 Formation of a stationary wave on a string attached to an immovable object

- The two colliding waves superimpose constructively to give a resultant of large amplitude at $t = 0$ s. As the reflected waves move out of phase with the incident waves, the resultant waves decrease in amplitude.

- One-quarter of a period $\left(t = \dfrac{1}{4}T \right)$ later the two waves are 180° out of phase and they superimpose destructively. At $t = \dfrac{1}{2}T$, constructive interference occurs and the resultant amplitude is at its maximum again. This is repeated with destructive interference and constructive interference occurring at $t = \dfrac{3}{4}T$ and $t = T$ respectively. The result of these is the formation of a wave profile that does not travel and appears stationary (Fig 14.3).

- Elements on the string oscillate with different amplitudes vertically. The points with the largest displacements are known as antinodes (A). See Fig 14.4. The points on the string with no oscillations are known as nodes (N). They are midway between adjacent antinodes.

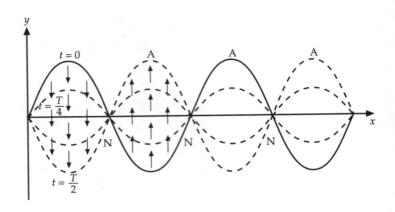

Fig 14.4 Nodes and antinodes of a stationary wave

	Stationary	Progressive
Amplitude	Varies from a maximum of $2A$ at the antinodes to 0 at the nodes. It depends on the position along the wave.	Same for all particles in the wave motion if no energy is lost
Frequency	All particles (or E field) vibrate with SHM with the frequency of the stationary wave.	All particles (or E field) vibrate with SHM with the frequency of the progressive wave.
Wavelength	Twice the distance between a pair of adjacent nodes or antinodes.	Distance between any two consecutive points on the wave with the same phase.
Phase	Phase of all particles or E field in a segment between two adjacent nodes is the same. Particles and E field in the adjacent segment of length $\lambda/2$ have a phase difference of π radians.	All particles or E field within one wavelength have different phases.
Wave profile	The wave profile does not advance.	The wave profile advances with the speed of the wave.
Energy	Energy is retained within the vibratory motion of the stationary wave.	Energy travels in the direction of propagation of the wave.

Table 14.1 Comparison of Stationary and Progressive Wave Motion

Stationary waves on vibrating wires (Melde's Experiment)

- A piano wire of length L is held taut by connecting one end to a pulley and weight and the other end to a vibrator. A signal generator is used to increase the frequency of vibrations. The progressive wave produced travels towards the pulley with a constant velocity v. When it superimposes with the reflected wave of the same velocity, a stationary wave is obtained.

- The simplest mode of vibration is known as the fundamental frequency or the 1st harmonic (Fig 14.4a). When the frequency is doubled, another stationary wave is formed. This is known as the 1st overtone or 2nd harmonic (Fig 14.4b). Further increases in frequency produce standing waves in Fig 14.4c and 14.4d.

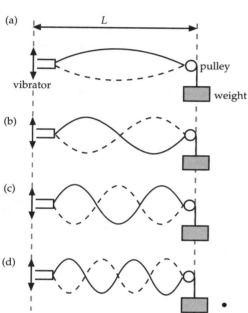

Fig 14.4   Melde's experiment

  Fundamental frequency or 1st harmonic

$$\lambda_1 = 2L; \quad f_1 = \frac{v}{\lambda_1} = \frac{v}{2L}$$

  1st overtone or 2nd harmonic

$$\lambda_2 = L; \quad f_2 = \frac{v}{\lambda_2} = \frac{v}{L}$$

  2nd overtone or 3rd harmonic

$$\lambda_3 = \frac{2L}{3}; \quad f_3 = \frac{v}{\lambda_3} = \frac{3v}{2L}$$

  3rd overtone or 4th harmonic

$$\lambda_3 = \frac{2L}{4}; \quad f_4 = \frac{v}{\lambda_4} = \frac{2v}{L}$$

- In general, for nth harmonics,

$$\lambda_n = \frac{2L}{n} \text{ where } n = 1, 2, 3 \ldots$$

- The frequency f_n of the nth harmonics is given by $f_n = \frac{v}{\lambda_n}$

  where v is the velocity of either one of the progressive waves that causes the stationary wave.

- The velocity of the progressive waves is given by

  $v = \sqrt{\frac{T}{\mu}}$ where T is the tension in the wire and μ is the mass per unit length. This velocity remains constant when frequency changes.

- If the piano wire is plucked, a number of different stationary waves can be produced simultaneously. The fundamental frequency and many of the overtones are present in the resulting vibrations.

333

- **Stationary waves in air columns** (closed pipe)

  If the air in a pipe that is closed at one end is disturbed by a source of sound (e.g. vibrating reed), a progressive longitudinal (sound) wave travels along the air column and is reflected at its end to form a stationary longitudinal (sound) wave.

  (a) The fundamental or the frequency of the lowest note is shown in Fig 14.5. The node is located at the closed end while the antinode is at the open end (Fig 14.5a). Molecules oscillate with maximum displacement at the antinode and zero displacement at the node (Fig 14.5b). The converse is true for pressure variation.

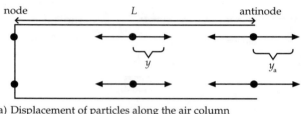

(a) Displacement of particles along the air column

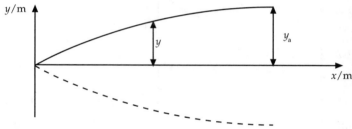

(b) Displacement-distance graph

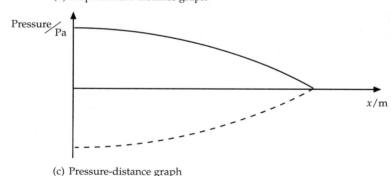

(c) Pressure-distance graph

Fig 14.5   Stationary waves in a closed pipe

  (b) Pressure is always a maximum at the node and zero at the antinode. This is possible only when the wavelength is correctly matched to the length of the pipe.

- Table 14.2 summaries the wavelength and frequency of the fundamental and the first two overtones. A displacement-distance graph has been superimposed on to the closed pipe. The speed of the progressive wave in air at a particular temperature is v.

334

Mode		Wavelength	Frequency
Fundamental		$\lambda_1 = 4L$	$f_1 = \dfrac{v}{\lambda_1} = \dfrac{v}{4L}$
1st overtone		$\lambda_2 = \dfrac{4}{3}L$	$f_2 = \dfrac{v}{\lambda_2} = \dfrac{3v}{4L}$
2nd overtone		$\lambda_3 = \dfrac{4}{5}L$	$f_3 = \dfrac{v}{\lambda_3} = \dfrac{5v}{4L}$

Table 14.2   Formation of stationary waves in a closed pipe

- **Stationary waves in air column** (open pipe)
  An open pipe is one in which both ends are open. The wavelengths and frequencies of the stationary waves are shown in Table 14.3.

Mode		Wavelength	Frequency
Fundamental		$\lambda_1 = 2L$	$f_1 = \dfrac{v}{\lambda_1} = \dfrac{v}{2L}$
1st overtone		$\lambda_2 = L$	$f_2 = \dfrac{v}{\lambda_2} = \dfrac{v}{L}$
2nd overtone		$\lambda_3 = \dfrac{2}{3}L$	$f_3 = \dfrac{v}{\lambda_3} = \dfrac{3v}{2L}$

Table 14.3   Formation of stationary waves in an open pipe

- Determination of the wavelength, frequency and speed of sound using a calibrated cathode ray oscilloscope.

- The apparatus shown in Fig 14.6 produces stationary waves from which the wavelength, frequency and speed of sound are obtained.

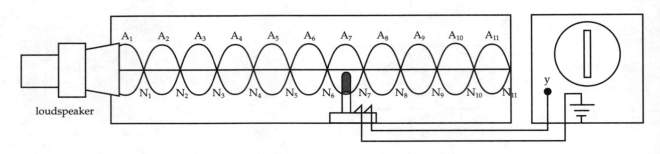

loudspeaker

Table 14.6   Determination of the speed of sound with stationary waves

(a) Signals from an audio-frequency generator fed to a loudspeaker produces sound waves of unknown frequency in an enclosed tube. The incident and reflected waves interfere to produce stationary waves.

(b) A microphone is used to measure distances between nodes. It is connected to the input (Y) and the earth terminal of a cathode ray oscilloscope (CRO).

(c) To measure the wavelength λ, a suitable Y-gain is chosen and the time-base is switched off. The microphone is moved from N_1 through 10 antinodes to N_{11}. The CRO will show a vertical trace which will vary from a maximum at the antinode to a minimum at the node. If the distance from N_1 to N_{11} is 0.750 m, the distance from one node to the adjacent node

$$= \frac{0.750}{10}$$
$$= 0.075 \text{ m}$$

Wavelength
$$\lambda = 2 \times \text{distance from one node to the next}$$
$$= 2 \times 0.075$$
$$= 0.150 \text{ m}$$

(d) To measure frequency, the time-base is set to a suitable frequency (e.g. 0.1 ms cm^{-1}). With a suitable Y-gain, a sinusoidal curve is obtained on the screen (Fig 14.7).

336

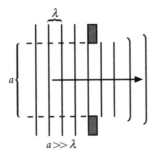

Fig 14.7 Sinusoidal curve of signals from an audio-frequency generator

The distance between two crest $x = 4$ cm
The period $T = x \times$ time base
$$= 4 \text{ cm} \times 0.1 \text{ ms cm}^{-1}$$
$$= 0.4 \text{ ms}$$
$$= 4 \times 10^{-4} \text{ s}$$

(e) The velocity of the sound wave is found from
$$v = f\lambda$$
Velocity of sound $= (2500 \text{ Hz}) (0.150 \text{ m})$
$$= 375 \text{ m s}^{-1}$$

DIFFRACTION I

- Diffraction is the spreading of wavefronts through a narrow slit or around an obstacle by the superposition of secondary wavelets from the emerging wavefront.

- The spreading of the wavefronts becomes more prominent when the size of the slit approaches the wavelength of the waves.

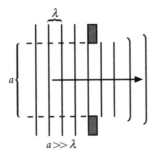
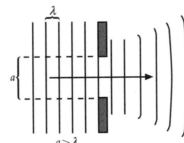
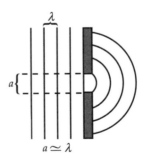

- Three types of diffraction effects are considered in this chapter. They are the diffraction of
  (a) single slit,
  (b) double slits (Young's interference experiment),
  (c) multiple slits (Diffraction Grating).

337

Diffraction from a single slit

- Consider monochromatic light of wavelength λ passing through a narrow slit of width a. If the light comes from a distant object, the waves incident on the slit will be planar.

- The diffracted pattern obtained is illustrated in Fig 14.8. Regions of bright (maxima) and dark (minima) bands can be seen. The graph of intensity as a function of the angular displacement $\sin \theta$ is shown in Fig 14.8.

- The central bright fringe has several times the intensity and twice the width of any other fringes.

- Rays coming from the slit arrive at O with no optical path difference (Fig 14.8a) and they interfere constructively. In the vicinity of O, the significance of the path difference increases, hence the intensity decreases.

- At the position of the first minimum (Fig 14.8b), the optical path difference between RS and PQ is $\dfrac{\lambda}{2}$. They interfere destructively. Furthermore, all rays in the region TUSR interfere destructively with all rays in the region RSQP. This results in a dark band.

$$\sin \theta_2 = \frac{\lambda}{a} \ (\text{1st minima})$$

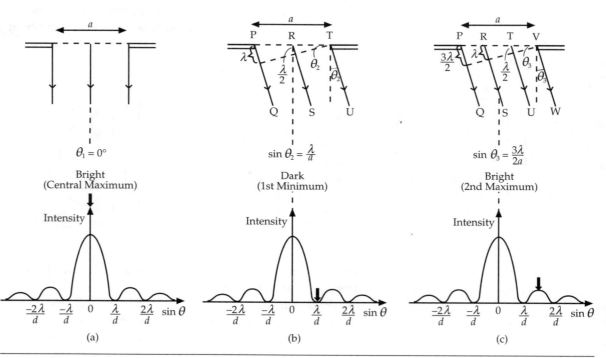

Fig 14.8   Diffraction patterns from a single slit

- At the position of the second maximum (Fig 14.8c), the optical path difference between TU and RS is $\frac{\lambda}{2}$. They interfere destructively. All rays in the region TUSR will interfere destructively with the rays in the region RSQP. However, light from the region VWUT will still reach the screen to form a bright band but this will not be as bright as the central band.

- In general, the angular displacement θ of the minima is given by $a \sin \theta = n\lambda$ where $n = \pm 1, \pm 2, \pm 3, \ldots \ldots$
  (a) If $a \gg \lambda$, θ is very small.
  $$\left(\sin \theta \approx \theta = \frac{\lambda}{a} \text{ for the first minima} \right)$$
  Diffraction patterns cannot be seen.
  (b) If $a = \lambda$, $\theta = 90°$ for the 1st minima. This means that the diffracted wave reaches all parts of the geometrical shadow.
  (c) If $a \ll \lambda$, the central maximum of the diffraction pattern covers the entire geometrical shadow.

Diffraction from a double slit

- Diffracted waves from two slits pass through each other to form interference patterns. The experimental set up to produce this effect is illustrated in Fig 14.9. Typical values for D and d are about 1 m and 0.5 mm respectively.

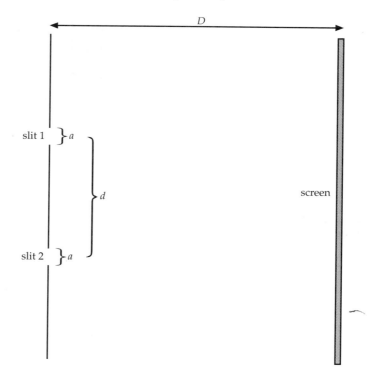

monochromatic light source

Fig 14.9   Diffraction from a double slit (Not drawn to scale)

339

INTERFERENCE I

- Interference is the superposition of two or more wave trains from coherent sources. The following conditions must be observed.
  - (a) The sources must have the same or roughly equivalent amplitude.
  - (b) The sources must be coherent. This means that
    - (i) waves are in phase or move with a constant phase difference,
    - (ii) waves have the same frequency and wavelength.
  - (c) Transverse waves must not be polarised.

- Two coherent sources can be obtained by splitting light from the same source. Two methods can be used to do this.
  - (a) Division of wavefront
    Fig 14.10 shows two slits S_1 and S_2 placed in front of a single source of wave or a laser. Waves can be seen spreading out from the two slits. The narrower the slit the greater is the spreading. The phenomenon is known as diffraction. The diffracted wavefronts from S_1 and S_2 merge to form interference pattern on screen C.

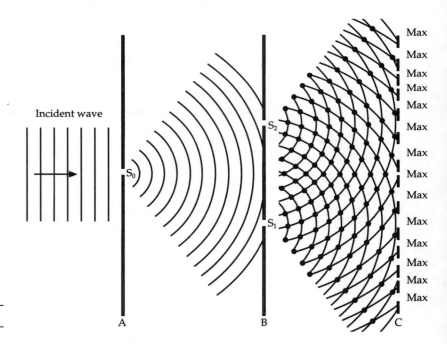

Fig 14.10

  - (b) Division of amplitude
    This is the partial reflection and partial transmission of waves when a wave train is incident on a semi-reflecting surface.

Young's Two-Slit Experiment

- Fig 14.11 is the experimental set-up for Young's two-slit interference experiment. The geometrical properties for the interference fringes are illustrated in Fig 14.11a. Light from a monochromatic source of wavelength λ is diffracted at S_1 and S_2 and falls on a screen placed at a distance D from the slits. Since S_1O and S_2O are equidistant, light waves arriving at O are in phase. Constructive interference occurs and central bright fringe is produced at O (Fig 14.11b). As one moves away from O along the screen alternate bright and dark fringes can be seen.

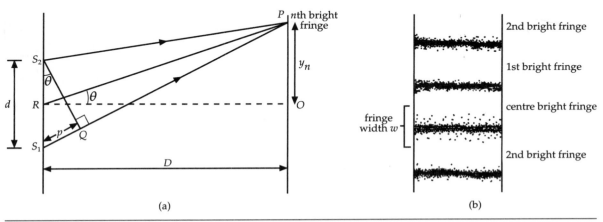

(a) (b)

Fig 14.11 Arrangement for producing interferences fringes

- From $\Delta S_2 S_1 Q$, $\sin \theta = \dfrac{p}{d}$ where p is the path difference between S_1P and S_2P.

  From ΔRPO, $\tan \theta = \dfrac{y_n}{D}$

  As $D \gg d$, $\theta < 0.1$ radian

  This means that $\sin \theta \approx \tan \theta$

  Hence $\dfrac{p}{d} = \dfrac{y_n}{D}$

  $$p = \frac{y_n d}{D}$$

  where y_n is the distance from the centre bright fringe to the n bright fringe.

  (a) Condition for bright fringes

  In general, for a bright fringe to occur (Fig 14.12), $p = n\lambda$ where n is an integer

  i.e. $n\lambda = \dfrac{y_n d}{D}$ ———— (1)

341

From equation (1), the nth fringe is given by

$$y_n = \frac{n\lambda D}{d}$$

The $(n + 1)$th fringe $y_{n+1} = \dfrac{(n + 1)\lambda D}{d}$

∴ The fringe width is given by: $w = y_{n+1} - y_n$

i.e. $w = \dfrac{\lambda D}{d}$

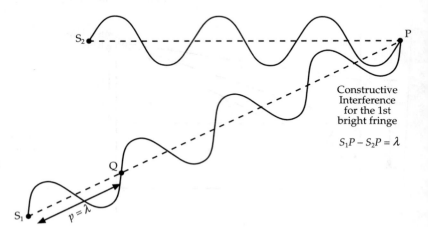

Constructive Interference for the 1st bright fringe

$S_1P - S_2P = \lambda$

Fig 14.12   Construction interference

(b) Condition for dark fringes
In general, for a dark fringe to occur

$$p = \left(n + \frac{1}{2}\right) \text{ where } n \text{ is an integer}$$

If $n = 0$, the path difference $= \dfrac{1}{2}\lambda$

Destructive interference occurs at P and a dark fringe is observed (Fig 14.13).

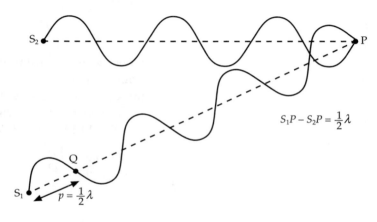

$S_1P - S_2P = \frac{1}{2}\lambda$

Fig 14.13   Destructive interference

- If the slits used in Young's interference experiment is such that $a \ll \lambda$, interference pattern obtained will have the same intensity as illustrated in Fig 14.14.

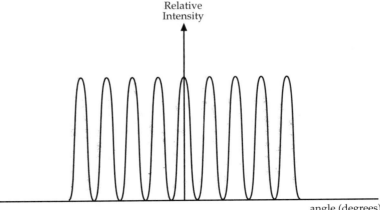

Fig 14.14

- In practice, the condition $a \ll \lambda$ is difficult to achieve. For slits that are wider, the interference fringes are not of equal intensity. This is because the diffraction of the waves modifies the intensity of the interference fringes. As the intensity of the diffraction pattern decreases to zero at its first minima, the intensity of the interference fringes will decrease likewise. In fact, the intensity of the fringes fits exactly into the diffraction pattern produced by the individual slits. In Young's experiment the central fringe is the brightest. The intensity decreases on either side of the central fringe (Fig 14.15).

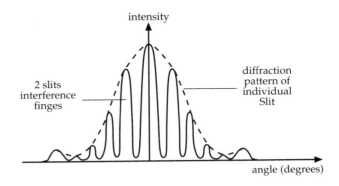

Fig 14.15 Intensity distribution for two slit interference

- If the two slits were made much narrower, the envelope of the diffraction pattern would be larger. More fringes of lower intensity and with the same separation can be seen in the central maximum (Fig 14.16).

343

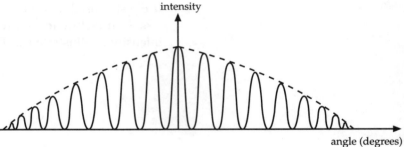

intensity

angle (degrees)

Fig 14.16

Two-source interference in a Ripple Tank

- Two spherical dippers S_1 and S_2 attached to the same vibrator will oscillate with the same frequency. When they are placed on the water surface of a ripple tank, two sets of coherent waves are formed. They spread outwards and the overlapping waves will produce interference fringes (Fig 14.17).

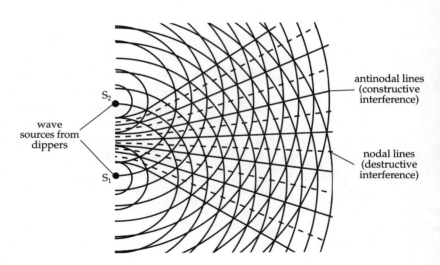

wave sources from dippers

S_2

S_1

antinodal lines (constructive interference)

nodal lines (destructive interference)

Fig 14.17 Interference fringes in the ripple tank

- When waves are exactly out of phase, destructive interference occurs. These can be seen along nodal lines. When waves are completely in phase with each other, constructive interference occurs. These can be seen along antinodal lines, midway between nodal lines.

Two-source interference using microwaves

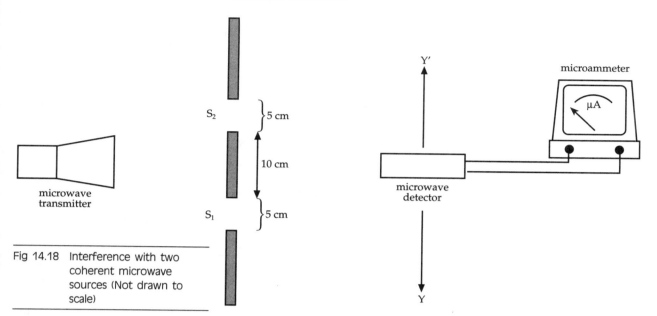

Fig 14.18 Interference with two coherent microwave sources (Not drawn to scale)

- The apparatus in Fig 14.18 can be used to study interference when microwave is used. As the microwave detector is moved along YY', the variation of the micro ammeter readings indicates constructive and destructive interferences along YY'.

 Blue light is used in Young's double slit experiment. Describe and explain what will happen to these fringes if
(a) the screen is moved closer to the slits,
(b) the separation of the slits is decreased,
(c) the light source is moved closer to the slits,
(d) the two slits are each covered with a small sheet of Polaroid and one of these Polaroid is rotated slowly.

 (a) Fringe separation $= \dfrac{\lambda D}{d}$ where λ is the wavelength of light, D is the distance from slit to screen and d is the separation of the two slits. When screen is moved closer to the slits, D decreases, hence, fringe separation will decrease.
(b) If the separation of the slits is decreased, d will be smaller and fringe separation will increase.
(c) Fringe separation is affected by changes in λ, D and d only. Changing the distance from light source to the slits will not affect the fringe separation.
(d) When one of the two sheets of Polaroid is rotated, the intensity of the fringes will decrease and disappear when the polarising directions of the two sheets of Polaroid are perpendicular to each other.

Diffraction from Multiple Slits

- If multiple slits were used, the fringes will be much sharper. If the separation of the slits were decreased further, sharp and widely separated fringes could be seen (Fig 14.19). The central maximum is called the zero order fringe. Subsequent bright fringes are known as 1st, 2nd and 3rd order fringes. Intensity distribution shown in Fig 14.19 can be obtained by using diffraction grating.

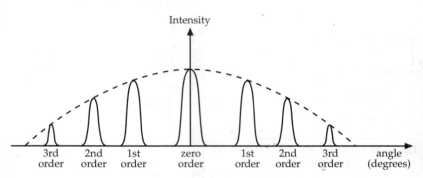

Fig 14.19

DIFFRACTION GRATING

- Diffraction grating consists of many fine equidistant parallel lines ruled onto a transparent glass slide. In some gratings, 1000 lines could be drawn on 1 mm of glass. Light could pass between the lines but not through them. The separation of the lines is known as grating spacing (d). Each slit acts as a centre of secondary disturbance.

- Fig 14.20 shows plane wavefronts of monochromatic light incident perpendicularly onto the diffraction grating. The emergent wavefront from each of the slits is diffracted through a wide angle. The superposition of the multiple wavefronts produces constructive interference illustrated in Fig 14.20.

  (a) In Fig 14.20a, the path difference between adjacent rays is zero. Constructive interference occurs when these rays are focused onto a screen by a convex lens. A central bright fringe or zero order fringe is formed.

  (b) In Fig 14.20b, the path difference between adjacent rays is λ. Constructive interference occurs when parallel rays are inclined at an angle θ_1 to the horizontal. The 1st order bright fringe is obtained when

  $$\sin \theta_1 = \frac{\lambda}{d}, \text{ i.e. } d \sin \theta_1 = \lambda.$$

  (c) In Fig 14.20c, the path difference between adjacent rays is 2λ. Constructive interference occurs when parallel rays are inclined at an angle θ_2 to the horizontal. The 2nd order bright fringe is obtained when

  $$\sin \theta_2 = \frac{2\lambda}{d}, \text{ i.e. } d \sin \theta_1 = 2\lambda.$$

346

(d) In general, if the path difference between adjacent rays is $n\lambda$, where n is an integer, the nth order bright fringe occurs when $d \sin \theta = n\lambda$.

n is also known as an order of diffraction.

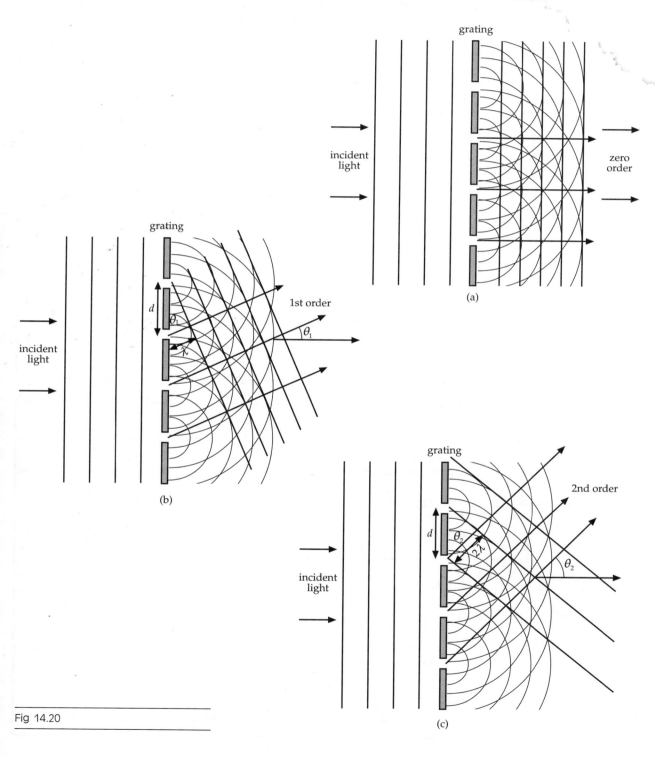

Fig 14.20

347

Q A diffraction grating has 5000 lines ruled over 1 cm of glass. It is illuminated normally by monochromatic light of wavelength 6×10^{-7} m.
(a) At what angle will the first-order maximum occur?
(b) What is the highest order maxima that can be seen?

A (a) Grating spacing $d = \dfrac{0.01}{5000} = 2 \times 10^{-6}$ m

Using $d \sin \theta = n\lambda$, 1st order maximum occurs when $n = 1$
θ is the angle at which the 1st order maximum occurs.

$$\sin \theta = \frac{\lambda}{d}$$

$$= \frac{6 \times 10^{-7}}{2 \times 10^{-6}}$$

$$= 0.3, \ \theta = 17°$$

(b) Since the maximum value of $\sin \theta = 1$,

$\dfrac{n\lambda}{d} \leq 1$ where n is the highest order maxima that can be seen.

$$n \leq \frac{d}{\lambda}$$

$$n \leq \frac{2 \times 10^{-6}}{6 \times 10^{-7}}$$

$$n \leq 3.3$$

Hence the highest order maxima is 3.

Q (a) What do you understand by a progressive wave? Illustrate your answer by reference to a transverse progressive wave.
(b) What conditions must be satisfied in order that two-source interference fringes may be observed?
(c) A double slit with slit separation 0.800 mm is situated a distance 2.50 m from a thin jet of high-speed smoke as shown in Fig 14.21.

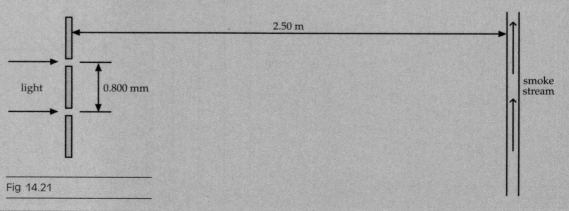

Fig 14.21

348

The double slit is illuminated with coherent light of wavelength 589 nm. Fringes are observed in the moving smoke. Calculate the separation of these fringes.

(d) State with a reason the change, if any, that would be observed in the pattern of fringes if the following adjustments were made in the experimental arrangement. In each case, only one adjustment is made and all other arrangements are as in (c).

    (ii) The coherent light of wavelength 589 nm is replaced with coherent monochromatic red light.

    (ii) The speed of the smoke stream is doubled.

    (iii) The direction of the smoke stream is rotated through 45° as shown in Fig 14.22.

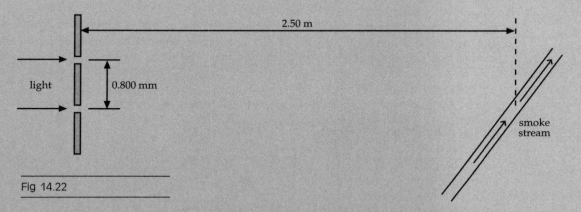

Fig 14.22

    (iv) The smoke stream is replaced by a fixed screen.

Cambridge

(a) A progressive wave is one in which the wave profile carries energy and momentum away from the source of disturbance.

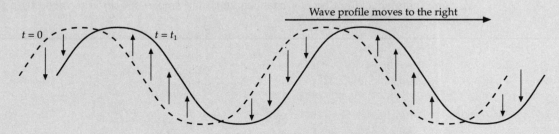

The figure shows a transverse progressive wave on the water surface in a ripple tank. Every particle on the surface oscillates sinusoidally in different phases. Alternate sections of the wave profile at $t = 0$ s move in different directions. The wave profile seems to move to the right at a later time ($t = t_1$) although each of the particles does not.

(b) Conditions that must be satisfied:

    1) The sources must have the same or roughly equal amplitude.

    2) The sources must be coherent.

    3) Transverse waves must not be polarised.

    4) Slit separation should be of the order of 10^{-4} m.

    5) Screen to slit ratio should be of the order of 3000.

(c) If w is the separation of the fringes, then

$$w = \frac{\text{(wavelength)} \times \text{(slit to screen distance)}}{\text{slit separation}}$$

$$= \frac{(589 \times 10^{-9}) \times (2.50)}{0.800 \times 10^{-3}}$$

$$= 1.84 \times 10^{-3} \text{ m}$$

(d) (i) Since monochromatic red light has the largest wavelength among the visible spectrum, the fringe separation will increase if red light is used.

(ii) The speed of the smoke stream is very small in comparison to the speed of light. No changes will be observed even if the speed of the smoke stream is doubled.

(iii) The 2nd maximum above O appears at B on the smoke stream. The fringe separation has increased. The 2nd maximum below O appears at A. The fringe separation has decreased.

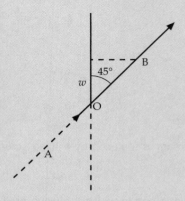

(iv) The unidirectional uniform motion of the smoke particles moving with negligible relative velocity with each other provide a reflecting surface that is similar to the surface of a fixed screen. There should not be any changes when the smoke stream is replaced by a fixed screen.

350

Exercise 14

Multiple Choice Questions

1   Two coherent monochromatic waves of equal amplitude are brought together to interfere on screen. Which one of the following graphs correctly represents the variation of intensity with position x across the pattern of fringes?

A intensity

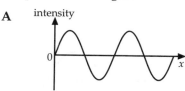

B intensity

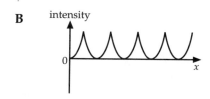

C intensity

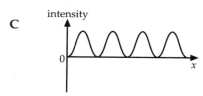

D intensity

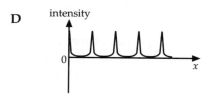

2   Fig 14.23 shows two identical loudspeakers driven in phase from a common audio-frequency source.

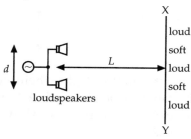

Fig 14.23

When a student moves from X to Y, the intensity of the note he hears is alternatively loud and soft. Adjacent loud and soft regions may be made closer together by
A   decreasing the amplitude.
B   decreasing distance d.
C   increasing distance L.
D   using a higher frequency.

3   Under which of the following sets of conditions will the separation of the bright fringes of a double-slit interference pattern be greatest?

	distance between slits	distance from slits to screen	wavelength of source
A	small	small	short
B	small	large	short
C	small	large	long
D	large	small	short

4   Fringes of separation y are observed in a plane 1.00 m from a Young's slit arrangement illuminated by yellow light of wavelength 600 nm. At what distance from the slits would fringes of the same separation y be observed when using blue light of wavelength 400 nm?
A   0.33 m   B   0.67 m
C   0.75 m   D   1.50 m

5   Progressive waves of frequency 300 Hz are superimposed to produce a system of stationary waves in which adjacent nodes are 1.5 m apart. What is the speed of the progressive waves?
A   100 m s^{-1} B   200 m s^{-1}
C   450 m s^{-1} D   900 m s^{-1}

6   A microwave transmitter emits waves that reflect from a metal plate, as shown in the diagram. A detector picks up the stationary waves produced. R, S and T are three adjacent points at which the meter shows zero intensity.

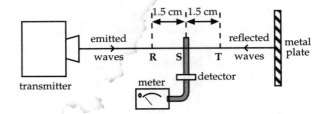

What is the frequency of the emitted waves?

A 9.0×10^6 Hz

B 2.0×10^8 Hz

C 1.0×10^{10} Hz

D 2.0×10^{10} Hz

7   A monochromatic plane wave of speed c and wavelength λ is diffracted at a small aperture. The diagram illustrates successive wavefronts.

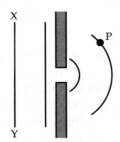

After what time will some portion of the wavefront XY reach P?

A $\dfrac{3\lambda}{2c}$ B $\dfrac{2\lambda}{c}$

C $\dfrac{3\lambda}{c}$ D $\dfrac{4\lambda}{c}$

8   The length l of an air column is slowly increased from zero while a note of constant frequency is produced by a loudspeaker placed above it.

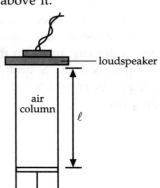

When l reaches 17 cm the sound increases greatly in volume.
What is the wave length of the sound wave produced by the loudspeaker?

A   8.5 cm   B   17 cm

C   34 cm   D   68 cm

9   The diagram shows the displacements at the same instants of two waves, P and Q, of equal frequency and having amplitudes of Y and $2Y$, respectively.

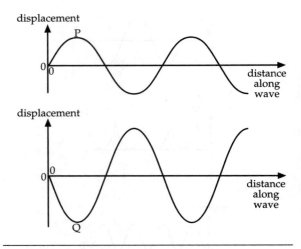

Fig 14.24

The waves are superimposed to give a resultant wave.
What is the amplitude of the resultant wave and what is the phase difference between the resultant wave and wave P?

	amplitude of resultant wave	(phase difference between resultant wave and wave P)/radians
A	Y	0
B	Y	π
C	3Y	0
D	3Y	π

10   Monochromatic light incident on an adjustable single slit produced on a screen the diffraction pattern shown below. (Fig 14.24)

352

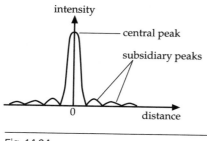

Fig 14.24

When the width of the slit was reduced,

A the intensity of all the peaks increased and the width of the pattern decreased.

B the intensities of all the peaks remained unchanged and the width of the pattern increased.

C the intensities of all the peaks decreased and the width of the pattern remained unchanged.

D the intensities of all the peaks decreased and the width of the pattern increased.

Structured Questions

1 (a) (i) State what is meant by the *diffraction* of a wave.

(ii) The diagrams of Fig 14.25 and Fig 14.26 represent wavefronts approaching a wide gap and a narrow gap respectively.

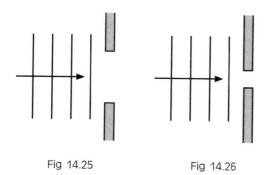

Fig 14.25   Fig 14.26

Draw on each diagram lines, illustrating diffractions, to represent the wavefronts after passing through the gaps.

Cambridge

2 This question is about the superposition of waves.

(a) (i) What is meant by the term *stationary wave*?

(ii) Describe an experiment to show how a stationary wave may be set up.

(b) (i) Explain the meaning of the term *diffraction*.

(ii) How does the width of the aperture through which a wave is passing affect the diffraction of the wave?

(c) A beam of red light from a laser is shone normally on a diffraction grating. Bright light is seen emerging at certain angles as shown in Fig 14.27. Use the principle of superposition to suggest a qualitative explanation of this effect.

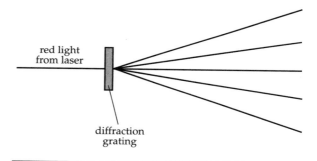

Fig 14.27

(d) A diffraction grating with a grating spacing of 2.20×10^{-6} m is used to examine the light from a glowing gas. It is found that the first order violet light emerges at an angle of 11.8° and the first order red light at an angle of 15.8° as shown in Fig 14.28.

(i) Calculate the wavelengths of these two colours.

(ii) Describe and explain what will be observed at an angle of 54.8°.

(iii) Without making any further calculations, draw a sketch similar to Fig 14.28 showing the whole pattern observed.

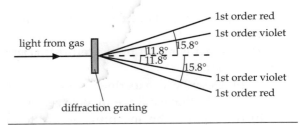

1st order red
1st order violet
light from gas
11.8° 15.8°
11.8°
15.8°
1st order violet
1st order red

diffraction grating

Fig 14.28

Cambridge

3 (a) State what is transferable by a *progressive* wave.

(b) Two microwave sources S_1 and S_2 are situated as shown in Fig 14.29. The waves emitted by the two sources are in phase and are polarised in the same plane.

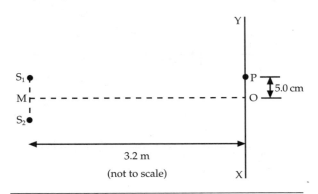

Fig 14.29

A microwave detector is placed on a line XY which is parallel to, and 3.2 m, from the line joining S_1 and S_2. M is the midpoint of the line joining S_1 and S_2. The line from M perpendicular to the line S_1S_2 meets XY at O. The detector produces an output which is proportional to the displacement of the wave.

With only S_1 switched on, the change with time of the detector output measured at P, a distance of 5.0 cm from O, is as shown in Fig 14.30.

The waveform detected at P for S_2 only is shown in Fig 14.30.

(i) Use Fig 14.30 to determine
   1. the period of the waves,
   2. the phase difference between the waves at P,
   3. the ratio $\dfrac{\text{intensity at P of wave from } S_1}{\text{intensity at P of wave from } S_2}$.

(ii) Using your answer to (i) 1., show that the wavelength of the microwaves from S_1 and S_2 is 2.5 cm.

(iii) S_1 and S_2 are switched on together, with the emitted waves in phase. The detector is moved from P along the line OY, in the direction away from O. State and explain the approximate distance that the detector must be moved before the intensity is a maximum, given that there is no maximum between O and P.

(iv) Make an estimate of the separation of the sources S_1 and S_2.

Cambridge

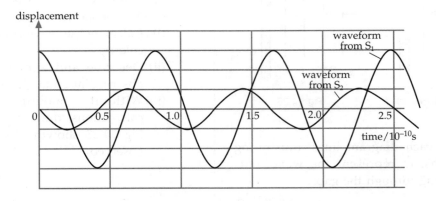

Fig 14.30

354

SUPERPOSITION

Whenever two or more waves are travelling in the same region simultaneously, total displacement at any point is equal to the vector sum of their individual displacement at that point.

Diffraction

Diffraction is the spreading of wavefronts through a narrow slit or around an obstacle by the superposition of secondary wavelets from the emerging wavefront.

in → **Single Slit**

$a \sin \theta_n = n\lambda$
$n = \pm 1, \pm 2, \ldots$

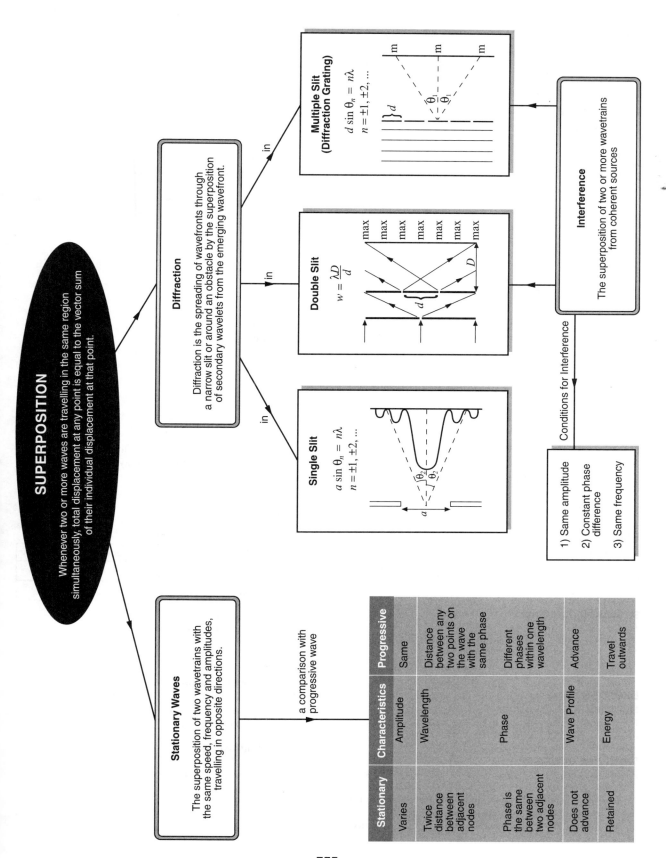

in → **Double Slit**

$w = \dfrac{\lambda D}{d}$

in → **Multiple Slit (Diffraction Grating)**

$d \sin \theta_n = n\lambda$
$n = \pm 1, \pm 2, \ldots$

Interference

The superposition of two or more wavetrains from coherent sources

Conditions for Interference

1) Same amplitude
2) Constant phase difference
3) Same frequency

Stationary Waves

The superposition of two wavetrains with the same speed, frequency and amplitudes, travelling in opposite directions.

a comparison with progressive wave

Stationary	Characteristics	Progressive
Varies	Amplitude	Same
Twice distance between adjacent nodes	Wavelength	Distance between any two points on the wave with the same phase
Phase is the same between two adjacent nodes	Phase	Different phases within one wavelength
Does not advance	Wave Profile	Advance
Retained	Energy	Travel outwards

355

Answers

Exercise 1
Multiple Choice Questions
1	A	2	C	3	A	4	A	5	B
6	B	7	D	8	D	9	A	10	C
11	C								

Structured Questions
1 energy (J); pressure (N m^{-2});
  electrical charge (A s);
  electrical resistance (V A^{-1})
2 kg s^{-1}
3 kg m^{-1}s^{-2}
4 (a) (i) velocity   (ii) weight
     (iii) momentum   (iv) gravitational field strength
  (b)

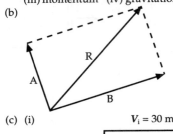

  (c) (i)

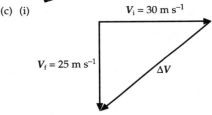

     (ii) −5 m s^{-1}
     (iii) 39.1 m s^{-1}; 39.8° to the horizontal

Exercise 2
Multiple Choice Questions
1	C	2	A	3	B	4	D	5	D
6	D	7	C	8	C	9	D	10	D
11	D	12	D						

Structured Questions
1 (a) 2.00, 3.3 mA
  (d) (i) 3.04%   (ii) (610 ± 20)Ω
2 (c) (i) 2.8%   (ii) (92 ± 3) N m^{-1}
  (d) 4.26%

Exercise 3
Multiple Choice Questions
1	B	2	A	3	B	4	D	5	B
6	C	7	D	8	C	9	D		

Structured Questions
1 (a) (i) 20.0 m s^{-1} (ii) 2.0 m s^{-2} (iii) −6.0 m s^{-2}
     (iv) 300 m   (v) 250 m
  (b) The object decelerates uniformly from 30 m s^{-1} until it
      comes to rest momentarily. In the next instant, the object
      moves off in the opposite direction with uniform
      acceleration until it reaches the velocity of 5 m s^{-1}.

2 (a) (i) less than 15 m s^{-1} (ii) 7.5 m s^{-1}
     (iii) 13 m s^{-1}
  (b)

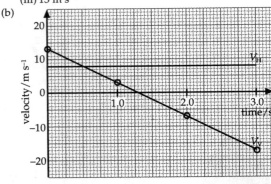

  (c) 8.45 m

Exercise 4
Multiple Choice Questions
1	C	2	D	3	D	4	A	5	D
6	C	7	D	8	B	9	B	10	D
11	D								

Structured Questions
2 (a) $v = \dfrac{u}{2}$ (b) $\dfrac{KE_{after}}{KE_{before}} = \dfrac{1}{2}$
  (c) It is converted into heat which is lost to the environment
      and an increase in internal energy.

4 (b) (i) $\dfrac{1}{2}MU^2 = \dfrac{1}{2}MV^2 + \dfrac{1}{2}mv^2$
         $MU = MV + mv$
     (ii) $\dfrac{m}{M} = 1$

5 (a)

collision	momentum	kinetic energy	total energy
elastic	✓	✓	✓
inelastic	✓		✓

  (b) (i) 1. Inelastic
         2. 6.0×10^7 m s^{-1}
     (ii) 4.0×10^6 m s^{-1}

Exercise 5
Multiple Choice Questions
1	B	2	D	3	B	4	A	5	A
6	C	7	B	8	D	9	A	10	C
11	B	12	D						

Structured Questions
1 (a) $F_1 + F_2 + F_3 = 0$
  (b) $F_4 + F_5 + F_6 + F_7 = 0$ & $\Sigma\tau = 0$

2 (d) (i)

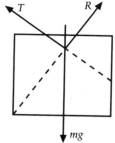

(ii) 9.73×10^7 kg

(iii)

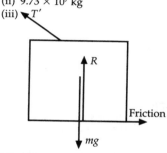

3 (b) 3   (c) 2, 3, 4   (d) 1500 N m

Exercise 6
Multiple Choice Questions

1 A	2 C	3 D	4 C	5 B
6 D	7 A	8 B	9 B	10 B
11 A				

Structured Questions

1

	truck	car
mass	3000 kg	1000 kg
velocity	20 m s^{-1}	40 m s^{-1}
momentum	60 000 kg m s^{-1} 6.0×10^4 kg m s^{-1}	40 000 kg m s^{-1} 4.0×10^4 kg m s^{-1}
kinetic energy	600 000 J 6.0×10^5 J	800 000J 8.0×10^5 J
stopping time	3.0 s	2.0 s
stopping distance	30 m	40 m

2 (b) (i) 1. 2.05 cm
          2. PE $= (0.15)(10)(0.0205)$
              $= 0.031$ J

   (ii) 1) KE $= \dfrac{0.031}{0.25} = 0.12$ J

        2) $v = \sqrt{\dfrac{2 \times 0.12}{0.011}} = 4.7$ m s^{-1}

        3) -4.1 m s^{-1}
   (iii) 1) 0.10 kg m s^{-1}
         2) 0.65 N

3 (c) (i) 10.1 kJ   (ii) 3.53 kJ   (iii) 17.4 m s^{-1}
   (d) (i) 16 N

Exercise 7
Multiple Choice Questions

1 C	2 D	3 C	4 C	5 A
6 D	7 D	8 C	9 D	10 A
11 C	12 C	13 B	14 A	15 A

Structured Questions

1 (i) 2583 MJ   (ii) 9.0 N kg^{-1}
2 (a) See Text

   (b) $mg = \dfrac{GM_m}{(R + h)^2}$

        $g = \dfrac{GM_m}{(R + h)^2}$

   (c) (i) 1.66 N kg^{-1} (ii) 3.46×10^8 m
3 (b) (ii) (1) 7.27×10^{-5} rad s^{-1}
             (2) 3.08 km s^{-1}
             (3) 0.224 m s^{-2}
             (4) 537 N
             (5) 6.00×10^{24} kg

Exercise 8
Multiple Choice Questions

1 C	2 D	3 A	4 B	5 A
6 C	7 B	8 D	9 D	10 B
11 A	12 B			

Structured Questions

1 A particle moving in a circle with constant speed
   (a)

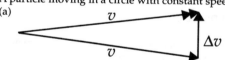

   (b) $\delta\theta = \dfrac{\delta v}{v}$, $\delta\theta = \dfrac{\delta s}{r} = \dfrac{v\delta t}{r}$,

        hence $\delta v = \dfrac{v^2 \delta t}{r}$

   (c) $a = \dfrac{v^2}{r}$; directed towards the centre of circular motion

2 (i) 1.62 m s^{-2}
   (ii) Tension and weight of bob

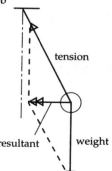

357

(iii) 9.38°
(iv)

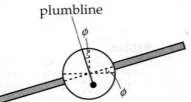

plumbline

3   (a) Use a stroboscope to determine the frequency of rotation
        and calculate from $\omega = 2\pi f$.
    (b) 351 m s^{-1}, 1.90×10^5 m s^{-2}
    (c) The centripetal force ($F = m\,a$) is large as acceleration a,
        is large. This exceeds the molecular binding force
        between the blade and the turbine.
    (d) 1.37×10^5 N

Exercise 9
Multiple Choice Questions
1   B   2   D   3   A   4   B   5   D
6   A   7   C

Structured Questions
1   (b) (i) 1. 6.38×10^{-21} J
              2. 2.76×10^3 m s^{-1}
        (ii) 1230 K

Exercise 10
Multiple Choice Questions
1   C   2   D   3   D   4   D   5   A
6   B

Structured Question
1   (a) See Text
    (b) independent of thermometric property of a material.
    (c) (i)   resistance thermometer
        (ii) thermocouple
        (iii) mercury-in-glass or thermocouple.
2   (a) See Text
    (b) See Text
    (c) (i) thermocouple   (ii) pyrometer
3   (a) See Text   (b) −0.15°C
4   (a) (b) See Text
5   (a) 79.3°C

Exercise 11
Multiple Choice Questions
1   B   2   D   3   D   4   C   5   B
6   D   7   B

Structured Question
1   (a) See Text
    (b) See Glossary
    (c) (i) (ii) See Text
    (d) (i) See Text

(ii)

	Solid which contracts on melting	Solid which expands on melting
DU	+	+
q	+	+
w	+	−

2   (a) See Text   (b) See Text
    (c) Increase in internal energy of a system
        = Heat entering system + work done on the system
    (d) (i) 768 kg   (ii) 8.83×10^7 J
        (iii) 1.28 kg m^{-3} (iv) 599 m^3
    (e) 2.59×10^7 J   (f) 6.24×10^7 J

Exercise 12
Multiple Choice Questions
1   C   2   D   3   B   4   D   5   D
6   D   7   A   8   D   9   C   10 D

Structured Question
1   (a) 50 Hz   (b) 100π rad s^{-1}
    (c) $x = (0.0030$ m$) \sin ((100\pi$ rad s^{-1}) t)
    (d) (i) ±0.9 m s^{-1}
        (ii) Particles can move through the equilibrium position
             in two opposite directions.
    (e) (i) 0.044 J   (ii) See Text

Exercise 13
Multiple Choice Questions
1   D   2   C   3   A   4   C   5   B
6   D   7   A   8   B   9   D   10 C
11 D   12 B   13 B   14 D   15 B
16 B

Structured Questions
1   (a) Frequency is the number of wave crests that pass a fixed
        point in each second.
    (b) 0.125 m
2   (a) A progressive wave is one in which the wave profile
        carries energy and momentum away from the source of
        disturbance.
    (b) $v = \dfrac{\text{distance}}{\text{time}} = \dfrac{\lambda}{T} = f\lambda$
    (c) (i) 0.4 m   (ii) 800 Hz   (iii) 320 m s^{-1}
        (iv) $\pi/2$ radians (v) 4   (vi) 16
    (d) Sound wave as the wave speed is 320 m s^{-1}.
3   45°

Exercise 14
Multiple Choice Questions
1   C   2   D   3   C   4   D   5   D
6   C   7   C   8   D   9   B   10 D

Structured Questions
1   (i) See Glossary
    (ii)

2 (a) (i) See Glossary
       (ii) See Text
   (b) (i) See Glossary
       (ii) The diffraction of the wave increases as the width of the aperture decreases.
   (c) Each slit on the diffraction grating acts as a centre of secondary disturbance. The emergent wavefront from each slit is diffracted through a wide angle. The superposition of the multiple wavefronts produces constructive interference at certain angles.
   (d) (i) $\lambda_V = (2.20 \times 10^{-6})(\sin 11.8°)$
           $= 4.49 \times 10^{-7}\,m$
           $\lambda_R = (2.20 \times 10^{-6})(\sin 15.8°)$
           $= 5.99 \times 10^{-7}\,m$
       (ii) At 54.8°, the 3rd order maximum for red light overlapped with the 4th order maximum for blue light to give purple light.
       (iii)

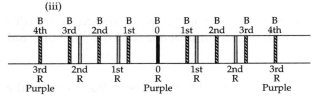

3 (a) Energy
   (b) (i) 1. $T = 8.37 \times 10^{-11}$ s

          2. Phase difference $= \dfrac{\pi}{2}$

          3. $\dfrac{\text{Intensity at P of wave from } S_1}{\text{Intensity at P of wave from } S_2} = \dfrac{3^2}{1^2}$

             $= \dfrac{9}{1}$

       (ii) $\lambda = v\,T = (3.08 \times 10^8)(8.37 \times 10^{-11})$
            $= 0.02511\ m = 2.5\ cm$
       (iii) 15 cm
       (iv) 40 cm

359

Glossary

Glossary of terms used in Physics

Absolute zero of temperature: the lower fixed point on the thermodynamic scale of temperature; it is considered to be the lowest possible temperature in the universe.

Absolute scale of temperature: a theoretical temperature scale that does not depend on the thermometric property of a material.

Acceleration: the rate of change of velocity with respect to time. It has the SI units of m s^{-2}.

Acceleration of free fall: the rate of change of velocity of an object when it falls freely towards the Earth's surface under the sole influence of the gravitational pull of the Earth. It is denoted by the symbol g and has a numerical value of 9.81 m s^{-2}.

Accuracy: the proximity of the observed reading on an instrument to the true or actual value of the physical quantity being measured.

Ammeter: an electrical instrument that measures the electric current in a circuit.

Amount of substance: the number of moles of a substance (see moles).

Ampere: the constant current that exerts a force of 2×10^{-7} N per metre length on two straight, parallel and infinitely long wire of negligible cross-sectional area when that current flows through the two wires. It is the SI unit of an electric current and is represented by the symbol A.

Amplitude: the maximum displacement from the equilibrium position to the crest or trough of a sinusoidal wave.

Angular displacement: the angle through which a rotating axis turns. It is usually measured in radians.

Angular velocity: the rate of change of angular displacement with respect to time. It is measured in rad s^{-1}.

Anode: positive electrode

Antinodes: points of maximum displacement in a stationary wave

Atmosphere: a unit of pressure equal to 1.01×10^5 Pa or 760 mm Hg

Atmospheric pressure: the pressure at a point due to the weight of the air column above it

Atom: the smallest part of an element that can exist naturally.

Atto: a prefix used in the metric system of units to denote a sub-multiple of 10^{-18}

Avogadro constant: the number of atoms in exactly 0.012 kg of carbon-12 and has a numerical value of 6.02×10^{23} mol^{-1}. It is denoted by N_A or L.

Barometer: a device that measures atmospheric pressure.

Base quantity: one of the seven arbitrarily chosen physical quantities that is used to define other physical quantities in the SI system.

Base unit: a unit of base quantity that is used to define the SI units of other physical quantities.

Boiling: the process in which a liquid changes into vapour at a definite temperature.

Boiling point: the temperature of a liquid as it changes into the gaseous state when the saturated vapour pressure of the liquid equals to the external pressure acting on it.

Boltzmann constant: the ratio of the molar gas constant R to the Avogadro constant N_A.

Boyle's law: the pressure (p) of a given mass of gas at constant temperature is inversely proportional to its volume (V).

Brownian motion: the continuous and random movement of tiny microscopic particles suspended in a fluid.

Cathode Ray Oscilloscope (CRO): an electronic instrument that uses the cathode ray tube to convert electrical signals into a displacement-time graph on the CRO's screen from which essential information such as amplitude and the period of a signal could be measured.

Cathode: negative electrode

Celsius scale of temperature: a scale of temperature that is adjusted to agree with the thermodynamic scale of temperature.

Centi: a prefix used in the metric system to denote sub-multiple of 10^{-2}.

Centigrade scale of temperature: an empirical scale of temperature in which the lower and upper fixed points are the freezing and boiling point of water respectively.

Centre of gravity: the single point in a body through which the entire weight of that body appears to act.

Centre of mass: the single point in a body through which the entire mass of that body appears to act.

Centripetal acceleration: the acceleration of a moving object that is always directed towards the centre of the circular path on which the object is travelling.

Centripetal force: the force on a moving object that is always directed towards the centre of the circular path on which the object is travelling.

Charles' law: the volume (V) of a fixed mass of gas at constant pressure is directly proportional to its thermodynamic temperature (T).

Compression: a region of higher pressure in a medium

Compressive forces: two equal but oppositely directed forces acting on an object that reduces it length.

Coherent sources: two sets of waves that have a constant phase difference; have the same frequency and wavelength and are not polarised.

Condensation: the process whereby a substance in the vapour state changes into the liquid state.

Conditions of equilibrium for forces acting on a body: (1) the vector sum of all forces acting on a rigid body must be zero, (2) the vector sum of all external torques acting on a rigid body must be zero.

Conduction (thermal): the transmission of heat from a region of higher temperature to a region of lower temperature through collision of particles within that medium.

Conductor (electrical): a material that allows the free movement of electric charges.

Conservation of energy: energy cannot be created or destroyed but can be changed from one form to another.

Conservation of linear momentum: the total momentum of a closed system of colliding particles remains constant if no external forces act on that system.

Constructive interference: the interaction of two or more waves at a point such that the amplitude of the resultant wave is greater than the amplitude of the individual waves.

Convection: the transmission of heat from a region of higher temperature to a region of lower temperature through the movement of heated fluid.

Coulomb: the charge flowing pass a point in a electric circuit due to the passage of one ampere of electric current flowing for one second. It is the SI unit of an electric charge and is represented by the symbol C.

Couple: two equal and oppositely directed parallel forces that do not lie on the same line of action.

Crest: the highest point on a wave.

Critical damping: a system that does not oscillate but returns to the equilibrium position in the shortest possible time.

Current (electric): the rate of flow of charge with respect to time.

Damped oscillations (light): a system which oscillates about the equilibrium position with deceasing amplitude over a period of time.

Deceleration: the decrease of velocity of an object.

Density: mass per unit volume of a substance.

Destructive interference: the interaction of two or more waves at a point such that the amplitude of the resultant wave is smaller than the amplitude of the individual waves.

Diffraction: the spreading or bending of waves at the edge of an obstacle or when waves pass through an aperture.

Diffraction grating: a device made of glass or transparent plastic that produces line spectra when light passes through hundreds of parallel and equally spaced lines ruled on it.

Diffusion: the process by which different gases or liquids mix as a result of rapid and random spreading of their component atoms, molecules or ions.

Displacement: the distance moved in a specific direction.

Drag forces: the frictional forces experienced by an object when it moves through a fluid or when the fluid flows pass the object.

Dynamics: the study of forces and energies that are associated with the motion of a body.

Elastic collision: a collision in which the total kinetic energy and momentum of the colliding bodies are conserved.

Elasticity: the property of a material that enables it to return to its original shape and dimensions when the applied stress is removed.

Elastic constant: a constant of proportionality that is numerically equal to the ratio of the applied force to the extension of an elastic material.

Electromagnetic spectrum: a wide range of electromagnetic waves arranged in ascending order of wavelengths.

Electromagnetic waves: transverse waves consisting of electric and magnetic fields that oscillates perpendicularly to each other.

Electron: an elementary particle with a rest mass (m_e) of 9.11×10^{-11} kg and elementary charge (e) of 1.60×10^{-19} C.

Electron diffraction: the spreading of electrons to form a pattern of rings on a screen as it passes through a thin gold foil or crystalline material.

Electric charge: the smallest quantity of discrete charge carried by an electron. It has the symbol e and has a value of 1.60×10^{-19} C.

Empirical scale of temperature: a temperature scale based on the linear variation of a thermometric property with temperature.

Energy: a measure of the stored ability within a system or body to do work. It has the SI unit of joules (J).

Equations of motion: a set of equations that relates the displacement s, initial velocity u, final velocity v, acceleration and time.

Equilibrium (thermal): see thermal equilibrium

Escape velocity: the velocity that a body must be given on the surface of a planet in order for it to just escape from the gravitational pull of that planet.

Experimental error: the difference between a value obtained through experiments and the true value.

Evaporation: the process by which energetic molecules leave the surface of a liquid to form vapour or gas.

Fixed point: a temperature at which a reproducible and measurable physical change occurs.

First law of thermodynamics: the heat transferred to a closed system increases its internal energy ΔU and causes the system to do work ΔW on its surroundings during the change.

Fluid: a liquid or a gas.

Force: a physical quantity that can change the shape of an object, the direction of its motion and its acceleration.

Forced oscillations: oscillations produced when a body is subjected to an oscillatory external force.

Free fall: the motion of a body through a gravitational field whereby the only force acting on it is its weight.

Free body diagram: a force diagram that shows all forces acting on a single body without including its surroundings or environment.

Freezing: the process in which a liquid changes into a solid without a change in temperature.

Frequency: the number of oscillations or vibrations per second.

Friction: a force that tends to prevent or oppose motion between two objects in contact.

Gas: a state of matter in which molecules move with large random velocities and are separated from each other with large intermolecular distances.

Gravitation: the mutual attraction between masses.

Gravitation field: a region of space where the effects of gravitational force is experienced by a mass.

Gravitational field strength at a point: the force on a unit mass placed at a point in a gravitational field.

Gravitational potential at a point: the work done in bringing a unit mass from infinity to a point in a gravitational field.

Gravitational potential difference between two points: the work done in bringing a unit mass from one point to the other in a gravitational field.

Hall probe: an electronic instrument that uses the Hall effect to measure magnetic field strength.

Heat: the thermal energy that flows from a region of higher temperature to a region of lower temperature.

Heavy damping: a system that do not oscillate and will take a long time to reach the equilibrium position due to large frictional or resistive force acting on it.

Heat capacity: the amount of heat required to raise the temperature of the entire body by one degree kelvin. The SI unit is Joules per kelvin ($J\ K^{-1}$) and its symbol is C.

Heat transfer: the process where thermal energy flows away from a body through thermal conduction, convection and radiation.

Hertz: the SI unit of frequency.

Hooke's law: force is directly proportional to the extension in a spring or wire if the limit of proportionality is not exceeded.

Homogeneity: the necessary condition that validates a physical equation by requiring all units of the physical quantities on the left- and right-hand side of the equation to be the same.

Ice point: the equilibrium temperature of a mixture of pure ice and water at standard atmospheric pressure.

Ideal gas: a hypothetical gas made up of a large number of small molecules that moves randomly and collides elastically with each other and obeys the ideal gas laws.

Ideal gas law: an equation that describes the state of an ideal gas and has the following form: $pV = nRT$ where p = pressure of the gas; n = number of moles; V = volume of the gas; R = molar gas constant; T = temperature of the gas in kelvins.

Impulse: the product of the force (F) acting on a body and the time interval (Δt) over which the force acts.

Inelastic collision: a collision in which linear momentum is conserved but kinetic energy is not conserved.

Inertia: a measure of the resistance to changes in motion of a body.

Infrared: an electromagnetic wave of wavelength 10^{-7} to 10^{-3} m in the electromagnetic spectrum.

Insulator (electrical): a material that do not allow electric charges to flow through easily.

Instantaneous acceleration: acceleration at a particular time.

Instantaneous velocity: velocity at a particular time.

Intensity (of a wave): the rate of flow of energy per unit area perpendicular to the direction of the wave.

Internal energy (of a thermodynamic system): the sum total of the kinetic and potential energies of all atoms and molecules in that system.

Interference: the superposition of two or more wavetrains from coherent sources to form a new wave pattern.

Joule: the work done when a force of one newton moves its point of application a distance of one metre in the direction of the applied force. It has the SI unit of newton metre.

Kelvin: the fraction 1/273.16 of the temperature difference between absolute zero and the triple point of water. It is the SI unit of thermodynamic temperature.

Kilo: the prefix used to indicate the multiple of 10^3 of any units. It has the symbol of k.

Kinematics: a branch of mechanics that describes the motion of a particle without reference to the force or energy that causes the motion.

Kinetic energy: the energy possessed by a mass due to its motion. It is a scalar quantity.

Kinetic theory of gases: A theory describing the physical properties of gases through the application of Newton's laws of motion on colliding gas molecules and offers an explanation on why gases obey the gas laws.

Lift: the upward force exerted on an aeroplane caused by air flowing over the upper and lower wings of a moving plane at different speeds.

Limit of proportionality: the point on a stress-strain curve at which the line changes from being linear (straight line) to non-linear (a curve).

Linear momentum (of a body): the product of mass and velocity of the body.

Liquid: a fluid in which molecules are not bounded in a rigid structure but each molecule is free to move through the body of the fluid and still maintain close proximity with other neighbouring molecules.

Longitudinal waves: progressive waves in which the direction of vibrations of particles in the wave is along the line of flow of energy.

Manometer: a mercury-filled U-tube that is used to measure the pressure difference of a fluid.

Mass: a measure of a body's resistance to changes in motion. It is a base quantity with the SI unit of kilogram.

Mean square speed: the average value of the square of the molecular speeds.

Measurement: the comparison of a physical quantity with a calibrated measuring instrument in order to associate that physical quantity with a magnitude.

Measurement error — see experimental error

Microwaves: electromagnetic waves with wavelengths that range from about 1 mm to about 10 cm.

Molar mass: the mass of one mole of a substance.

Mole: the SI base unit for the amount of substance.

Moment of a force (about a point): the product of the force and the perpendicular distance from the line of action of the force to the point.

Newton: the force which produces an acceleration of 1 m s^{-2} when it is applied to a mass of one kilogram.

Newton's first law of motion: an object at rest will remain at rest and an object in motion will continue in motion at constant speed in a straight line in the absence of a resultant force.

Newton's second law of motion: the rate of change of momentum of an object is directly proportional to the resultant force acting on that object and has the same direction as the force.

Newton's third law of motion: action and reaction are always equal but oppositely directed on two different bodies.

Newton's law of gravitation: a point mass will attract another point mass in any part of the universe with a force that is directly proportional to the product of the masses and inversely proportional to the square of the distance between them.

Node: a point on a stationary wave where the amplitude of oscillation is zero.

Parallax error: arises when the eye is not positioned vertically above the scale to be measured.

Parallelogram law of vector addition: the resultant of two vectors acting at a point P is represented by the diagonal of a parallelogram formed by the two vectors and its origin is at P.

Path difference: the extra length travelled by a wave when it is compared with another.

Period: the time taken to generate a complete wave or to complete one oscillation of a vibrating system.

Phase (of a particular point in an oscillation): the fraction of the oscillation measured from an initial chosen point and expressed in degrees (°) or radians (rad).

Phase difference: a measure of the extent to which a wave is out of phase with a reference wave and expressed in degrees (°) or radians (rad).

Physical quantities: quantities that are measurable and can be expressed as a numerical value and an acceptable standard or unit.

Pitch: the frequency of a sound wave.

Plastic deformation: the permanent change in structure of a material and the corresponding drastic change in shape and size when the material is subject to stress that is close to its breaking value.

Potential energy in a system: the energy stored by virtue of its position, shape, configuration or state of the system.

Power: rate of work done or energy transfer.

Pressure: the force acting perpendicularly per unit area.

Pressure law: the pressure of a fixed mass of gas at constant volume is directly proportional to the absolute scale of temperature.

Principle of moment: the sum of the clockwise moments about a point must be equal to the sum of the anticlockwise moments about the point when the body is in equilibrium.

Principle of superposition: whenever two or more waves are travelling in the same region simultaneously, the total displacement at any point is equal to the vector sum of their individual displacement at that point.

Process: a change in the thermodynamic variables in a system.

Progressive waves: waves that carry energy from one point to another through oscillation or vibration within the medium.

Random errors: unpredictable deviations from the actual value such that each reading has an equal chance to fall above or below the actual value.

Random motion: the motion of an atom or molecule in a fluid whose velocity changes in an erratic or unpredictable manner as a result of collisions with other atoms or molecules.

Resistance thermometer: a thermometer which relies on the change in resistance of a wire as temperature changes.

Resonance: a system oscillates with maximum amplitude when it is subjected to an oscillatory force whose driving frequency is equal to the natural frequency of the system.

Resultant: the name given to a vector whose effects are entirely the same as the combined action of two or more vectors.

Root mean square speed: the square root of the mean square speed of the molecules of a gas.

Scalar quantity: a physical quantity which has magnitude but no direction.

Simple harmonic motion: the to and fro motion of a particle about an equilibrium position such that its acceleration is proportional to the displacement from the equilibrium position and is always directed towards that position.

Specific heat capacity: the amount of heat required to raise the temperature of 1 kg of a substance through 1 K or 1°C.

Specific latent heat of fusion: the quantity of heat required to change 1 kg of a substance from solid state to liquid state without a change in temperature.

Specific latent heat of vaporisation: the quantity of heat required to change 1 kg of a liquid to vapour without a change in temperature.

Speed: distance travelled per unit time. The SI unit of speed is m s^{-1}.

Speed-time graph: displays the variation of speed of an object with time.

Stationary wave: a wave formed by the superposition of two waves which are travelling in opposite directions, and which have the same speed, frequency and amplitudes. The resultant wave stores vibrational energy and its wave profile does not move through the medium but remains stationary.

Steady state: the condition reached when the temperature of a body attains a constant value when heat gained by the body is equal to heat lost by the body.

Steam point: the temperature of steam maintained at standard atmospheric pressure when it is in thermal equilibrium with pure water.

System: a well-defined quantity of matter bounded entirely by a real or imaginary surface.

Systematic error: an inherent error in an instrument or in a technique which causes a random set of readings to be distributed consistently around an average that is significantly different from the actual value.

Temperature: a measure of the degree of hotness of an object.

Terminal speed: the constant speed attained by a body when the upward net force acting on it balances the downward weight as it falls freely through a fluid.

Thermal equilibrium: a state in which every part of a body attains the same temperature when heat gained by the body is equal to the heat lost by the body.

Thermocouple: a thermometer which uses the electromotive force (emf) generated between two dissimilar junctions to measure a difference in temperature.

Transverse waves: progressive waves in which the direction of vibrations of the waves is perpendicular to the line of flow of energy.

Trough: the lowest point on a wave.

Thermodynamics (first law): the heat ΔQ transferred to a closed system increases its internal energy ΔU and causes the system to do work ΔW on its surroundings during the change.

Torque: moment of a couple.

Triple point: the single temperature at which pure ice, water, and water vapour co-exist together in thermal equilibrium.

Uncertainty: the spread of values on either side of a measurement.

Vector: a physical quantity which has both magnitude and direction.

Velocity: the rate of change of displacement.

Velocity-time graph: displays the variation of velocity of an object with time.

Wavefront: the crest of a wave or a line that joins all identical points on a wave with the same phase.

Wavelength: the distance between two successive crests or two successive troughs.

Work done (by a force on a body): the product of the force and the distance moved in the direction of the force.

Zero error: the systematic error of a measuring instrument when the scale reading of that instrument does not read exactly zero when there is nothing being measured.

Zeroth law of thermodynamics: If two bodies X and Y are separately in thermal equilibrium with a third body T, then X and Y are in thermal equilibrium with each other.

Appendices

APPENDIX A

a) Addition and Subtraction of Uncertainties

(i) Let $S = A + B$ and δS, δA and δB be the absolute uncertainties of S, A and B respectively.

Then $S \pm \delta S = (A \pm \delta A) + (B \pm \delta B)$

The biggest value that S could take is
$$S + \delta S = (A + \delta A) + (B + \delta B)$$
$$= (A + B) + (\delta A + \delta B)$$

The smallest value that S could take is
$$S - \delta S = (A - \delta A) + (B - \delta B)$$
$$= (A + B) - (\delta A + \delta B)$$

Hence, $S \pm \delta S = (A + B) \pm (\delta A + \delta B)$

The absolute uncertainties in S can be written as $\delta S = \delta A + \delta B$

(ii) Similarly, let $D = A - B$ and δD, δA and δB be the absolute uncertainties of D, A and B respectively.

Then $D \pm \delta D = (A \pm \delta A) - (B \pm \delta B)$

The biggest value that D could take is
$$D + \delta D = (A + \delta A) - (B - \delta B)$$
$$= (A - B) + (\delta A + \delta B)$$

The smallest value that D could take is
$$D - \delta D = (A - \delta A) - (B + \delta B)$$
$$= (A - B) - (\delta A + \delta B)$$

Hence, $D \pm \delta D = (A - B) \pm (\delta A + \delta B)$

The absolute uncertainties in D can be written as $\delta D = \delta A + \delta B$

When two independent readings are added to, or subtracted from each other, their respective absolute uncertainty must be added to find the absolute uncertainty of the sum or difference of the two readings.

b) Multiplication and Division

(i) Let $P = A \times B$ and δP, δA and δB be the absolute uncertainties of P, A and B respectively.

The biggest value that P could take is
$$P + \delta P = (A + \delta A)(B + \delta B)$$
$$= AB + A\delta B + B\delta A + \delta A\delta B$$
$$= AB + (A\delta B + B\delta A)$$

We neglect $\delta A\delta B$ as it is small compared with $A\delta B$ and $B\delta A$.

The smallest value that P could take is
$$P - \delta P = (A - \delta A)(B - \delta B)$$
$$= AB - A\delta B - B\delta A + \delta A\delta B$$
$$= AB - (A\delta B + B\delta A)$$

Again, we neglect $\delta A\delta B$ as it is small compared with $A\delta B$ and $B\delta A$.

Hence $\quad P \pm \delta P = AB \pm (A\delta B + B\delta A)$

And $\qquad \delta P = A\delta B + B\delta A$

Dividing both sides by AB,

$$\frac{\delta P}{AB} = \frac{A\delta B}{AB} + \frac{B\delta A}{AB}$$

$$\frac{\delta P}{P} = \frac{\delta B}{B} + \frac{\delta A}{A}$$

(ii) Let $Q = \frac{A}{B}$ and δQ, δA and δB be the absolute uncertainties of Q, A and B respectively.

The biggest value that Q could take is

$$Q + \delta Q = \frac{A + \delta A}{B - \delta B}$$

$$\delta Q = \frac{A + \delta A}{B - \delta B} - \frac{A}{B} = \frac{B\delta A + A\delta B}{B(B - \delta B)}$$

$$\delta Q = \frac{B\delta A + A\delta B}{B^2}$$

neglecting $B\delta B$ as it is small in comparison with B^2

Similarly, the smallest value that Q could take is

$$Q - \delta Q = \frac{A - \delta A}{B + \delta B}$$

$$-\delta Q = \left(\frac{B\delta A + A\delta B}{B^2}\right)$$

The fractional error in Q can be written as

$$\frac{\delta Q}{Q} = \frac{\frac{B\delta A + A\delta B}{B^2}}{\frac{A}{B}}$$

$$\frac{\delta Q}{Q} = \frac{\delta A}{A} + \frac{\delta B}{B}$$

When two independent readings are multiplied together or divided, their respective fractional uncertainty must be added to find the fractional uncertainty of the multiplication or division of the two readings.

APPENDIX B
Basic mathematics for A level Physics
Algebra

1. Equation of a straight line

$$y = mx + c$$

where m is the gradient and c is the intercept.

If (x_1, y_1) and (x_2, y_2) are co-ordinates on a straight line, the gradient m of the line is

$$m = \frac{y_2 - y_1}{x_2 - x_1}$$

2. In a quadratic equation $ax^2 + bx + c = 0$, the roots of the equation are

$$x = \frac{-b \pm \sqrt{b^2 - 4ac}}{2a}$$

   i) $b^2 - 4ac > 0$ (the roots are real and different)
   ii) $b^2 - 4ac < 0$ (the roots are imaginary)
   iii) $b^2 - 4ac = 0$ (the roots are equal)
   iv) $b^2 - 4ac \geqslant 0$ (the roots are real)

3. Rules for logarithms
   If $\log_a M = n$ then $a^n = M$
   $\log_a MN = \log_a M + \log_a N$

   $\log_a \dfrac{M}{N} = \log_a M - \log_a N$

   $\log_a M^n = n \log_a M$
   $\log_a b \quad = $ (to any suitable base)
   $\ln e^{kx} \quad = kx$

4. Indices

   $$x^{\frac{1}{a}} = \sqrt[a]{x}$$

   $$x^{-a} = \frac{1}{x^a}$$

   $$(x^a)(x^b) = x^{(a+b)}$$

   $$\frac{x^a}{x^b} = x^{(a-b)}$$

   $$(x^a)^b = x^{ab} = (x^b)^a$$

   Common symbols used
   $<$ means smaller than
   $>$ means greater than
   $\ll$ means very much smaller than
   $\gg$ means very much greater than
   $\approx$ means approximately equal
   $/$ means divide
   $\propto$ means proportional
   $<x>$ means average value of x
   Σ means sum of
   x or δx means small change in x
   $\sqrt{}$ means square root

Geometry and Trigonometry

1. $\cos A = \dfrac{\text{adjacent}}{\text{hypotenuse}}$; $\sin A = \dfrac{\text{opposite}}{\text{hypotenuse}}$; $\tan A = \dfrac{\text{opposite}}{\text{adjacent}}$

    $\sec A = \dfrac{\text{hypotenuse}}{\text{adjacent}}$; $\cos A = \dfrac{\text{hypotenuse}}{\text{opposite}}$; $\cot A = \dfrac{\text{adjacent}}{\text{opposite}}$

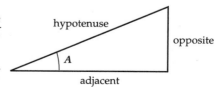

373

$$\cos^2 A + \sin^2 A = 1 \qquad\qquad \tan 2A = \frac{2 \tan A}{1 - \tan^2 A}$$

$$1 + \tan^2 A = \sec^2 A \qquad\qquad \cot 2A = \frac{\cot^2 A - 1}{2 \cot A}$$

$$\cot^2 A + 1 = \text{cosec}^2 A$$
$$\cos (A + B) = \cos A \cos B - \sin A \sin B$$
$$\cos (A - B) = \cos A \cos B + \sin A \sin B$$
$$\sin (A + B) = \sin A \cos B + \cos A \sin B$$
$$\sin (A - B) = \sin A \cos B - \cos A \sin B$$

$$\tan (A + B) = \frac{\tan A + \tan B}{1 - \tan A \tan B}$$

$$\tan (A - B) = \frac{\tan A - \tan B}{1 + \tan A \tan B}$$

$$\cos 2A = \cos^2 A - \sin^2 A = 2 \cos^2 A - 1 = 1 - 2 \sin^2 A$$

$$\sin 2A = 2 \sin A \cos A = \frac{2 \tan A}{1 + \tan^2 A}$$

$$\sin \theta \approx \tan \theta \approx \theta \text{ and } \cos \theta \approx 1 \text{ for small angle } \theta$$

2.

x	0 / 0°	$\frac{\pi}{6}$ / 30°	$\frac{\pi}{4}$ / 45°	$\frac{\pi}{3}$ / 60°	$\frac{\pi}{2}$ / 90°	π / 180°	$\frac{3\pi}{2}$ / 270°	2π / 360°
$\cos x$	1	$\frac{\sqrt{3}}{2}$	$\frac{1}{\sqrt{2}}$	$\frac{1}{2}$	0	1	0	1
$\sin x$	0	$\frac{1}{2}$	$\frac{1}{\sqrt{2}}$	$\frac{\sqrt{3}}{2}$	1	0	-1	0
$\tan x$	0	$\frac{1}{\sqrt{3}}$	1	$\sqrt{3}$	∞	0	∞	0

3. Trigonometric relationship for triangles

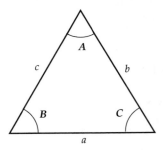

$$\frac{a}{\text{Sin } A} = \frac{b}{\text{Sin } B} = \frac{c}{\text{Sin } C}$$

$$a^2 = b^2 + c^2 - 2\, b\, c \cos A$$

Length of arc $s = r\theta$ where θ is the angle in radians and r is the radius of the circle.

Calculus

$$\frac{d}{dx}(x^n) = nx^{(n-1)}; \int x^n dx = \frac{1}{n+1}x^{(n+1)} + c$$

$$\frac{d}{dx}(\sin mx) = m \cos m \, x; \int \cos mx \, dx = \frac{\sin mx}{m} + c$$

$$\frac{d}{dx}(\cos mx) = -m \sin m \, x; \int \sin mx \, dx = \frac{-\cos mx}{m} + c$$

$$\frac{d}{dx}(\tan mx) = m \sec^2 m \, x; \int \sec^2 mx \, dx = \frac{\tan mx}{m} + c$$

$$\frac{d}{dx}(\ln x) = \frac{1}{x}; \int \frac{1}{x} dx = \ln x + c$$

$$\frac{d}{dx}(e^{ax}) = ae^{ax}; \int e^{ax} dx = \frac{e^{ax}}{a} + c$$

APPENDIX C

Important terms concepts	Equations	Description
Mass of one atom or molecule (m)	$m = \dfrac{M}{N_A}$	M = Molar Mass N_A = Avogadro Constant
Number of moles of a substance (n)	$n = \dfrac{m'}{M}$ $n = \dfrac{N}{N_A}$	m' = mass of the substance M = Molar Mass N = number of atoms or molecules N_A = Avogadro Constant
Components of a vector	$R_x = R \cos \theta$ $R_y = R \sin \theta$ $R = \sqrt{R_x^2 + R_y^2}$ $\tan \theta = \dfrac{R_y}{R_x}$	$R_x = x$−component of R $R_y = y$−component of R
Equations of motion	$s = \dfrac{1}{2}(u + v)t$ $v = u + at$ $s = ut + \dfrac{1}{2}at^2$ $v^2 = u^2 + 2as$	s = displacement u = initial velocity v = final velocity a = acceleration

Important terms/concepts	Equations	Description
Equations of motion for projectile motion	$y = \frac{1}{2}(u_y + v_y)\,t$ $v_y = (u \sin \theta) - gt$ $y = (u \sin \theta)\,t - \frac{1}{2}gt^2$ $v_y^2 = (u \sin \theta)^2 - 2\,gy$ $x = u_x t$	y = vertical displacement u = initial velocity u_y = y component of u v_y = y component of v u_x = x component of u x = horizontal displacement t = time of flight g = gravitational acceleration
Momentum (p); Change in momentum (Δp) Force (F)	$p = mv$ $\Delta p = mv - mu = Ft$ $F = \dfrac{d(mv)}{dt}$ $F = ma$ $F = v\dfrac{dm}{dt}$	m = mass v = final velocity u = initial velocity Force is equal to the rate of change of momentum a = acceleration $\dfrac{dm}{dt}$ = rate of change of mass
Conservation of momentum	$m_1 v_1 + m_2 v_2 = m_1 u_1 + m_2 u_2$	m_1 = mass of 1st object m_2 = mass of 2nd object u_1 = initial velocity of m_1 u_2 = initial velocity of m_2 v_1 = final velocity of m_1 v_2 = final velocity of m_2
Pressure (P)	$P = \dfrac{F}{A}$ $P = h\rho g$	F = force acting perpendicularly on unit area A = area h = depth of fluid ρ = density of fluid g = gravitational acceleration
Stokes' Law	$F = 6\pi\eta vr$	F = magnitude of the viscous force η = coefficient of viscosity v = velocity of sphere r = radius of sphere
Hooke's Law	$F = kx$	F = tension in the spring k = spring constant x = extension of the spring

Important terms / concepts	Equations	Description
Conditions for equilibrium	$\Sigma F = 0$ $\Sigma \tau = 0$	ΣF = vector sum of all forces acting on a rigid body $\Sigma \tau$ = vector sum of all external torques acting on a rigid body
Work done (W)	$W = Fs \cos \theta$ $\Delta W = P \, \Delta V$	F = force s = displacement P = pressure of a gas ΔV = change in volume
Gravitational Potential Energy (PE, U, W, or E_p)	$E_p = mgh_2 - mgh_1$	m = mass g = gravitational acceleration h_1 = height at level 1 h_2 = height at level 2
Kinetic Energy (E_k, K, KE or W)	$E_k = \frac{1}{2}mv^2 - \frac{1}{2}mu^2$	m = mass of object u = initial speed of object v = final speed of object
Elastic Potential Energy (E_e)	$E_e = \frac{1}{2}kx^2$	k = spring constant x = displacement
Conservation of Mechanical Energy	$K_1 + U_1 = K_2 + U_2$	K_1 = kinetic energy of mass before impact U_1 = potential energy of mass before impact K_2 = kinetic energy of mass after impact U_2 = potential energy of mass after impact
Force as a function of x ($F(x)$)	$F(x) = -\dfrac{dU(x)}{dx}$	$U(x)$ = potential energy function
Power (P)	$P = \dfrac{W}{t} = Fv$	W = work done t = time F = constant force v = velocity
Efficiency (E)	$E = \dfrac{P_0}{P_i} \times 100\ \%$	P_o = useful power output P_i = power input

Important terms / concepts	Equations	Description
Newton's Law of Gravitation	$F = G\dfrac{m_1 m_2}{r^2}$	F = gravitational force m_1 = point mass of particle 1 m_2 = point mass of particle 2 r = distance between m_1 and m_2 G = universal gravitational constant
Gravitational Field Strength of a point mass	$g = \dfrac{F}{m}$	F = gravitational force m = point mass
Gravitational Potential Energy (U)	$U = -\dfrac{GMm}{r}$	M = mass m = mass r = distance between M and m G = universal gravitational constant
Gravitational Potential (ϕ)	$\phi = -\dfrac{GM}{r}$	M = mass r = distance from a point to the centre of M G = universal gravitational constant
Centripetal force (F)	$F = \dfrac{mv^2}{r} = mr\omega^2$	m = mass v = tangential velocity ω = angular velocity r = radius of circular path
Equation of State	$PV = nRT$ $PV = \left(\dfrac{m'}{M}\right)RT$ $PV = m'rT$ $PV = \left(\dfrac{N}{N_A}\right)RT$ $PV = NkT$	P = pressure of a gas V = volume R = molar gas constant T = temperature n = number of moles m' = mass of gas M = molecular mass in kg $r = \dfrac{R}{M}$ N = number of molecules N_A = Avogadro constant $k = \dfrac{R}{N_A}$ (Boltzmann constant)

Important terms / concepts	Equations	Description
Kinetic theory of gases	$PV = \frac{1}{3}Nm <c^2>$ $P = \frac{1}{3}\rho <c^2>$ $\frac{1}{2}m<c^2> = \frac{3}{2}k T$ $U = \frac{3}{2}NkT = \frac{3}{2}n R T$ $c_{\text{r. m. s.}} = \sqrt{<c^2>}$	P = pressure of a gas V = volume N = number of atoms m = mass of 1 atom ρ = density of gas $<c^2>$ = mean square speed k = Boltzmann constant T = temperature n = number of moles R = molar gas constant $c_{\text{r. m. s.}}$ = root mean square speed
Empirical Centigrade scale	$\theta = \left(\dfrac{X_\theta - X_0}{X_{100} - X_0}\right) 100°C$	θ = temperature in YC X_θ = thermometric property at temperature θ X_0 = thermometric property at melting point X_{100} = thermometric property at boiling point
Ideal gas scale	$T = 273.16\left(\dfrac{P}{P_{tr}}\right)$	T = temperature in K P = pressure of gas at temperature T P_{tr} = pressure of gas at triple point
Specific latent heat of fusion (l_f) Specific latent heat of vaporisation (l_v)	$l_f = \dfrac{Q}{m}$ $l_v = \dfrac{Q}{m}$	Q = latent heat m = mass
Specific Heat Capacity	$c = \dfrac{C}{m}$ $c = \dfrac{Q}{m(\theta_f - \theta_i)}$	C = heat capacity m = mass Q = amount of heat transferred θ_f = final temperature θ_i = initial temperature
First Law of Thermodynamics	$\Delta U = \Delta Q + \Delta W$ $a = -\omega^2 x$	ΔU = change in internal energy ΔQ = transfer of heat to a system ΔW = work done on the system

Important terms / concepts	Equations	Description
Simple Harmonic Motion	$a = -\omega^2 x$ $v = \pm\omega\sqrt{x_0^2 - x^2}$ $x = x_o \sin \omega t$ $v = x_o \omega \cos \omega t$ $a = -x_o \omega^2 \sin \omega t$ $E_K = \dfrac{1}{2}m\omega^2 (x_o{}^2 - x^2)$ $E_P = \dfrac{1}{2}m\omega^2 x^2$ $E_T = \dfrac{1}{2}m\omega^2 x_o{}^2$	a = acceleration v = velocity ω = angular velocity x_o = amplitude x = displacement E_K = kinetic energy E_P = potential energy E_T = total energy
Wavelength (λ) Frequency (f) Phase (ϕ)	$\lambda = \dfrac{v}{f} = vT$ $f = \dfrac{1}{T}$ $\phi = 2\pi\left(\dfrac{x}{\lambda}\right)$ $\phi = 2\pi\left(\dfrac{t}{T}\right)$	v = speed of wave f = frequency T = period x = distance λ = wavelength t = time taken
Intensity (I)	$I = \dfrac{P}{A}$ $I = \dfrac{P}{4\pi r^2}$ $I = 2\pi^2 f^2 \rho v A^2$	P = power A = area r = radius of sphere f = frequency ρ = density v = speed of wave A = amplitude
Diffraction in Double Slit Diffraction in diffraction grating	$w = \dfrac{\lambda D}{d}$ $d \sin \theta_n = n\lambda$	w = fringe width D = distance from slit to screen d = distance between slits n = order of diffraction λ = wavelength of light d = grating spacing θ_n = angle for the n−order maximum

Index

382